Khyron's Claim

RAYNA TYLER

ISBN: 978-1-953213-01-3

CHAPTER ONE

Celeste

My instincts, at least when it came to sensing danger, were finely honed and rarely wrong. Something wasn't right. I could feel it in my core, had felt it for several days now. Yet when I leaned against the ornately carved wall of rock bordering the terrace and stared down at the city of Aztrashar, I didn't see anything suspicious.

Maybe I was mistaken and should blame the tension thrumming through my body on boredom. My friends Sloane, Laria, Cara, Burke, and I were temporary houseguests in the home of the drezdarr, the leader of the ketaurran people. I'd been stuck in the city way longer than I'd expected, and all I wanted to do was return to the human settlement and home.

We'd successfully completed our mission by rescuing Vurell, the physician who'd been abducted by mercs, and returning him along with an antidote to stop the toxin that was slowly killing the drezdarr. Supposedly, the male I had yet to meet wanted to thank my friends and me personally for saving his life. So instead of heading home, we'd been asked to stay. It was the drezdarr's polite way of ordering

1

us to remain in the city until he had completed the sleep-induced healing process necessary for the drug to work.

I hadn't assisted the vryndarr, the drezdarr's elite warriors, with the mission or risked my life to save their leader. I'd done it because the toxin was a threat to many lives, human and ketaurran alike. I had no interest in being thanked for the role I played in the rescue. If I hadn't known punishment for refusing a ketaurran leader's request was severe, I'd have left the day after we arrived.

Other than the few times Sloane and I had ventured to the trader's market, I had nothing to do but wait and visited the terrace frequently. I tipped my chin into the breeze, warmed by the early afternoon sun, and stared at the deep-green sky, where a cluster of blue-gray clouds had formed along the horizon signaling an oncoming storm.

Feeling confined and edgy, my patience gone, I decided to indulge my curiosity about the drezdarr and headed for his personal quarters. It probably wasn't a good idea and meant major trouble if I got caught. Since I wasn't big on following rules anyway, I decided it was worth the risk. With any luck, the drezdarr would be awake so I could get my thank-you, then leave.

I crept down the corridor leading to his private rooms, pausing outside Burke's sleeping chamber long enough to hear him arguing with Vurell. Both males were obstinate and strong-willed and had differing viewpoints on whether or not the injuries Burke had received during our rescue attempt had healed enough for him to be allowed out of bed. I stifled a grin and silently slipped past the open doorway undetected.

Surprisingly, there were no guards standing in the hallway outside the closed doors of the drezdarr's quarters. I knew I shouldn't be here, but couldn't force myself to walk away. After taking several deep breaths to calm my racing heart, I pressed on the door and slipped inside.

The interior of the room was dimly lit. Large wooden panels had been secured over the window areas to block out the sunlight. I waited for my eyes to adjust, then perused my surroundings. To the right sat a long desk and chair. Filling the area to the left was a massive bed, the frame constructed from stone much like the rest of the building.

From where I stood, I could see the large outline of a body beneath the blanket on top of the bed. I heard a male groan, not a normal sleep-laden noise, but the pain-filled moan of someone in the throes of torment. The heartfelt and overwhelming need to comfort him was too strong, so I cautiously inched closer.

After one glimpse and a shocked gasp, I clamped my hand over my mouth. Even with the sweat soaking the dark hair and plastering it to the skin around his face, I recognized the male before me. I knew the face all too well. It belonged to the male who had abandoned me, the male responsible for shredding my heart and letting my family die.

He was as handsome as I remembered, yet during the years since I'd last seen him, he'd matured, transformed into an even more appealing male. The contours of his face had sharpened, his jaw becoming more prominent. His body had filled out too. His chest was broader, his muscles more defined. I knew if he opened his eyes, they'd be an azure shade of blue, intense, intelligent, and, on rare occasions, sparkling with humor.

He fisted the blanket at his sides, the movement exposing his chest. His scales had lost their luster, were no longer a vibrant blue but a dull ash. "Oh, Khyron," I whispered, unable to resist running my fingertip along his arm.

He groaned again, this time with less agony and a hint of a smile forming on his lips. He sniffed the air, then the end of his tail, which had been hanging limply over the edge of the bed, curled upward, possessively ensnaring the back of my legs. It reminded me of another time, a happier time when we'd…

"Celeste, you should not be in here." The sound of Vurell's voice made me jump. He rushed to my side, his gaze focused on Khyron's tail, his tone admonishing. "What did you do to the drezdarr?"

The drezdarr? I'd been so focused on Khyron's condition that I'd forgotten whose room I'd crept into. Along with the realization came renewed anger. Not only had he deserted me, but he'd failed to tell me he was a member of the ruling family. I inhaled a deep breath, ignored Vurell's question, and stared at Khyron's deteriorating state, wondering if we'd risked our lives for nothing? "Were we too late?" I rasped, speaking around the constriction in my throat. No matter how much I hated what he'd done. No matter how much I'd never wanted to see him again, I didn't want him to die. Never that.

"No, the drezdarr owes your friends and you his life." Some of the harshness disappeared from his voice. "Unfortunately, healing from the toxin is painful. The additional drugs I gave him will ensure he rests during the remainder of the process. I expect a full recovery within the next few days."

I avoided looking at Vurell, blinking away the moisture forming in my eyes. I'd sworn long ago that I would never shed another tear for Khyron, not ever.

I ran my hand along his tail, then removed it from my leg. "Good, then I'll still get a chance to cut out his heart." The words, though cruel and unlike me, were empty. I'd never follow through with the threat. They were simply a way to release my anger and ease some of my hurt.

I should have been exhilarated, felt some sort of satisfaction at seeing Vurell's uneasy scowl as I turned and rushed from the room. Instead, I felt nothing. Nothing but a familiar emptiness and regret.

***

Khyron

Pain was nothing new. I had suffered it for weeks, but never to the extent caused by the toxin being purged from my system. The sleeping state that Vurell had induced was not deep enough to numb my body or force me to relax as he had stated. My mind filled with memories, jumping from one moment to the next, a continual trip from the present to the past. The physical pain I could endure. It was the emotional torment, having to relive losing my ketiorra, the one female I could claim as a mate, that was unbearable.

The memories started with the day I met Celeste. It was near the onset of the war, weeks before my sire died, not long before I would take on the role of drezdarr.

The war had been started by Sarus, my sire's sibling, a greedy male whose desire to rule the planet outweighed any thought of the destruction he would cause to all the inhabitants living on Ketaurrios.

It had been reported that some of Sarus's males had been targeting humans, and I had been traveling with my sire's soldiers, visiting the settlements and offering protection.

I was young, arrogant, and convinced I did not need any males acting as my guards. I had gotten good at losing them when I wanted to be by myself. At the time, the vryndarr, the males responsible for protecting the drezdarr, traveled with my sire; otherwise, I never would have gotten away from the males.

Once I was alone, I heard the sound of female laughter and followed it until I found Celeste and her sister Maria. I learned the younger female had a habit of wandering off from their home, which was why they were in the wooded area to begin with.

Since ketaurrans rarely visited the settlements, Celeste believed I was one of Sarus's males. She tried to take my head off with a large stick before shoving me into one of several puddles of water created by a recent storm. Later, after introductions, I'd questioned Celeste about straying away from her home without the protection of a male. She had found my question amusing, stating she could take care of herself and did not need a male's help. She had further insulted my ego by pointing out that I was the one who was soaked and covered with sandy mud.

My mind skipped ahead several weeks to the last time I saw Celeste, a heavy weight settling on my chest. I had just received word that my sire needed me to join him. It was evening, and we stood outside the dwelling she shared with her family. I was holding her in my arms, wiping away her single tear and promising to return.

I was ripped from the memory of our final kiss and transported to another time. A time of great loss. A time when I was forced to live through my sire's death, then received the news that Celeste and her entire family had been slaughtered by some of Sarus's men. The pain tearing through my heart was no less excruciating than it had been all those years ago.

In my mind I visualized my fists clenching, my agony released with a moan. Then I heard my name spoken in the soothing sound of Celeste's voice. I could smell her scent, feel her human fingertips caressing my scales, and appreciated the way her long legs fit nicely within the possessive curl of my tail.

No image accompanied what I assumed was a part of my imagination. Though it could not be real, I embraced the moment anyway, my tension slowly easing. When I heard the anger in her voice and felt her hand on my tail, dislodging it from the warmth of her soft curves, I experienced my earlier agony all over again.

I refused to lose her, and fought to regain the memory.

The more I struggled, the more I drifted in and out of a foggy haze until my body finally reacted by jolting me awake. I forced my heavy lids open, half expecting to see Celeste standing next to me. Instead, I was greeted by Vurell's frowning face, his dark eyes filled with concern. I groaned, disappointed that what seemed so real had been another torturous dream. Yet, if what I had sensed was truly my imagination, then why was the room filled with her unique scent, and why were my scales tingling?

"Khyron, how are you feeling?"

I wanted to spare my friend any hurt and did not tell him that the unconscious state he had induced only minimized my suffering. It did not relieve it. "Better." I pushed to a sitting position. The aftereffects of the drugs I had been given left my head groggy and my stomach nauseous.

Vurell did not seem convinced. He crossed his arms, unwilling to budge or allow me to leave the bed. I did not have enough strength to battle the male, at least not yet, so I sighed and pressed my back to the headboard.

"How long was I asleep?" I asked.

"Only a few days, but you should not be awake yet," Vurell growled.

Movement near the open doorway leading into the hallway outside my sleeping chamber drew my attention. Thrayn, the youngest member of the vryndarr, stepped into view and gave me a brief nod. His light brown hair was secured at his nape with a strip of leather, and his vest stretched across his muscled chest. Judging by the way his hand rested on the hilt of his blade and the glint in his pale green eyes, he was determined to protect me. He would not be there unless Jardun, the male I had left in charge, had assigned him the task. "Why is there a guard posted outside my room?"

"I requested his presence." Vurell crossed his arms.

"Why?" Someone had already tried to take my life by dosing me with a deadly toxin. Had something else happened while I was recovering?

"Because of the female." His cheeks flushed from pale peach to a dark orange.

"What female?" My heart raced, invigorated for the first time in weeks. Was it possible Celeste was alive, that what I thought was my imagination was real, that she had been in my room?

"The human female who threatened to cut out your heart. Though it is unclear whether or not she would actually hurt you, I did not want to take the chance."

Celeste had a temper, and the threat sounded exactly like something she would say. I hid my grin, certain Vurell would not appreciate my amusement. "Does this female have a name?"

Frustrated, Vurell swiped his hand through his hair. "Of course she has a name. Why would you—"

The last of my patience dissolved, and I snapped, "Her name."

As always, Vurell ignored my harsh tone. "Celeste. Her name is Celeste."

A female with the same name could not be a coincidence. After all these years, I knew in my heart it was her, my ketiorra. No amount of nausea, throbbing in my head, or nagging from an annoying physician was going to stop me from going after her. I smiled, then pushed the blanket aside and moved to the other side of the bed.

"Where do you think you are going?" Vurell circled the end of the bed, intent on blocking my escape. "You are not yet fully healed and must continue to rest."

"I am done resting. Now take me to see this female."

CHAPTER TWO

Celeste

My skin still tingled from having Khyron's tail wrapped around the back of my legs. It was a reminder of another time, a time filled with happy memories. Memories I'd spent years trying to bury.

I clenched my fists and stormed down every hallway leading back to the quarters I shared with my friends, not caring who noticed. He'd lied to me. Okay, it wasn't exactly a lie, but not telling me he was the drezdarr, or at least related to the drezdarr when we'd first met, wasn't exactly being truthful either.

In my angry haste, I took a corner too sharply and almost collided with Zaedon, one of the ketaurran males who'd been on the mission to rescue Vurell. He was also a vryndarr and someone I'd enjoyed being around.

His scales were a similar blue to Khyron's but his eyes were a dark turquoise and his chestnut hair had light cinnamon streaks. Though I found his appearance striking and his humor enjoyable, we'd never be anything more than friends.

"Zyrdena, are you all right?" Concern furrowed his

brow, not a common look for the easygoing warrior.

Shortly after we'd met, he'd started addressing me with the nickname that translated to "little princess" in his language. I knew it was his way of teasing me, but I'd grown fond of hearing it nonetheless.

"Fine." I sidestepped to his right, not in the mood to answer any questions.

He blocked the move, placing his hand gently on my shoulder. "Has someone offended you?" He rested his other hand on the hilt of the sword attached to the belt circling his hips.

I released an exasperated sigh. Even though he knew I could wield any number of blades and was trained to take care of myself, it didn't prevent him from being overprotective. Ketaurran males were hardwired to protect all females. It was a part of their culture, so I couldn't fault him for his reaction.

"No, no one has offended me." I patted his hand. "I was running late to meet with Sloane and wasn't paying attention to where I was going." I hated myself for lying, but how could I tell Zaedon I had a history with the male he was sworn to protect, or that Khyron was the reason I planned to leave?

"Then I will not keep you." There was skepticism in his gaze, but it did not stop him from removing his hand and stepping aside so I could pass.

I paused in the doorway of the rooms I shared with Sloane, Cara, and occasionally Laria because she spent her nights with Jardun in his quarters. Sloane was seated at a corner table inside the main gathering room, sharpening one of her many blades. Laria and Cara had pushed the furniture against a wall and were using the center of the room to spar. The headlock Cara had on Laria didn't last long, and she ended up on the floor with a thud.

"Hey, guys," I said as I headed for my room. I was still too upset to talk and was determined to pack before anyone could change my mind, myself included.

Once inside my room, I grabbed my pack off a shelf and began stuffing the few belongings I'd brought with me inside. Our home at the settlement wasn't quite as elaborate as the drezdarr's. I was going to miss sleeping in a plush bed and using the bathing room's large tub with a polished sandstone finish.

By the time I'd gathered the new items I'd bartered for at the market the day before, all three of my friends had strolled into the room, with Sloane plopping on the end of the bed.

"What are you doing?" Laria held up one of my shirts, her concerned green gaze focused on my bag.

She was the most sensible out of all of us, the one we always relied on when we got into trouble. Only this time, what was broken, she couldn't fix. "Leaving." I snagged the shirt along with my new pair of boots and stuffed them into the bag, then secured the bindings.

"You can't leave." Sloane reached for my bag. "We've been ordered to stay. You'll be breaking the drezdarr's law, and he'll have you tossed in a cell."

"Let him try." After a brief tug-of-war, I released my grip on the bag, and Sloane toppled off the bed and landed on the floor.

"Hey, not fair," Sloane said.

"Why don't you tell us what's going on, and maybe we can help." Cara held out her hand and pulled Sloane to her feet.

Images of Khyron burst into my mind, along with the heart-crushing pain of seeing him again after all this time. I didn't want to tell them or get them involved, but I had no choice. "It's him. He's here, he's…"

"Who is *him*?" Cara asked. "Can you be more specific?"

I'd never shared Khyron's name with my friends. They only knew the male who'd broken my heart was a ketaurran I'd met shortly after the war started, that I'd been devastated when he left and never came back.

Laria gasped. "Oh no." She was the first one to figure

out my cryptic rambling.

"You're talking about *the guy*, aren't you?" Sloane had finally caught on. She left my bag on the floor and returned to her spot on the bed.

I nodded. "And before you start asking me a bunch of questions, you need to know that he's the draeking drezdarr." Using the ketaurran curse word to refer to Khyron didn't make me feel any better.

Sloane gasped. "Nooo."

"Yes, and that's why I need to leave," I rasped.

Laria draped her arm across the back of my shoulders. "Celeste, you know we'll support whatever you want to do, but I can't leave with you, not without talking to Jardun first."

Her relationship with the leader of the vryndarr was one of the few good things to come out of our mission. It had been difficult for Jardun and the other males to accept our fighting abilities, so when Laria first met him, I had my doubts as to whether or not they'd be able to get past their differences and act on their obvious attraction.

Being stranded on an unfamiliar planet with no hope of ever returning to Earth hadn't been easy. Shortly after our arrival, a power struggle within the ruling family forced the ketaurrans into a war, a deadly battle that left the rest of the inhabitants fighting for survival, my friends and me included. We'd all incurred losses, family members we cared about. And even though I envied Laria's happiness, I was thrilled she'd found someone who respected and adored her.

I swallowed through my tightening throat. I knew I could always count on my friends to be there for me no matter what I decided to do. "I know. That's why I'm going by myself." I held up my hand to keep Sloane from arguing.

"Fine." The way she grunted and crossed her arms reminded me of Garyck, the grumpier of the three vryndarr who'd gone on the mission with us.

I turned to Laria. "If it's okay with you, I'd like to take Trixie." Trixie was the name she'd given her transport. She loved the vehicle, and borrowing it would be asking a huge favor. A favor I'd never ask if the settlement hadn't been too far away to reach without some form of transportation. If she turned me down, I'd be forced to take one of the drezdarr's solarveyors. Then he could add stealing to the list of my offenses.

"Of course, but I don't think you should be traveling alone," Laria said.

"I can help with that." Cara tucked one of her wild chestnut curls behind her ear. "You two stay here and smooth things over with the drezdarr. I'll go back to the settlement with Celeste."

"Are you sure?" I hadn't been looking forward to making the trip by myself and was relieved to hear her volunteer. "What about disobeying the drezdarr? If he sends someone after us…"

"Well, if he does, I'm sure Laria and Sloane will make sure he has no idea where to find us." Cara grinned. "Won't you?"

"Absolutely," they said at the same time, then grinned.

"Besides, I haven't been home in a while and need to check in with my grandparents anyway," Cara said.

We all worked with Burke, which was how we'd ended up on the mission to save Khyron's life and crossed paths with Cara. During the war, Burke had formed a small team of rebels who'd stayed together afterward and continued to help the surviving humans. Most of the time, Laria, Sloane, and I acquired supplies. It usually meant dealing with mercs in unsafe areas and taking a lot of dangerous risks.

Cara had secretly volunteered to investigate the rumors that some Earth laser weapons had been discovered in the damaged remains of the *Starward Bounty*, the exploration spacecraft that had been our home prior to the crash.

A male named Doyle, a mean and nasty excuse for a human, had transformed the vessel into a mercenary compound. When we found Cara, she'd been working undercover, disguised as a teenage boy.

Ketaurran weaponry wasn't technologically advanced. Fighting was done with knives and swords, and because the humans had lost a lot in the crash, they'd learned to adapt.

Burke had been worried that if the laser weapons did exist and got into the hands of Sarus's old supporters, the inhabitants of the planet could find themselves in another war. A war they wouldn't be able to win or even survive.

"Give me a couple of minutes to grab my things, then we can leave." Cara rushed from the room, giving me time to hug my friends and say our goodbyes.

***

Khyron

Celeste was alive. I was almost certain of it after making Vurell describe the female who had visited my room in more detail. She had been in my home for days, and if I had known, I never would have allowed Vurell to induce sleep. I would have gladly suffered additional agony if it meant seeing her beautiful face again.

Relief was one of many emotions bombarding my system. Worrying about Celeste's anger at my betrayal was another. Annoyed with my friends for delaying my departure, I hastened along the corridor. After I'd bathed and changed into clean clothes, Jardun and Thrayn had refused to let me leave my room until Vurell had examined me thoroughly and ensured the toxin had been purged from my system. Because the warriors who had sworn to protect my life were also my friends, they did not fear me the way a ketaurran soldier would.

Though some of my strength had returned, I was not strong enough to best the persistent males; otherwise, I would have already arrived at the quarters Celeste shared with her friends. Arguing would have done no good and only wasted more time, so I agreed to their request.

"Are you certain about this?" Jardun walked alongside me, his heavy footsteps on the stone flooring matching mine.

I could hear the worry in his voice, his concern about my well-being. I understood his trepidation. He had witnessed my devastation when I learned about Celeste's death and had to be wondering how I would react if this female was not her.

I would also be meeting his Laria for the first time. Besides being one of the females who had risked her life to save mine, she was his love, his mate. Her acceptance of me and his way of life mattered a great deal to him. Things would not go well if I caused problems with one of her friends.

At the moment, making a good impression was the least of my concerns, not when every instinct I possessed longed to find Celeste and claim her as my ketiorra.

"Perhaps you are experiencing side effects from the drugs," Thrayn, who was following behind us with Vurell, said.

His comment earned him an over-the-shoulder glare from Jardun.

"There was nothing wrong with the medication I gave him," Vurell huffed. "You watched me perform the examination yourself and…"

"Enough." I interrupted their bickering. "Celeste is the female I once knew, and there is nothing wrong with me." The latter part of my statement was untrue, but I would not admit it out loud. My body was still weak from the effects of the toxin. My muscles straining and begging for rest did not stop me from continuing my hurried stride.

I turned the remaining corner, hesitating long enough outside the female's quarters to inhale a deep breath before walking through the open entryway leading into the main gathering room. I sniffed the air, catching a whiff of her lingering scent, then glanced around the room expecting to find her, only to be disappointed.

Instead of Celeste, I found two human females pulling a lounger away from a wall and returning it to the center of the room. The doors to all the adjoining sleeping chambers were closed. If Celeste was hiding behind one of them, it would do her no good, because I was not leaving. Not until I had a chance to speak with her.

Jardun had not exaggerated when he had informed me the females were true warriors. They both wore blades sheathed at their hips. The taller one had golden hair and green eyes that sparkled with intelligence. She acted as if she knew who I was and seemed undaunted by my presence.

The other female had dark hair and blue eyes that shimmered with mischief. She might be shorter, but she was no less imposing. When she stopped what she was doing to cross her arms and glare at me, I wondered if my abrupt entrance had somehow offended her. Whatever the cause, I had no intention of making it worse by demanding to see Celeste. If what Jardun had told me about the females was correct, they were strong-willed and loyal to one another. A confrontation would do more harm than good, so I nodded at Jardun to take the lead.

Jardun stepped around me, approaching the taller female and taking her hand. "Khyron, this is Laria, my ketiorra." He tipped his head toward the other female. "And this is Sloane."

Sloane leaned in front of Laria and spoke to Jardun as if I could not hear her. "He's the drezdarr, right? Is he expecting us to bow or do something like kiss his boots? Because there's no way it's going to happen."

"Sloane." Laria snapped at her friend under her breath while keeping her irritated gaze focused on me.

"What? It was an honest question. It's not like we got handouts on royal protocol when we crash landed here."

Her humor was refreshing, and it was the first time in a

long time that the chuckle rumbling from my chest felt so good. It was easy to see why Celeste had chosen to call these females her friends. "There are no special protocols, not for those responsible for saving my life."

"Speaking of lives, should you be up this soon?" Zaedon stood in the entryway grinning, his turquoise gaze mildly concerned.

I should have known news of my awakening would spread quickly.

"He has looked better." Garyck, another vryndarr and friend, appeared next to Zaedon. His golden-scaled frame was slightly larger than Zaedon's and consumed the remainder of the opening. After giving Zaedon a nudge, he moved farther into the room. His amber gaze immediately jumped to Sloane before returning to me.

Was it possible the male who'd suffered more than most during the war, and rarely showed any emotions, had taken an interest in the female? Perhaps I had missed more than I thought by waiting to meet my guests.

"I have already stated that I am fine." I appreciated their concern, but I was losing patience and wanted to address my original purpose for being here. "I wish to speak with Celeste."

I had no idea how much of my relationship with Celeste had been shared with the females, but judging by the way they tensed at my request, they knew enough and were not happy about it.

"You can't. She's not here," Laria said.

"But her scent…" Maybe I had just missed her and she had gone to another part of the building.

Zaedon furrowed his brow. "Are you certain? I saw her in the hallway earlier, and she stated that she was on her way to meet with Sloane." He glanced around as if he suddenly realized something else, something important. "Where is Cara?"

Laria glanced at Jardun, then back at me. "They're both gone."

"What do you mean, gone?" Zaedon's raised tone was out of character for the male.

The muscles in my chest tightened, making it hard to breathe. "Gone where?"

"Even if we knew, which I'm not saying we do, we wouldn't tell you because it's none of your business." Sloane fingered the hilt of the blade sheathed on her hip.

"Little one," Garyck warned as he positioned himself between Sloane and me. "You cannot speak to the drezdarr is such a manner."

"I'll speak to him any draecking way I want to, and parts will disappear if he does anything to hurt my friend." Sloane made her insinuation clear when her angered gaze focused on my groin.

I had angered females before, but it was the first time one had dared to make such a threat. I resisted the urge to take a step back or protectively place my hand over the parts she referred to.

"That is enough." Garyck grabbed Sloane around the waist and hoisted her over his shoulder.

Sloane squirmed, kicked, and pounded her fists on Garyck's back. "Put me down, you overgrown lizard."

"Not until you promise there will be no use of your blades." Garyck squeezed the back of her thigh. "Or removing of any parts."

Sloane groaned and stopped struggling. "I promise, at least for now, so put me down."

As soon as her feet touched the ground and she was facing me again, I said, "I assure you I care deeply for my ket...for Celeste. I would never harm her." I never got the chance to tell Celeste she was my ketiorra and would not announce the claim to others until I told her first.

"Really." Laria took a step forward and swatted Jardun's hand when he reached for her. "If you cared so much about her, then you shouldn't have abandoned her."

"Laria, he..." I held up my hand to stop Jardun's defense.

"You are right." Her words would not have cut so deeply if they had not been true or my guilt so heavy. "I cannot undo the past. I simply wish to speak with her." To hold her in my arms, beg for her forgiveness, convince her we belong together.

Quick-paced thuds echoed in the outer corridor and drew everyone's attention to the entryway. A young ketaurran soldier rushed into the room, clutching his midsection. He skidded to a stop, then bowed his head. "I am sorry to interrupt, drezdarr." He turned his attention toward Jardun. "Two of the human females have taken the transport you asked me to protect."

Laria smiled, then turned and leaned into Jardun. "You had someone guarding Trixie?"

Jardun wrapped an arm around her waist. "I promised you I would not let anything happen to her." He narrowed his gaze at the soldier. "Apparently, my orders were not fulfilled."

The young male jutted out his chin. "My apologies, but the dark-haired one distracted me while the one with curls attacked me from behind." He noticed my frown, then quickly added, "I await whatever punishment I am due."

I remembered what it was like to be a young male and how easily a beautiful female could sway my thoughts. I also considered the fact that the soldier had no knowledge of Celeste's and Cara's fighting abilities. I could not dismiss his actions, but I could ensure that his punishment was not severe.

"Return to your post. We will discuss this matter later," I said.

"Of course." After several backward steps and a near collision with the doorframe when he spun to leave, the soldier shuffled from the room.

I turned back to the group. "Would someone please tell me who this Trixie person is? I was unaware that there were more than four females in your group."

Jardun grinned. "Trixie is the name Laria gave her

transport."

"I see." Though I did not comprehend why humans tended to name inanimate objects, I was aware of the practice.

"I assume you know their destination?" Zaedon sounded more than a little curious.

Laria shifted slightly but remained encircled within Jardun's arms. "I do."

"Would you mind sharing that information?" I strained to keep the irritation out of my voice.

"Are you planning to go after her?" Sloane asked.

"Yes, that is my plan."

Laria shared a knowing look with Sloane, then said, "I'll tell you where they went on one condition."

"Whatever you wish." I would gladly give her anything she wanted for the information.

"You take us with you." Laria swept her hand at those surrounding her.

"Agreed. Now…"

"Khyron, do you think it is wise to leave the city?" Jardun released Laria and moved closer to me. "Someone has tried to take your life, and you are not totally healed from the poisoning."

Vurell pushed away from the wall where he had been standing with Thrayn, listening to the conversation. "Perhaps you should let them go after Celeste and bring her back here."

Standing for such a long period of time had taken some of my strength, and I longed to drop on the nearby lounger. I knew Vurell had been watching me closely and any sign of weakness would reinforce his insistence that I return to my bed.

"Good luck with that." Sloane's response saved me from answering.

I was certain Celeste had left because of me. Forcing her to return was no way to gain her trust and would only make things worse.

"Sloane's right. If you want to speak with her, you'll have to go to her. And even then, she might not be willing to listen," Laria said.

I grasped Jardun's shoulder. "You are my oldest friend. Would I be able to stop you from going after your ketiorra, your Laria?"

"No, but I am not the leader of our people either. As your vryndarr, it is my responsibility to ensure your safety." Jardun held up his hand to keep me from arguing. "But as your friend, I must insist that we stop wasting time and prepare to leave immediately."

Vurell groaned. "If Khyron is going, then I will be going with him. Someone needs to make sure the stubborn male does not have a relapse."

"I have never been to the human settlement and would like to go as well." Thrayn took a step forward. "If there is trouble, you will need more males to protect you."

I rubbed my forehead. "You can all accompany me, but there will be no soldiers and you"—I pointed at Thrayn—"can tell Raytan he will be staying behind to address any issues that arise in my absence."

Raytan had a temper, wasn't going to be happy about being left behind, and would be difficult to deal with. As expected, Thrayn looked as if I had smacked him in the jaw. With a small amount of satisfaction, I addressed the females. "How soon can you be ready to leave?"

CHAPTER THREE

Celeste

I stared out the transport's viewing pane, watching the occasional beam of sunlight burst from behind the numerous dark clouds lining the late-afternoon green sky. The storm had gotten closer, the direction we traveled heading directly into it. My mind was filled with thoughts of Khyron. Concentrating was difficult, so letting Cara operate the controls had not been a problem.

Living on Ketaurrios had taken some getting used to. The planet had varying terrains, some portions similar to deserts, the ground a combination of dirt and sand. There were no defined seasons in the weather. Most of the time it was hot during the day and almost cold in the evening. Storms were random, appearing at any time and ranging from mild drops of water to heavy rains that could last several days.

Since all mechanical transportation was solar powered, traveling could take longer than expected and depended a lot on the weather. It was never a good idea to go anywhere without making sure the solars had been fully charged first. Even with the threat of rain, we had plenty of power to drive the remaining two or so hours to the settlement.

"You know the drezdarr is going to punish that soldier who was guarding Laria's transport, don't you?" Cara pushed several buttons on the control panel to increase the vehicle's speed now that we'd cleared the edge of the city.

I still couldn't believe there was someone guarding Trixie. I'd bet anything Jardun had something to do with it. I remembered him telling Laria on the day we'd met that he wouldn't let anything happen to her transport.

"We didn't have much of a choice. It's not like he was going to let us take the transport if we'd asked nicely." I actually felt bad for the young ketaurran male. Not only had I distracted and disarmed him by implying sexual favors, but Cara had knocked him to the ground with one kick to his gut. The poor guy's ego would be bruised way more than his backside, especially when the other males heard how an unarmed female at least six inches shorter than he had gotten the better of him.

"Besides, I can't"—I shook my head and stifled the sob pushing its way along my throat—"go back." Though deep down, there was a part of me that could. I was never one who did much crying, yet after seeing Khyron, I couldn't keep my memories of the past from resurfacing, and struggled with the overwhelming need to be alone and shed some tears. On top of my erratically emotional state, the uneasiness I'd been experiencing before I'd gone to his room had intensified from the moment we left the city.

She reached across the gap between our seats and touched my arm. "I know."

That was the thing I liked about Cara the most. She always understood and gave her support without asking any personal or prying questions.

I returned to staring outside, doing my best not to think about the ramifications of what Cara and I now faced for disobeying the drezdarr's orders to remain in his home. Well, if Khyron wanted to enforce his law, he'd have to come and find me first. Not that I thought he would. He hadn't cared enough to come back for me years ago before he became the drezdarr, when it really matter the most. So I had no reason to believe he'd care enough to waste his time tracking me down now.

Before Vurell caught me in Khyron's room, he'd told my friends and me that he thought it would take several more days for the antidote to purge the toxin from his system. Even if someone mentioned my name, Khyron had been asleep when I sneaked into his room. Since I'd left before he could see me, there was no way he'd know I was the same person from his past. I also knew I could count on Laria and Sloane making sure he never found out.

"It looks like the worst part of the storm passed through here already." Cara slowed the transport to keep from barreling through the water that had pooled on the uneven road.

Traveling could be treacherous. The environment was harsh, and nothing was paved, only worn by constant use. We'd reached an area consisting mainly of rock, where the road wound its way through a gap between stacks of boulders sitting higher than a one-story dwelling.

Laria's vehicle was an older, smaller model, and could move faster than the larger solarveyors. It was an ideal size for traveling unnoticed and escaping bad situations, which happened a lot when we did acquisition jobs for Burke. It wasn't, however, great for dealing with the aftereffects of bad weather.

We didn't have to worry about interior flooding because the base of the transport sat high off the ground. The sand and dirt, when combined with water, became so slick, the transport had trouble maintaining traction. Our biggest problem was sliding and ending up stuck in a crevice or slamming into an outcropping of rock.

"Good, then we should make the settlement shortly after dark." I couldn't complain about the past week's accommodations. They were great, but I missed being home, spending time with my other friends and the children orphaned by the war.

Cara had barely maneuvered through the water and reached an area where the ground was flatter and the stacks of rocks were much lower when the transport lurched forward. She tapped the brakes hard and swerved to keep from driving over a jagged mound that would've torn up the underbelly of our vehicle.

Unless we were being chased, I never secured the safety strap on my chair, and the jerky maneuver flung me out of my seat. Luckily, I reacted quickly, bracing my hands on the edge of the control panel, preventing my head from hitting metal.

"What was that? Did we hit something?" I asked, settling back into the chair and reaching for the strap.

"I didn't see anything on the road. That felt like something slammed into us from behind." Cara pressed a button, and the transport accelerated. "Check the rear side panel and see if there's something back there."

The walls of rock coupled with the winding, narrow road made seeing behind the transport from the control area nearly impossible. "On it." I pushed out of my seat and grabbed the overhead bar that stretched the entire length of the vehicle seconds before we received another hit.

"Hang on!" Cara shouted, struggling to right the transport and keep us from scraping against rock.

As soon as the swerving stopped, I continued working my way to the back. On the next curve in the road, I spotted a solarveyor. I didn't recognize the two males manning the controls, but they were definitely human. Even with our accelerated speed, it wouldn't take the other vehicle long to catch up with us again. I didn't want to be back here when they did, so I turned and headed back to my seat.

"You were right, it's a solarveyor. There were two guys

at the controls." I slid into the chair and snapped the safety strap into place.

"Anyone you recognize?" Cara asked.

"Nope, no idea who they are." Laria, Sloane, and I dealt with mercs on occasion, but I couldn't think of anyone who'd intentionally come after us.

"Could be road bandits, but I've never heard of them traveling this far north." The road straightened, and Cara accelerated again.

"Don't they usually go for larger transports?" I asked.

"Yeah."

The rear of the vehicle received another, much harder hit. The impact vibrated along the hull and jolted us sideways. The engine sputtered, making a loud, shrill whine before jerking to a stop.

No matter how many buttons Cara pushed, the transport didn't rev back to life. "They must have damaged the engine." She slammed her fist on the panel. "We aren't going anywhere, not without doing some major repairs first."

Draeck. This was the first time I'd ever borrowed Trixie, and for once, I was glad Laria wasn't around so she wouldn't see what had happened to her. I unsnapped the strap across my lap with a growl, then shoved out of my chair. The guys responsible were about to experience some pain. I moved around Cara, who was already out of her seat, and rushed to the storage unit hidden inside a side panel.

"You have got to be kidding me." Cara was staring out the side pane at the two males heading for our transport's sealed access door.

"What?" I stopped what I was doing to glance in her direction.

"It's Rick and Neil. They're Doyle's men."

"How did they find us?" I didn't know the males, but I hadn't spent weeks living with them at the compound in the Quaddrien, a desolate desert area the humans had nicknamed the wastelands, like Cara had.

"Don't know, but the good news is there are only two of them." Cara moved away from the pane and engaged the security lock on the door.

"And the bad news?" I pulled out two swords and a thin blade. I slipped the blade into the sheath hidden inside my boot, then held a sword out to Cara.

"They have laser weapons." She waved at the blade. "Those aren't going to do us any good."

A loud bang, a fist against metal, echoed through the interior, followed by a male's angry bellow. "Open the door, or we'll blast it."

"Cara, I know you can hear me. All we want is what you stole from Doyle," the other male said.

"Sorry, Rick. I have no idea what you're talking about." Cara raised her voice at the sealed door.

"Do you think they're looking for the toxin?" The antidote for Khyron wasn't the only thing Vurell had taken during the rescue. He'd also grabbed vials containing several different poisons.

"Possibly, though they're not very bright if they think we'd bring them with us, or just hand them over. Since the drezdarr's home is heavily guarded, it's more likely they were waiting for someone to leave the city so they could take hostages, hoping to make a trade," Cara said.

Cara's theory made sense. It also explained my uneasiness the past few days.

"Open the damn door, Cara." The other male's snarl was followed by a ping on the hull.

Cara noticed my troubled look. "Don't worry, the exterior is too thick for them to blast through. I'm more concerned about Rick being able to override the security. That lock isn't going to keep them out for long, so if there's anything else in here we can use to protect ourselves, now's the time to share."

This wasn't the first time the transport had been attacked. It didn't happen a lot, but it did happen. Laria,

Sloane, and I had gotten good at finding our way out of situations far worse than this. "I've got an idea." I moved to the opposite wall, then used the edge of my blade to remove a thick sheet of metal. "I've never used this as a shield for a blaster, but I think it will work." I kept my voice low as I positioned the panel in the middle of the floor parallel to the door.

Cara grabbed the other end to help me keep it upright. "Okay, so now what?"

"You still any good with a knife?" I retrieved the thin blade I'd hidden in my boot.

Cara smiled and took the blade. "Better with my fists, but I can hit what I aim at."

CHAPTER FOUR

Khyron

The solarveyor we took for our trip to the settlement was a much larger solar-powered version of a transport and the same vehicle Jardun and the others had used to cross the Quaddrien. According to Laria, Cara was an excellent mechanic, had repaired the damage to the engine sustained during their escape, and assured her it was functioning properly.

It was a good thing the vehicle could accommodate a large number of people. Not only had the males who were present during my conversation with Laria and Sloane insisted on coming with me, so had Burke. Even though he was still recovering from the knife wound on his thigh, several cracked ribs, and extensive bruising, which he received from Doyle during the mission to rescue Vurell, he objected to being left behind.

Vurell refused to leave the toxins and antidote he had removed from the compound with his assistant, Kren. He wanted to keep them safe and had been adamant they accompany us on the trip. I agreed with his decision. One of the toxins was the same poison I was recovering from.

It was specifically engineered for ketaurrans, was harmless against humans, and not something I wanted anyone else to access.

During the rescue, Cara had destroyed the laboratory, hindering Doyle's ability to recreate the poison. What I did not know was whether or not more of the toxin existed elsewhere. Until I learned the information and discovered the identity of the person who'd attempted to take my life, I thought it best to keep the deadly liquid and its cure guarded by those I trusted.

I stretched my legs across one of the bench seats and stared out the viewing pane at the last rays of sunlight peeking through the steadily growing storm clouds. So far, the precipitation had been light and scattered. I feared it wouldn't be long before we encountered sheets of water, which would hinder our visibility and slow our travel.

No sooner had we departed from the city than an uneasy feeling, a gut-tightening dread, began snaking its way through my system. My impatience to find Celeste and ensure she was unharmed grew stronger the longer we traveled. From my position at the back of the vehicle, I could easily view our progress through the panes in front of the control area and overhear the conversations between the other members in the group.

I clutched the cup of creevea Vurell had prepared for me, taking an occasional sip of the bitter yellow liquid and trying to relax. The drink, derived from a plant, had minor healing abilities and a natural stimulant to aid with exhaustion. He had taken the bench opposite me and, not long after supplying me with the drink, had fallen deeply asleep. I had no doubt he had spent the last few days watching over me and had neglected to take care of himself.

Jardun had taken a seat near the front with the others and currently had Laria sitting on his lap. Watching the attentive way the couple interacted with each other had envy and regret settling over my heart. If things in the past had gone differently, if I had made other choices, I might be sharing the same kind of relationship with Celeste.

Sloane's boisterous laughter drew my attention. She was seated in the copilot chair next to Garyck, who manned the vehicle's controls. She'd swung the seat sideways to face the males seated on the benches behind her. "Can I see your blade?" She held out her hand and wiggled her fingers at Thrayn.

The wary way Thrayn scrutinized Sloane was an expected reaction. I was fairly certain that before today, he had not interacted with the females much. Nor was he aware they were highly skilled with blades and had been trained in hand-to-hand fighting by Burke and several of his males.

He had been taught since birth that it was a ketaurran male's responsibility to protect females. Seeing the females as warriors and fighting alongside them was an entirely new experience. It required considerable adjustment, even for me.

"Let her see your knife, Thrayn. She will not hurt herself with it." Zaedon grinned and adjusted his long legs so they were crossed at the ankles.

"If you are sure." Thrayn did not sound convinced but reluctantly handed Sloane his knife.

She examined it as if it were a priceless jewel, carefully caressing the side of the blue-black blade with her fingertip. "Excellent craftsmanship."

"And quite expensive. Now, if you will…" He extended his hand, expecting her to return it.

Sloane snatched it out of his reach, her blue eyes sparkling with mischief. "How about a little wager?"

Thrayn narrowed his gaze, his interest piqued. "What kind of wager?"

"I'll bet you this exquisite blade that Celeste either refuses to have anything to do with Khyron, or she tries to take off his head with a knife the next time she sees him." Sloane glanced in my direction and grinned.

I shifted uncomfortably on my seat. At the moment, Sloane had the advantage of knowing Celeste better than I did. I already knew my first meeting with her after all these years was going to be difficult, but hearing her friend state it out loud was disconcerting.

"Impossible." Thrayn jerked upward and puffed out his chest. "There is no female on the entire planet who would not be happy to have the drezdarr's attention."

Thrayn gave me a confident nod. At the moment, I lacked the same confidence and decided not to comment.

"If you say so." Sloane tapped the blade against her palm.

Laria, who'd been resting her head on Jardun's shoulder, straightened so she faced Thrayn. "Don't do it, Thrayn."

He shrugged off her warning, then lowered his gaze appreciatively along Sloane's body. "What will you offer if you lose?"

It was obvious he had not observed Garyck's interest in the female. If he had, he would not risk bodily injury by perusing her in such a manner. I was thankful Garyck was facing away from the younger male and focusing on the controls.

Sloane shook her head. "Nah, not interested, but I do have ten cradasson that says I'll win." She got to her feet, removed her blade from the leather sheath attached to the belt on her hip, then replaced it with Thrayn's.

Garyck shot her a sidelong glance and growled. "Little one, what are you doing?"

I wasn't sure what intrigued me more, Garyck's use of the uncomplimentary way he addressed Sloane or the fact that she continued to let him.

"Nothing." She raised her head long enough to shoot a glare in his direction, then removed the blade from the sheath. "I wasn't going to keep it. I just wanted to make sure it was going to fit after I won it."

Thrayn snorted and held out his hand. "You assume

too much, female. I agree to your terms and look forward to receiving the coins when *I* win our wager." He accepted his blade and returned it to his hip.

"My *name* is Sloane, not female." She dropped back in her chair and pointed her knife in his direction. "*And* I never bet unless I know I'm going to win."

"I hope you weren't fond of that blade." Burke patted Thrayn on the shoulder as he pushed out of his seat and stretched his injured leg.

"Thrayn, I believe this trip is going to be good for you," Zaedon said.

Thrayn narrowed his eyes. "How so?"

Zaedon chuckled. "You are going to acquire many lessons on how to deal with humans, specifically the females."

"Laria, isn't that your transport in the road up ahead?" Burke placed a hand on the back of Sloane's chair and leaned closer to the viewing pane. "It doesn't look like it's moving."

"What? Where?" She pushed off Jardun's lap and moved closer to Burke.

I was up and standing behind Garyck's seat in seconds. We should not have caught up with them this easily, not unless there was a problem with their transport or something else had caused them to stop. I ignored the wave of nausea battering my body, refusing to believe I had finally found Celeste only to lose her again.

"There." Burke pointed at the vehicle sitting at an odd angle on the side of the worn road.

"It looks like the storm was heavy in this area. Maybe they had trouble with the solars." Jardun wrapped an arm around Laria's waist, pulling her back against his chest.

"Cara can handle almost any engine problem they might have had." Laria glanced at Jardun over her shoulder, her worried gaze catching mine. "Something about this doesn't feel right."

"Khyron…" Garyck slowed the vehicle's engine, the

use of my name a request on how to proceed.

"Approach with caution and be prepared for anything," I answered.

CHAPTER FIVE

Celeste

Using the metal panel as a shield had worked better than I'd expected. The only damage it sustained was from a single laser blast, which left a vertical burn mark across the center.

Cara had been right about Rick bypassing the security. We'd barely gotten into position before the access door opened. As soon as the males moved into view, we'd thrown our blades. Cara caught the guy closest to her in the shoulder, causing him to yelp and stagger backward, then drop his weapon to pull out the knife. I had a much better aim and nailed the other male's hand, the one gripping his laser weapon, the result a jerky discharge. After that, disarming them had been easy.

Neither of the male's injuries was life-threatening. Even though I had a good idea what would have happen to Cara and me if they managed to take us prisoner, I still retrieved a medical kit from an overhead storage unit, then cleaned and bandaged their wounds. Not that they were grateful. I had to listen to their complaints until Cara told them she'd remove male parts if they didn't stop whining.

The effort I expended to take care of their injuries might be moot. Life was difficult and dangerous. There were times when survival required doing unpleasant tasks. Whether or not they survived after I turned them over to Burke's men for interrogation was another matter. Fortunately, it was one of those times when someone else would have to deal with it.

The worst part of the whole situation was having to leave Trixie behind. I didn't have a choice, not after Cara informed me the damage to the engine was too extensive and would probably take days to repair. Since the transport Rick and Neil used to ram us wasn't much larger than ours, we'd have the same difficulty maneuvering it through the sandy mud caused by the storm. Towing our vehicle the remainder of the way to the settlement was not an option.

The road we were on wasn't heavily traveled, I still hoped nobody came along and stripped Trixie's parts before we returned for her. With any luck, I'd be able to persuade one of Burke's guys to head out first thing in the morning and tow her back to the settlement. I had no idea how long it would be before I saw Laria and Sloane again, but I hoped the transport was working perfectly before then.

I didn't want to spend the remainder of the trip worrying about Rick and Neil attempting to overpower us, so I rummaged through the storage units on their transport, looking for something to bind their wrists.

I found several sets of shackles, and by the quality of the metal, I assumed they were made from brugoran, an ore so strong that not even a ketaurran male could break out of them. "What do you think they planned to do with these?" I held one of the shackles up for Cara to see, then gave it a shake and rattled the chain.

Cara pursed her lips in disgust. "I can only imagine." She kept one of the laser blasters aimed at the males while I fastened the metal cuffs to their wrists.

"Take a seat on the floor over there." I motioned to a spot between the two long benches lining one of the walls.

"And no talking, or I might decide to follow through on my earlier threat." Cara aimed her weapon at Rick's groin.

Rick moved his hands protectively and shot a malicious glare in Cara's direction.

"You can't..." Neil sputtered, an angry red bursting across his cheeks. An elbow in the ribs from Rick had Neil clamping his mouth shut.

"Now that they're taken care of, what do you say we head home?" Cara walked over to the pilot seat.

"Works for me." I took the seat next to her, rotating it sideways so I could see Rick and Neil.

Within minutes Cara had the vehicle moving, then she spent the next hour telling me less than pleasant stories, some bordering on vile, about Rick, Neil, and the other males back at the compound. It was early evening by the time we reached the settlement. I had no sympathy and felt no remorse about what might happen to the males in the near future.

Once Cara parked in front of the building that served as Burke's home and a gathering place for the people who worked with him, we jerked Rick and Neil to their feet and led them out of the transport. It was dark outside but there was enough light coming from the room inside the building to see where we were going.

Rick glanced around as he stepped onto the platform near the building's entrance. "Where are we?"

Mercs rarely visited the settlements, preferring to do their business in one of the cities, usually in a run-down bar. Having Burke and his guys living here was a definite deterrent for Doyle and other males like him. None of the mercs I'd met over the years had as nasty a reputation or came close to being as deadly as Doyle.

"Not a place you want to be."

"Yeah, it was either here or take you back to the

Quaddrien and feed you to the snakkrils." Cara had a wicked sense of humor and grinned when Neil shuddered.

Being reminded of the snakelike creatures with short, clawed legs made me want to shudder too. The last time I'd seen one was during our mission to rescue Vurell, when we'd cut across the wastelands.

Not long into the trip the chaugwas—an animal that looked like an overgrown iguana—Laria had been riding was attacked by one of the poisonous creatures. If Jardun hadn't reacted quickly and killed the snakkril, Laria might not have survived the attack.

Later, during our escape, Doyle and his men chased our vehicle with their solarveyors. We couldn't outrun them, so we led them near the snakkril nests. At the time, I'd thought Laria was crazy when she'd suggested driving over the nests and been astonished when it actually worked. At the last minute, we'd averted our course, leaving Doyle and his crew to deal with the creatures.

I already knew Doyle had survived because he'd sent Rick and Neil after us. I assumed by Neil's reaction to Cara's statement that he'd also been onboard one of the solarveyors and lived through the snakkril attack.

With all the people coming and going from Burke's place, knocking wasn't required. I reached for the door handle and urged Neil inside ahead of me. Logan, Burke's second-in-command, along with Vince, another member of the so-called rebels, were lounging in two of the chairs scattered around the room and drinking ales. No doubt one of Nayea's homemade brews.

The older ketaurran woman had lost her ketiorra during the war and had made the settlement her home years ago. She was the resident doctor and utilized local plant life to concoct anything medicinal, from simple healing salves to birth control. Besides mothering the males and anyone else who worked with Burke, my friends and me included, she made the best alcoholic beverages in the area.

"Hey, guys," Cara said as she shoved Rick into the room.

Logan's dark gaze locked on the shackles, and he raised an inquiring brow. "New friends?"

Most of the males Burke had recruited were big guys, well-muscled from training and deadly with a blade. Logan's dark hair and eyes, along with the short growth of beard on his upper lip and chin, added to his threatening appearance.

Vince, on the other hand, was more laid-back. His eyes had more of an amber hue. When combined with his tawny hair and charming smile, the guy was all kinds of hot and had quite a few of the single females in the settlement chasing after him. If I hadn't lost my heart to Khyron years ago, I might have accepted one of his many offers to be more than good friends.

"Couple of Doyle's guys. They thought it would be fun to attack us on the way here." I gave Neil a nudge. "Do you have a cell available that we can use? I'm sure Burke will want to talk to them when he gets back."

"Not a problem." Vince lowered his half-empty glass, balancing it on his leg, then glancing behind me. "Where's Burke? Last time I saw him, he said he was heading to Aztrashar to meet with Laria, Sloane, and you."

"He found us." I was exhausted and preferred to keep things brief. Vince could get real chatty depending on how much ale he'd consumed.

"Speaking of Laria and Sloane? Why aren't they with you? I thought you three always traveled together." Logan took another long sip from his drink.

"Something came up, and they all decided to stay in the city a little longer. I expect them to show up in a few days, and Burke can tell you all about it himself." Actually, I had no idea how long they'd be waiting for Khyron to wake up or when they'd be coming home. I glanced at Cara, expecting her to correct me, but only received a smile and shrug.

"These two geniuses battered the back end of Laria's transport, so I'll need someone to take a solarveyor out in the morning and tow it back here so I can repair it," Cara said.

Logan snorted, pinning Neil and Rick with an empathetic look. "I wouldn't want to be either of you when Laria finds out what you did to Trixie."

"You can't keep us here." Rick jerked away from me. "Doyle will come looking for us, and when he does…"

None of us were intimidated by his threat, least of all Cara. She shook her head. "Do you really think Doyle cares what happens to you?"

Logan got to his feet and set his drink on a nearby table. "Cara, why don't you let me help you with them?"

"Can you also find a secure place to keep this?" Cara handed Logan her laser weapon.

"This one too." I handed over the one I was carrying.

Logan took the weapons and shook his head. "So the rumors were true?"

I didn't like the way Rick was suddenly paying close attention to our conversation. "Yeah, but we can talk about it later." Any discussions we had about the laser weapons needed to stay private. We couldn't risk any information getting back to Doyle.

After watching the way Doyle had gone after Burke during the short time we were prisoners in the compound, I believed all the stories I'd heard about the male. Something had happened to the guy's mind after the crash, his thinking turned crazy and unpredictable.

We hadn't been able to prove it, but my friends and I thought Doyle had connections with Sarus during the war. We'd all heard that the old drezdarr's power-hungry brother had been killed, but Jardun was convinced he hadn't died. If he was right, then Khyron's life, as well as those of all humans, was still in danger.

As much as I agreed with Cara that Doyle didn't care about his men, there was the possibility he might attack the settlement out of revenge, or if he thought the toxins were here. Rick and Neil might have valuable information that we needed. "Oh, and Logan." He was halfway across the room helping Cara take Rick and Neil to the back of the building.

"Yeah." He stopped and glanced over his shoulder.

"You might want to have Nayea take a look at their wounds. We wouldn't want them to die before Burke has a chance to talk to them."

***

Khyron

Garyck had barely gotten the solarveyor stopped behind Laria's transport before I hurried outside.

"Khyron, wait!" Jardun shouted.

I heard an exasperated growl and knew if I glanced over my shoulder, he'd right behind me. When I reached the exterior entrance, I found the door open, the interior empty.

There was no sign of Celeste or Cara anywhere. I sensed that whatever had transpired wasn't good, that we were too late. The throbbing in my head and the pressure in my chest were almost unbearable. I wanted to search for Celeste, but the area around us was vast, and looking without knowing what happened here first would do no good and be a waste of valuable time.

Was this going to be my punishment for failing her all those years ago? Hoping I would get another chance to make things right only to have the opportunity stolen from me, to have her stolen from me?

"Khyron." Zaedon interrupted my thoughts. "This is a laser burn." Zaedon ran his hand over the darkened area near the door's exterior frame. "The mark is similar to the ones on the hull of the solarveyor." He jutted his chin toward our transport.

"It appears whoever did this rammed them first, which damaged the engine and forced them to stop," Jardun said as he approached from the other side of the vehicle with Laria walking beside him.

Laria stood with her arms crossed and studied the transport's structure. I sensed a controlled anger burning within the depths of her intense green gaze.

"There is blood." Garyck scowled, then swiped the metal frame at the base of the door, his fingertip smudged with crimson liquid.

"I don't think it belongs to Cara or Celeste." Sloane appeared in the opening above him from inside the transport.

"What makes you think the females were unharmed?" The pale green on Thrayn's face had darkened as soon as Garyck mentioned the blood.

A female did not need to be a male's ketiorra for him to feel the overpowering need to protect her. It was an instinct built into our primal nature. All the ketaurran males in the group would be experiencing a similar response.

Mine was clearly the worst, almost to the point of debilitating. The need to find those responsible for taking Celeste from me sent rage rippling through me.

"Because someone removed a metal panel from the wall in here." She hitched her thumb over her shoulder. "My guess is they used it to protect themselves from the lasers. And since there're no burn marks inside the transport other than the one on the panel, I'm guessing they threw their blades before their attackers could do any shooting.

"Celeste and Cara wouldn't have given up without a fight. There'd be signs of a struggle… And way more blood." She sidestepped Garyck's bulky frame, then jumped to the ground. "Besides, Celeste *never* misses when she throws." She grinned at Thrayn, then gave my arm a pat as she moved to stand next to Laria.

"And since there aren't any bodies lying around…" I assumed the nudge Sloane gave Laria with her shoulder was meant to be comforting.

"Means she didn't want whoever did this dead." A hint of satisfaction spread across Laria's face.

I had not known the female long but easily recognized the signs of someone contemplating ways to exact revenge on those who had attacked her friend and damaged her transport.

The Celeste I remembered was strong-willed and determined to get her way when she wanted something. Based on Sloane's comment, my ketiorra had acquired numerous fighting skills since the last time I had seen her. The thought of meeting the female she had become had my tail twitching with anticipation. Now if we could only find her long enough for me to observe and admire these traits for myself.

"I think Sloane is right." Burke approached with Vurell from investigating the roadway up ahead.

The male had not healed completely, and I noticed a slight limp in his step.

"The tracks from the other vehicle head toward the settlement." Burke tipped his head. "This road is the only safe way to get in and out of the area. If someone had planned to take the girls, they wouldn't risk heading in that direction, and we would have seen them if they were returning the way they came."

In case their suppositions were incorrect, I did not want to waste any more time before going after Celeste. "Then we should follow the tracks and continue on to the settlement."

"Wait." Laria stepped into my path to keep me from returning to the solarveyor. "We can't just leave Trixie here. We have to take her with us."

"It is a transport. I am sure it will be fine until morning," I said.

Jardun moved behind Laria and glared at me as if I'd

speared him with a blade. It was understandable that he wished to keep her happy, but finding my ketiorra was more important. At least that was my assumption until Sloane appeared next to Laria, arms crossed and silently daring me to disagree with her friend.

Judging by the narrowed gazes of the other ketaurran males—with the exception of Thrayn—it appeared they agreed with the females. It did not seem to matter that I was the drezdarr, the leader of the planet's inhabitants, the one whose orders were supposed to be fulfilled without question. Knowing this was a battle I could not win, I sighed. "Do whatever you must to tow your Trixie."

***

Khyron

"Garyck, you can park in front of that large building over there." Burke had gotten up and now stood behind the pilot seat. "Right next to the transport I believe we were following."

It was late in the evening, but the storm had passed and the glow from the nearest of our two moons lit the sky. Time passed too slowly between finding Laria's transport and arriving at the settlement. Because of the growing darkness and the limited light provided by the guiding beam at the front of the solarveyor, we had to stop several times to confirm we were still following the other vehicle's tracks.

The anxiety strumming through my body refused to give in to my exhaustion. What little sleep I obtained during the drive did not last long and was interrupted each time we stopped.

Hearing we had finally reached our destination relieved some of my tension. Hopefully, the remainder of my stress would disappear once I saw Celeste and confirmed she was safe. Though I much preferred holding her in my arms, I was certain, after her parting words to Vurell, it was not something I could expect to happen anytime soon.

The minute I exited the transport, Laria appeared by my side and placed her hand on my arm. "Khyron, maybe you should let Sloane and me go in first."

I restrained my impatience. "I already gave you my word I would not hurt Celeste."

"It's not Celeste I'm worried about."

"I do not understand," Jardun said. "Do you really think she would try to harm him?" It was obvious by his concern that Celeste had earned my friend's respect. Yet the vryndarr, the role of protector, was present in the way he straightened his shoulders.

"Let's just say I'm not sure how she'll react and would prefer not to risk it," Laria said.

The Celeste I remembered had a temper, but I did not believe she would ever purposely hurt me. "I appreciate your concern, but I value Celeste's welfare over mine." I deserved her wrath and much more, but refused to share my opinion openly. I stepped up onto the platform surrounding the building and headed for the entrance before anyone else tried to stop me.

I did not think Zaedon cutting me off to reach the door ahead of me had anything to do with protecting me. Not when he rushed inside, then stopped once his gaze landed on the female with short curly hair sitting at the end of a long table and drinking what appeared to be an ale. "Cara." His usually friendly tone was curt and made me wonder what the female had done to annoy him.

"Zaedon." Her reply was just as curt, their gazes locked in a challenging stare until she noticed Laria and Sloane enter the room. She looked away from him with a smile. "Hey guys, I didn't expect you for another week or so." She set her drink on the table and pushed out of her chair.

"Told you it wasn't their blood." Sloane smiled at me with smug satisfaction, then crossed the room and wrapped her arms around Cara's neck.

I remembered when Celeste had introduced me to the human tradition of hugging. She would greet me with them a lot and I enjoyed letting her. They always led to holding her in my arms and kissing. If I continued to think about sampling her soft lips, my shaft would grow uncomfortably hard, undoubtedly noticeable. I immediately returned my attention to the conversation going on around me.

"Where's Celeste?" Laria asked before I had the chance. "Is she okay?"

"She's fine. Said she was tired and headed back to your place to get some sleep." Cara returned to her seat.

I was relieved that she was all right, yet frustrated that our meeting would be postponed again. As much as I longed to be near her, I would not enter her sleeping chamber without an invitation. I also considered her blade-wielding abilities and decided startling her would be unwise and possibly fatal.

One of the two human males sitting not far from Cara asked, "Damn, Burke, you look like hell. What happened?"

"My reunion with Doyle didn't go as well as I'd expected," Burke grumbled and took a seat in a chair near the wall.

"Might explain why we have two of his men in holding cells out back," the same male said.

"Before we start discussing private information, care to introduce your traveling companions?" The other male had been scrutinizing my friends and me since we'd entered the building.

"Everyone, this is Vince and Logan, my second-in-command." Burke tipped his head at the males in our group. "You already know Zaedon and Garyck."

The four males exchanged acknowledging nods, reminding me that they must have met when Jardun sent Zaedon and Garyck to ask for Burke's help in rescuing Vurell.

Burke shifted sideways and swept his hand through the

air. "This is Jardun, Thrayn, and Vurell, the drezdarr's physician. And in case you hadn't guessed, this is the drezdarr." He pointed in my direction.

"Khyron." I corrected, hating the formalities that came with the title. If my plans for the future collaboration were successful, I preferred to earn their respect via my leadership capabilities.

"It's an honor to meet you." Vince continued to clutch his drink as he got to his feet. "I met your father shortly after our ship crashed. He was a great man. I mean male. I was sorry to hear about his death."

"Thank you." I forced an appreciative smile and pushed away the resurfacing memories of that horrible time. A time I associated with pain and loss. A time that changed my life forever.

"Burke, you never said anything about bringing the drezdarr back with you before you left." Suspicion laced Logan's voice.

His reaction was not unexpected, nor the first time I had experienced similar disdain. After the war, some humans resented all ketaurrans for what had happened. I understood and did not blame them for their mistrust, but it was something I hoped to change in the future.

Burke straightened his shoulders. It was clear he did not like having his decisions questioned. I was afraid the discussion would quickly turn into an argument and interceded. "He was not made aware of the request until this morning, but has offered to provide me with a tour of the settlement." Now was not the time to discuss either my desire to see Celeste or my proposition, not until Logan was more comfortable with my presence.

My explanation did not seem to ease the tension radiating through the room. The males in my group remained near the closed door and protectively by my side. Even Vurell had not made an effort to integrate with the human males.

"Anyone thirsty? Nayea makes the best homemade ale

in the area."

In the short time I had been around Laria, I had grown to appreciate her intuitiveness, even more so as I watched her open a cabinet and retrieve several empty glasses, then place them on the table.

"Feel free to help yourselves." She poured a glass and brought it to me. She leaned close and whispered, "Why don't you sit down before you fall down?"

I had done my best to keep the poor condition of my scales covered, but keeping my exhausted, still-recovering state from appearing on my face was difficult. "Thank you." After accepting the drink, I took the closest chair, which happened to be next to Burke.

Laria took Jardun's hand and pulled him toward the table. Within minutes, everyone had poured themselves a drink from one of two large containers sitting in the middle of the table, then found a place to get comfortable either in a chair or leaning against a wall.

Sloane waited until everyone was settled before plopping down in the chair next to Cara. "Sooo, what happened to Trixie? And don't leave out any of the juicy details."

CHAPTER SIX

Celeste

I woke early, not long after the first rays of sunlight filtered into my room. I'd been telling the truth when I told Cara I was exhausted, more from emotional stress than our encounter with Doyle's men. I'd left Burke's dwelling shortly after Cara and Logan returned from locking up Rick and Neil. The place I shared with Laria and Sloane seemed overly quiet and empty, and didn't provide the comfort I'd been hoping for.

I should have asked Cara to come along and stay with me, because getting any restful sleep was hard without my friends there. Even the blue-green light from the glowing zapharite stones I kept next to my bed to keep away the nightmares hadn't helped as I'd expected. Instead, reliving memories of losing my parents and helplessly being forced to watch my sister die, my dreams were filled with images of Khyron painfully crying out from his bed and not being able to do anything to help him.

The only pleasant memory I retained from my dream about Khyron was the possessive way he'd curled his tail around the back of my legs. It was something I'd enjoyed from our previous time together, that and the way being in his arms always made me feel safe.

Not in the mood to be alone or deal with Logan and the possibility of more questions I didn't want to answer, I decided to visit Harper. Harper's fiancé had been killed during the first year of the war, and since then, she'd devoted herself to taking care of the homeless children. A motherly role for which she'd been truly suited.

Her two-story dwelling was the settlement's version of an orphanage or a children's home. Everyone who lived in the community referred to it as Harper's place. Things were hard enough for the children, so everyone refrained from calling it an orphanage so they wouldn't be reminded that they'd lost their parents.

The settlement wasn't huge, but the community, which consisted of homes and a few businesses, was spread out. Not everyone was fortunate enough to own a transport, so most of the inhabitants traveled everywhere on foot.

The handful of settlements, predominantly occupied by humans, was located on lush flatlands great for farming. Other than the rocky area filled with caverns in the distance, the area surrounding the community was covered with unusual plants and trees in brilliant shades of blue, yellow, and occasionally orange. The buildings in the ketaurran cities were constructed with a combination of stone and various versions of sand, a contrast to the settlements, which were mainly built from wood.

Between the mission and my extended stay in Aztrashar, I'd been away longer than I'd expected and missed my daily visits with the children. After a quick shower and changing into clean clothes, I took a shortcut between buildings and arrived just after the children had finished breakfast.

Melissa, a ten-year-old girl with two tawny braids on each side of her head, was a slow eater and still sitting at the table. She flashed a pair of chocolate-brown eyes in my direction. "Celeste, we missed you." She grinned and patted the bench she was sitting on, then scooted over to make room for me at the long table.

I tweaked one of her braids. "I missed you too." I snagged the last pytienna, a flat pancake made from meat and plants, off one of the serving plates, then sat next to her.

A few seconds later, Gabe and Ben, two of the boys I spent a lot of time teaching how to handle blades, entered the room with Harper following close behind them. Some of her curly auburn locks had escaped from the tie at her nape, and the flush on her face made her freckles more prominent.

She had her arms wrapped around a squirming two-year-old and was unsuccessfully trying to remove her hair from his tiny fist. I knew other half-human, half-ketaurran children existed, but Draejill was the only one I'd ever seen. He was the cutest thing ever with his golden locks and pale tangerine skin and scales.

I'd wondered more than once how different things would've been if Khyron hadn't left. If we'd stayed together, would we have one or more little ones just like Draejill?

Gabe saw me, and his eyes widened. "You're back. Does this mean we get a lesson today?"

A year separated the two dark-haired boys. Ben was twelve and the older of the two. They were the best of friends and always together, reminding me of the close relationship I had with Laria and Sloane.

"No lessons until you finish cleaning up and doing the dishes." Harper ignored their groans as they halfheartedly picked up dirty plates, then shuffled from the room. She walked to my end of the table, leaning forward to give me a hug. She glanced at the half-eaten pytienna in my hand, then asked, "Can I fix you something else to eat?"

"Thanks, but I'm good." I set down the cake and held out my arms.

"Go, Ceeste," Draejill said with a giggle, then launched himself from Harper to me.

I'd barely gotten him settled in my lap when I heard a whiny growl and glanced at the four-legged creature standing near my feet. He was the size of a small dog and had white tufts of fur sticking out between his violet scales. He dropped his rear on the floor and pawed my leg.

"Fuzzball, no begging," Harper scolded.

The cute little creature had been living in the house as the resident pet since Melissa found him over a year ago near the clearing where I practiced with the boys. We were pretty sure he'd been abandoned since we couldn't find his mother or any signs of other similar creatures. I'd made the mistake of calling him a fuzzball the first time I saw him, and somehow, the name stuck.

I shook my head when he ignored Harper and continued to whine. "Sorry, you heard her. No more food." I was as bad as the children when it came to the lovable little guy and would've shared my food with him if Harper hadn't been around.

Fuzzball groaned, then dropped down on his belly.

"If you won't let me make you any breakfast, at least let me get you a cup of freegea." Harper didn't give me a chance to answer before turning and heading for the kitchen.

Freegea was derived from an orange plant with brown stripes, whose name I could never remember. Since all the packaged coffee that survived the crash had been consumed long ago, it was the closest substitute we could find for the drink many of us had enjoyed back on Earth. Though it had a decent flavor, it lacked any natural stimulants, was a light brown color, and was the equivalent of drinking an herbal tea.

"Guess you'll be staying for a while." Melissa happily wiggled in her seat, then took a bite from her pytienna.

Everyone who'd met Harper knew it was pointless to argue with her. I untangled the end of my braid from

Draejill's grasp, then grinned at Melissa. "I guess so."

***

Khyron

I had learned long ago that resting deeply could cost me my life and had trained myself to be a light sleeper, but that night, I was overruled by my exhausted body. I did not wake until long after the sun had warmed my room, and felt slightly better than I had the day before.

While I prepared for the day, I contemplated everything I had discovered since leaving for the settlement and Cara's explanation about the attack on Laria's transport. I had a hard time reconciling the Celeste she described with the female I once knew, the female who had stolen my heart.

During the previous evening's conversation, I had learned that Burke's dwelling was not only his home but also housed some of the males who worked for him. He had additional sleeping quarters in the upper level and provided the members of my group with their own rooms. By the time discussions had ended, it was late. Laria and Sloane did not want to disturb Celeste, so they had decided to spend the night here.

Sitting on the end of the bed, I had one boot on and was reaching for the other when I heard a loud rap. The door opened, and Vurell walked inside before I had a chance to say anything. "You look exhausted, and the color of your scales has not returned to the extent I would like."

The male had never been good at greetings or respecting my boundaries. "Please, come in." I ignored his frown and finished tugging on my other boot, then got up to grab my belt and sword from the chair near the door. When Vurell crossed his arms and refused to move from the entryway so I could pass, I returned an equally menacing glare. "Stop hovering. I am fine."

"You are not *fine*."

If we were discussing anything but my health, I would agree. Emotionally, I was not fine and would not be until I saw Celeste.

Vurell held up his hand. "I know you wish to find the female, but it will do no good if you collapse at her feet."

"I do not care if I collapse at her feet as long as I can see for myself that she is unharmed." I wrapped the belt around my waist and secured the clasp, then adjusted the sword so it pressed against my right hip.

"She is that important to you?" The tightness in his jaw slackened, and he lowered his arms. "I did not realize she was your…"

So far, Jardun was the only one who knew the whole truth, and I planned to keep it that way. I shook my head to silence him. "A fact I would urge you to keep to yourself." The war had intervened all those years ago, and I never got the chance to tell Celeste she was my ketiorra.

Vurell nodded, then stepped out of my way.

Before I reached the outer hallway, Vurell said, "At least take Thrayn with you. He can drag your body back when the female finishes with you."

Annoyed, I scowled at him over my shoulder. "Your attempt at humor is not appreciated." As I headed for the gathering room, the sound of Vurell's laughter echoed behind me.

The aroma of cooked meat filled the air and reminded me I had not eaten much the previous day. I followed the scent to the cooking area, a room the humans referred to as a kitchen. Zaedon, Garyck, and Sloane were seated at a smaller version of the table in the main room. Their plates contained food from the platters scattered across the wooden surface. Laria and Jardun had yet to rise. I did not expect to see Cara. She had her own place and had left shortly before everyone retired.

Burke stood next to a counter pouring hot liquid into a

large mug. "Morning." He glanced in my direction. "We have some freshly brewed freegea. Want a cup?"

"Yes, thank you." I took a seat next to Zaedon and across from Sloane and Garyck.

"I assume you slept well. Your scales actually have some color today," Zaedon said.

It appeared I was not going to avoid having the state of my health be a topic of interest for my friends, a topic I was not going to encourage with a response.

Burke set a cup in front of me before taking a seat. "If you're interested, I'll take you on a tour of the settlement tomorrow...provided you're still in one piece when you get back from seeing Celeste." He hid his grin by taking a sip of his drink.

"Ignore him." Sloane handed me an empty plate from a stack sitting on the end of the table to her right. "Garyck decided our food wasn't good enough and went hunting this morning." She picked a piece of meat off her plate with her fingers. "It's not bad if you like your food overcooked."

Garyck grunted and snatched the morsel from her hand.

"Hey, I wasn't done with that." Sloane tried to grab it back but wasn't fast enough to stop Garyck from shoving it in his mouth.

I placed some food on my plate and ate while I half listened to Garyck and Sloane. Their banter consisted of him making noises and her responding as if she knew exactly what he meant.

"Khyron." I turned my head toward the sound of Thrayn's voice. "I believe you are in need of my assistance today, that you require an escort."

I was going to ask him where he got that idea until I saw Vurell sauntering into the room behind him, a huge smirk on his face.

"Until the humans are more comfortable with our presence, having someone accompany you is not a bad idea," Zaedon said.

I preferred to see Celeste alone but understood his concern. Arguing or ordering them to stay behind would do no good. They would follow me anyway, especially since I had already survived one attempt on my life. "I will take Thrayn with me." He hadn't interacted with the humans as much as the others had, and if Burke and the females agreed to the plans I had for the future, then learning more about their culture would be beneficial.

Impatient to be leaving, I washed down my last bite with the remainder of my freegea, then got to my feet. "Can you tell me where to find Celeste?" I directed the question to Sloane.

"Are you sure you don't want me to go with you?" Sloane asked after taking a sip of her drink.

Thrayn puffed out his chest. "I am going with him, and I assure you he will not need additional assistance from a female."

Sloane briefly narrowed her eyes, and I was certain she would do something to make Thrayn regret his statement.

Instead, she shrugged and settled back into her chair. "Suit yourself. Just remember our bet." She gave the blade strapped to Thrayn's hip an appreciative glance. "I'll expect you to hand over my blade when you get back."

Thrayn snorted and gripped the hilt possessively. "*My* blade will remain where it is."

"You can discuss ownership later. Right now, I would like to leave and find Celeste," I ordered.

After supplying me with instructions to her home, Sloane grinned. "Oh, and if she's not home, you might try Harper's place. It's the two-story building on the other end of the main street, the one with all the children running around."

"Thank you." I gave Sloane an appreciative nod and headed for the exit.

Though I had never been to this settlement, having humans stop and stare was not an uncommon experience.

Seeing two ketaurran males armed with swords and traipsing through their community had no doubt brought back unwanted memories of another time. A time when others of my kind had tried to take control and slaughtered humans for being different.

When I was younger, there was a time during the war when my sire was still alive when I had kept my identity secret and traveled with a group of soldiers rather than the vryndarr. We knew Sarus's men were targeting humans, so I had visited several of the settlements to ensure they remained protected. It was where I met Celeste. After the report of her death, the memories were too painful, and I refused to visit the human communities anymore.

Sloane's assumption that Celeste would not be in their dwelling had been accurate. A fact confirmed by an older ketaurran female named Nayea, but not until I had answered all her questions and she was convinced I was truly the drezdarr. After learning Celeste had gone to Harper's home, it had not taken Thrayn and me long to reach the dwelling.

It seemed that Celeste was well-liked within the community, because Harper was just as skeptical and protective as Nayea had been. She didn't care about my title and seemed even less impressed with Thrayn when he tried to intimidate an answer from her. After making him wait outside and listening to me apologetically answer all her questions, she finally told me where I could find Celeste.

Harper's instructions led us through a heavily wooded area some distance away.

"Are you sure the female provided you with an accurate location?" Thrayn asked.

I wondered the same thing until laughter came from the other side of a copse of trees with deep blue trunks, the upper branches covered with thorns.

"That wasn't bad. Try to keep your aim straighter when you throw." Hearing Celeste's voice made my heart race. I fought to keep my pace steady and my tail from happily swishing back and forth.

I moved through the trees and found her in a clearing with two young human males. They were facing away from Thrayn and me, focused on throwing knives at trees on the opposite side of the area. "Celeste." I wanted to get her attention before her next throw.

She cringed, then spun, poised with a knife in her hand. I did not believe she had it in her to cause me bodily harm, so I remained immobile and watched the blade sail through the air. I released the breath I was holding when it missed my head and plunged into the trunk of the tree behind me.

It was the first time I had ever seen Thrayn move his mouth without speaking. I was glad he had been too stunned to react and had not decided to dive in front of me.

"What are you doing here, and how did you know…"

She must have realized Laria and Sloane had told me where to find her. "I can't believe they…" She fisted her hands and continued to ramble. "Did Vurell tell you what I said? Is that why you're here?"

She had matured a great deal and was more beautiful than the last time I had seen her. Her body was lean, her muscles more defined. Her brown hair was pulled back in a single braid that reached the middle of her back. It glistened in the sunlight, and I longed to pull it free, to splay it across her shoulders. I had forgotten how her cinnamon eyes darkened and shimmered when she was angry. "He did." I held back a grin. "And no."

Celeste crossed her arms. "Then why are you here?"

Thrayn interrupted by placing a hand on the hilt of his sword and taking an intimidating step forward. "You do know there are consequences for attacking the drezdarr. He could have you thrown in a cell for attempting to take his life."

"You're not taking Celeste anywhere." One of the

young males clutched his blade and moved to stand in front of her. I guessed his age to be no more than eleven or twelve and admired the fierce way he tried to protect her from Thrayn.

I pinched the bridge of my nose. Further confrontation instigated by my vryndarr would not help the situation, and I wanted to throttle Vurell for insisting I bring the male with me. "Thrayn, enough. Go stand over there." I pointed to an area on my right, far enough away to keep him from interfering. "I believe I can speak for myself."

"Of course." Thrayn frowned and bowed his head, then stomped to the spot I had indicated. The arrogant male still had many things to learn about his new role as a vryndarr. I knew it would come in time, but at the moment, I did not have the patience to deal with him, not when it came to Celeste.

"Can we speak *alone*?" I glanced at the two young males.

Celeste placed a hand on each of their shoulders and squeezed. "You guys head back to Harper's place. I'll be there shortly."

"But what if he…" The taller of the two hadn't taken his dark eyes off Thrayn.

"I'll be okay. Now go…please."

They reluctantly dragged their feet, shooting frowns and glares at me over their shoulders before disappearing through the trees.

I had had plenty of time since leaving the city to ponder how this meeting would go. So far, nothing had gone as I had imagined. Celeste didn't budge, nor did she say anything, further proof my arrival had not made her happy.

I wanted to move closer but was afraid any movement might make things worse. "Do not be angry with your friends. It took a great deal of convincing for them to share your location."

"That still doesn't explain why you're here."

"I wanted to thank you for risking your life to save mine." There were many other things I wanted to tell her but knew now was not the time. They would have to wait until later. Now that I knew where she was and that she was safe, I had no intention of returning to the city until I told her everything I wanted to say.

"Seems like a long way to travel just to say thanks, but whatever, you're welcome. Now if you'll excuse me, I need to go." She spun on her heels, took a few steps, then stopped. "Oh, and Khyron?" She spoke without looking at me.

"Yes." I took a hopeful step forward.

"Enjoy your trip back to the city." Celeste strode in the direction the young males had taken, the sway of her hips accentuated with each irritated step she took.

After she disappeared through the trees, Thrayn appeared by my side. "I cannot believe she tried to kill you."

"Her aim was perfect." I retrieved her knife from the tree and smiled. "If she wanted to kill me, I would already be dead."

"Do you wish for me to go after her?" Thrayn asked.

"No, but I need some time alone and would like you to return to Burke's home to wait with the others."

Thrayn's gaze widened. "But who will protect…"

I cut him off with a glare. "I am quite capable of protecting myself."

After Thrayn left, I lowered myself to the ground near the closest tree, using the trunk to brace my back. I closed my eyes and let images of Celeste fill my thoughts. Not long into my musings, I heard rustling close by and assumed Thrayn had disregarded my order and returned. I forced my eyes open, ready to admonish him for disobeying, and found a young human girl with inquisitive brown eyes and braids on each side of her head peeking at me from behind a tree.

"Are you really the drezdarr?" she asked as she took

several hesitant steps into the clearing.

"I am, but you may call me Khyron." I smiled when she grinned. "And what is your name?"

She took a few more steps. "Melissa."

"What are you doing out here all alone?" I patted the ground next to me, then chuckled when she rushed to take a seat.

"I was watching Gabe and Ben train with Celeste. When I get a little older, she promised to train me too," she stated proudly.

"I have no doubt you will be very good at it."

She twisted her hands in her lap. "Celeste was really angry with you. What did you do to her?"

The intricacies that accompanied adult relationships were difficult to explain, and I did not want the child to worry. "It is complicated."

"Harper always tells us to apologize when we do something wrong. Maybe you should give Celeste flowers or something." Her smile widened. "The chirayka are her favorites."

I remembered Celeste's fondness for the deep purple blossoms. "That is a very good idea. Thank you."

Melissa jumped to her feet and eagerly held out her hand. "If you want, I can show you where to find some."

CHAPTER SEVEN

Celeste

I couldn't believe Khyron came all this way to thank me for saving his life, yet he couldn't tell me he was sorry for not keeping his promise, for not coming back for me years ago when I needed him the most. I'd been fuming by the time I'd returned to Harper's house to check on Ben and Gabe to let them know I was okay. The bravery the two boys had shown when they'd faced off against Thrayn, who was no doubt a vryndarr, hadn't surprised me. Their lives had been hard, and they'd grown up tough.

I didn't want to admit it, but I was thankful and admired the way Khyron defused the situation before anyone got hurt. It irritated me even more to realize the attraction was still there, that I couldn't stop noticing how handsome he was or worry about the pale condition of his scales.

Part of me wanted to spend more time with the children, but if Khyron was here, then so were Laria and Sloane.

I felt betrayed and more than a little angry with my friends for bringing him to the settlement, but my rational side didn't fault them. Khyron had always been charming and could be very persuasive when he wanted something. Since our relationship ended so long ago, I had no idea what that something was, but I intended to find out, and I was certain my roommates had the answer.

When I walked out of the woods, I noticed a familiar transport sitting on the road in front of Harper's house. It belonged to Joe, a middle-aged guy who traveled between the few remaining settlements selling and trading goods. Most of his inventory consisted of clothes made by some very talented ketaurran females from several of the cities. There was a market area set up on the other end of the community for all visiting traders. Whenever Harper needed clothes for the children, that was where she'd go to get them. Joe knew traders weren't allowed to solicit homes, so I found it strange to discover his vehicle parked here.

I opened the door to the rear entrance and heard raised voices coming from the front of the dwelling.

"I said no. Now please leave." Harper had her back to me and was trying to keep a guy I didn't recognize near the front door and out of her home. He appeared to be in his late twenties, maybe early thirties. The uneven cut of his hair and the long bangs covering his forehead made it hard to tell for sure. He hadn't seen a bath in a day or two, and his clothes looked as if he'd been sleeping in them.

Ben and Gabe stood off to the side, holding Draejill's hands between them. Ben nervously rocked from one foot to the other. Gabe fisted his free hand, possibly contemplating going for the blade on his hip so he could help Harper. Draejill's lower lip quivered, and he'd soon be shedding tears.

I didn't care who this guy was. Nobody got away with upsetting the children, not when I was around. Fueled by a new wave of fury, I walked farther into the room. "What's going on here?"

"Celeste, thank goodness." The stiffness in Harper's

shoulders relaxed, and she shot a relieved glance in my direction.

"Just some honest trading," the guy said as he inched to his left, giving me a better view. "Name's Travis. And you are?" His grin, along with the way his dark, narrow-set eyes roamed up and down, then stopped when they reached my breasts, made me shudder.

"I'm the one asking the questions." I placed my hand on my hip, ready to draw my blade if necessary, then realized I'd left it in the tree after I'd thrown it at Khyron. I had a thinner blade in my boot, but bending over to grab it would cost me valuable time if he figured out what I was doing and reached for Harper.

"No need to get upset. I was just telling the girly here that I know of a good home for the little one over there." He pointed at Draejill, the movement enough to cause the tears I'd predicted to trickle down the child's pale orange face.

"Good home, my…" Harper huffed. "He was trying to negotiate a trade."

"Where's Joe, and why do you have his transport?" I asked, even though I was pretty sure I already knew the answer.

"He was sick of trading, decided to retire." Travis tapped the side of his leg.

I had a feeling Travis was lying, that something bad had happened to Joe, that there was a good chance he was dead. Even if Joe had decided to stop trading, which was doubtful, vehicles were hard to come by, and he never would have gotten rid of his transport.

More than likely, this guy was a bandit or slaver pretending to be a trader. There was no point in explaining the settlement's rules about trading. If I was right, he was a greedy lowlife who had no use for rules and took what he wanted. He was dangerous, and I needed to get him out of the house and away from the children. "We're not interested in your offer, so I think you should leave."

"Who's going to make me? You?"

"If I have to, yes." I'd need to act quickly if I didn't want anyone other than Travis to get hurt.

"Sure you will." Travis dismissed me with a laugh, then stepped to his right. "I'll be taking the little one with me."

"Don't you touch him." Harper backed away from Travis and placed herself protectively in front of the boys.

I felt small fingertips brush the back of my bare arm. I risked a quick glance over my shoulder and found Gabe standing behind me so Travis couldn't see him. He'd unclasped the sheath from his belt and held it out in front of him. Amazed by his ingenuity, I forced back a grin, nodded, then reached behind me. As soon as Gabe pressed the hilt against my palm and tugged on the sheath, I shouted, "Hey, Travis!"

The second Travis jerked his head in my direction, I released the knife.

His eyes widened, and he stepped to the left, the throw I'd meant for his shoulder slicing his forearm and ending up in the wall behind him. Travis growled, his disbelieving glare jumping from the blood trickling down his arm to me.

I had already retrieved the blade in my boot by the time his shock had worn off.

I glared at Travis, poised to throw again. "You can either leave now, or the next one takes out an organ." This wasn't Earth. There were no prisons, no long-term places to keep criminals. And if I was alone, I wouldn't hesitate to take his life, because I knew if he got the chance, he wouldn't hesitate to take mine. The children had witnessed enough death in their short lives, and I didn't want them to see what I was capable of or give them another nightmare to deal with.

"And she won't miss." Gabe moved next to Harper. She'd scooped up Draejill, who now had his head on her shoulder and was sobbing against her neck.

"Nope, she won't," Ben added with a bob of his head.

When Travis didn't respond right away, I was afraid he wouldn't heed my warning. "This ain't over." He shoved the door open and strode outside.

I followed far enough to watch him get in Joe's transport and drive away. Letting him leave was probably a mistake, but there was nothing I could do about it. Even if I ran all the way to Burke's place to get another vehicle, Travis would be long gone.

I'd still need to let Burke or one of his guys know what had happened. At the moment, I was more concerned about Harper and the children. I returned my blade to its hiding spot in my boot, then turned to go back inside.

"Is he okay?" I asked, glancing at Draejill, who was no longer crying.

"A little shaken up, but I think he'll be fine." Harper tenderly rubbed his back.

"Nice job." I mussed Gabe's hair, then added, "Both of you" so Ben wouldn't feel left out.

Ben, always the worrier, furrowed his brow and looked at me, then Harper. "You're not going to scold Celeste for throwing knives in the house, are you?"

"No." Harper draped an arm around his shoulder and smiled. "I think under the circumstances, we'll let it go this time."

***

After leaving Harper's, I decided to head for Burke's place to let someone know about Travis's attempt to take Draejill. I knew there was a good chance Khyron might be there, but the child's safety was more important than dealing with the personal issues I had with the drezdarr. Luckily, I ran into Logan halfway to my destination. He promised to relay the information on to Burke and also send word to the other settlements so they could be on the lookout for Travis. Our settlement wasn't the only one with orphans or children with human and ketaurran parents. There was always the chance that Travis would try to steal another child.

Logan was good at disguising his emotions, always presenting a hardcore exterior. But underneath his tough persona was a softy when it came to children. I'd bet anything that after he talked to Burke, he'd be stopping by to check on Harper and spend some time with the kids.

Once that was out of the way, it was time to track down Laria and Sloane and find out what the heck was going on and how Khyron had known where to look for me. The clearing in the woods was fairly secluded. Ketaurrans rarely visited the settlement, and if he'd arrived on his own, very few would've told him where to find me.

There were only a couple of places my friends might be, so I decided to start with our shared home first. I was glad when I arrived and didn't see any of the vryndarr hanging around. I didn't mind spending time with Zaedon and Jardun. Even Garyck, with his grumpy attitude, had kind of grown on me. The male rarely had much to say, and Sloane was the only one who understood his grunts and snorts. The ketaurran males were also Khyron's friends and protectors, and I didn't need them relaying any part of my conversation with Laria and Sloane back to him.

I found Laria in the kitchen rifling through bare shelves that hadn't been stocked since the last time we'd traveled.

"Celeste." Concern replaced her smile. "Is everything all right?"

"No, everything is not all right." I might be mad, but it didn't stop me from giving her a hug, then punching her in the arm. "And a heads-up would have been nice." I didn't need to tell her I was referring to Khyron.

"It was late when we got back, so Laria and I stayed at Burke's place. When we got back home, you were gone." Sloane walked into the kitchen, stopping a few feet away from me. "Are you going to punch me too if I give you a hug?"

"I should, but no." I held out my arms and accepted her embrace. It was hard to stay mad at either of them for very long.

"Do you two want to tell me what happened? I thought you weren't going to tell anyone where I went."

"About that." Laria hopped up on a counter, a hint of red flushing her cheeks. "Khyron woke up right after you left, and he was pretty adamant about finding you."

I leaned against the counter next to her. "Why?" Khyron wanting to find me specifically didn't make any sense. He knew I'd threatened to cut out his heart, yet when we spoke in the clearing, it hadn't seem to bother him.

"Not entirely sure, but he was doing that sniffing thing when he reached our quarters and said something about being able to scent you," Laria said.

He'd been asleep when I was in his room. I remembered the way he'd caressed my legs with his tail. Had he been able to sense my presence?

Laria placed a hand on my shoulder. "I know you don't want to hear it, but I think he still cares about you."

"I have to agree," Sloane said. "You should have seen him when we found Trixie abandoned and he thought you'd been hurt. I thought for sure when Garyck showed him the blood that he was going to lose it. I didn't know ketaurran scales could get so pale. Not that Khyron's looked super healthy at the moment."

The mention of his scales reminded me that his body was purging itself of a poison that had almost killed him. I remembered his agonizing moans and wondered if he was still in pain. There was no way he'd healed completely after I left, yet he'd spent the majority of a day traveling in an uncomfortable solarveyor across rough terrain to find me. What did that say about the male? And what did it say about me and the way I'd reacted when he found me?

"Sooo, how did it go with Khyron? Did you try to take his head off?" Sloane clapped her hands together, her eyes beaming with curiosity.

My friend knew me too well, and I answered her with a smirk.

"Yes," Sloane squealed and jumped up and down.

Sometimes her childish antics were confusing, so I turned to Laria, since she was the more rational of my friends. "Care to explain?"

"I assume you met Thrayn," Laria said.

"If you mean the ketaurran male who threatened to toss me in a cell, then yes, I met him." And I'd been less than impressed.

"Well, Sloane and Thrayn had a bet about how you'd react when you saw Khyron again." She smiled. "Let's just say he's not going to be happy about giving her his blade."

"And it's a nice blade too." Sloan giggled. "Has a blue-black finish."

"I can't believe you didn't just steal it," I teased.

"I might have if Thrayn hadn't been so arrogant and in need of an adjustment about the way he viewed human females." Sloane dropped into a chair, then propped her feet on the edge of the table.

"Oh, and before I forget, Cara told us what happened with Trixie," Laria said.

"Wait, why aren't you mad? I promised to take care of her, and now she's damaged." I'd been so focused on Khyron, I hadn't realized until now that Laria was taking what happened to her transport better than I'd expected.

"Because I know Doyle's men are responsible, not you." Laria slowly curled her lips into a devious grin. "And I found out that Logan will be the one interrogating them later."

Logan was a nice enough guy but had a reputation for being ruthless when it came to protecting humans. I'd be surprised if Rick and Neil were still alive after he finished with them.

"That reminds me, we're invited to Burke's for the evening meal," Laria said.

"Khyron's still here, isn't he?"

"Yes, they all are."

My body was a conflicting mess of emotions. My stomach clenched into a tight knot while the rest of me warmed at the thought of being in the same room with Khyron again. Part of me wanted to see him, to be near him. Another part of me, my rational side, urged me to stay away. "You two have fun, because I'm staying here."

Sloane sighed. "Sweetie, you can't avoid him forever."

I crossed my arms defiantly. "Watch me."

"Well, it wasn't a request, and *you are* going," Laria insisted.

I pushed away from the counter. "If Khyron thinks he can come here and start ordering me around, then…"

"Khyron didn't say a word, and this has nothing to do with what's going on between you. Burke wants us there." Laria swept her hand through the air. "All of us."

"The guys should be done interrogating Doyle's men by then, and hopefully we'll know whether or not we should expect more trouble," Sloane said.

"Hey, guys. I wasn't eavesdropping, but I couldn't help overhearing." Cara strolled into the room. She had an open invitation and usually popped in and out whenever she wanted. "Doyle's insane, used to work for Sarus, and badly wants the toxins we stole." She walked over and took the chair next to Sloane. "So yeah, I'd say we should expect trouble, and a lot of it."

***

Khyron

My time with Melissa had been enjoyable. The chatty child had been amusing and enlightening. The majority of the information she'd shared pertained to the other children and herself. It saddened me to learn that so many young ones had been left without their parents to care for them. Celeste had always been very protective of her younger sister. She must have been devastated by the child's loss. Was that why she spent a great deal of time at Harper's and working with the young males?

After Melissa had shown me where to find the blossoms she'd insisted I give to Celeste, I had escorted her back home, then returned to Burke's dwelling. Thrayn, of course, was sulking, and the other members of my team were not happy that I had been out on my own without an escort.

Not long after my arrival, more of Burke's males made an appearance. They were part of a group who took turns patrolling the outlying perimeter areas bordering the settlement. Their presence was a deterrent to any bandits or mercs who were not intelligent enough to avoid the community.

During our introductions, I sensed the same uneasiness I'd experienced the evening before, though their trepidation was nowhere near the level of disdain I had sensed from Logan. And, for the second time, I wondered if something drastic had happened to the male during the war to cause the underlying hostility.

After our brief meeting, Burke had given our group, less Laria, Sloane, and Cara, a tour of the building he referred to as the command center. The building was much larger than it had appeared when we arrived. It was obvious in the layout and the way Burke commanded his males that he had utilized whatever military training he received on Earth.

"What is being done with the males who attacked Celeste and Cara?" I asked when we returned to the main room. I doubted Burke would allow them to leave. Then there was the matter of trying to harm my ketiorra. That alone guaranteed their deaths.

"Logan is getting ready to interrogate them if you'd like to watch," Burke said.

"Yes, thank you." Using pain to extract information

from another being was not a method I enjoyed, but it was necessary for continued survival, not only for my people, but also for the humans. Doyle's previous connection to Sarus, before we'd received word of his death, coupled with his current involvement with the toxin, made him a dangerous adversary. One whose actions I could not afford to ignore.

Later, after the evening meal Burke had scheduled—an event I hoped Celeste would be attending—we would be discussing the collaborative plans I envisioned for the future. Until then, observing the interrogation and discovering whatever Doyle's males had intended to do to Celeste and Cara was a priority.

I glanced at the males in my group, who also appeared eager to hear whatever information Logan could extract.

"We use the building behind this one for storage." Burke headed toward the back of the dwelling. "We haven't had to use them in a while, but there are a couple of small rooms where we've kept prisoners."

Vurell and Nayea, the same ketaurran female I had spoken with earlier, were already in the room. Vince had informed me she was the community's resident physician. She was kneeling on the floor next to the chair the male named Rick was bound to, with Vurell hovering next to her, his pale peach scales an interesting contrast to her dark orange ones.

Vurell picked up the small container sitting next to her on the floor. He dipped his finger into the thick yellowish-brown substance, then wrinkled his nose after sniffing it. "What is this concoction you have applied to the human's skin?"

Nayea frowned up at Vurell, snatched the container from his hand, then placed it back on the floor and out of his reach. "It is a healing salve I make from the suclorra plant." She finished binding the knife wound in the male's shoulder with a cloth.

"Interesting," Vurell said, helping her to her feet. "The

same plant can be used to make a poisonous toxin."

"Not many are aware of that fact. How did you know?" Nayea asked.

"If you two are finished comparing medical notes, we'd like to get started." Logan interrupted, then cracked his knuckles.

"It would be wise not to use your sharp tongue on me, or forget who tends your injuries." She leaned forward to retrieve her supplies, then pinned Logan with a sharp glare before giving him her back and smiling at Vurell. "If you would like to learn more about the ingredients, we can continue this conversation elsewhere."

"I would be very interested." Vurell held the door open and waited for her to leave in front of him.

Zaedon coughed to hide his amused grin. The action was not lost on Vurell. He paused to narrow his gaze in warning before exiting the room and slamming the door.

Jardun playfully elbowed Zaedon in the ribs. "Teasing Vurell is never a good idea."

"Jardun is right. You might want to avoid acquiring any wounds in the near future." I stifled a chuckle when Zaedon's smile faltered.

It was time to address getting the information we needed from Doyle's male, so I tipped my head in Burke's direction. "Whenever you are ready."

I remained in the far corner of the windowless room with Jardun and Zaedon so Burke and Logan could interrogate the male. I had Thrayn standing guard in the hallway and had asked Garyck to keep an eye on the females, not because I believed they were in any danger, but because he had suffered through being tortured himself and did not need to relive the memories. Neil, the other male, was being kept in another room similar to this one and would be questioned once they finished with Rick.

As leader of the planet's inhabitants, no one would argue with or try to stop me if I interfered with the questioning. I refused to abuse my position and chose not to challenge Burke's leadership. I had sworn to my sire before his death that I would carry on his wishes to unite the different races on the planet, not tear their worlds apart with the same lust for power Sarus had possessed.

I watched Burke's second-in-command. He seemed detached and determined to do whatever was necessary to get the information we needed, which included bruising and bloodying Rick's body, as well as his own knuckles.

Apparently, loyalty was not a requirement in the world of mercenaries. It had not taken long after Logan threatened to use a blade that Rick responded to his questions.

"What does Doyle want? Why did he send you?" Burke asked.

He'd been leaning against the wall to my right with his arms crossed, letting Logan do all the work. I had no doubt he would intervene if it became necessary.

Rick spit blood on the floor and gritted his teeth. "He sent us to retrieve what you stole from him."

"Be more specific," Logan insisted.

Rick jerked his head in my direction, his disgust for ketaurrans evident in his dark gaze. "He sent us to retrieve the toxins." He returned his attention to the floor, refusing to look at Logan when he answered.

My tail twitched, and dread slithered along my scales. There was something in the way he spat out the words, something in his tone, that made me doubt his truthfulness.

"And the females. Why did you attack their transport?" Logan asked, his hand fisted, ready to apply another punch if Rick refused to answer.

Thrayn's growl followed by "Female, you cannot go inside" filtered into the room from the hallway outside.

"Thrayn, I suggest you get out of the way. I really don't want to hurt you." After hearing Laria's raised voice, Jardun widened his eyes, then rushed to open the door.

"Am I too late?" She patted Jardun's chest, then shifted

sideways to get inside the room.

Jardun frowned. "Laria, you should not…"

"This is not my first interrogation." The determined glare she aimed at Zaedon and me threatened bodily harm if she received any arguments. "It was my transport they damaged, so I'm staying."

So far, Laria had been helpful when it came to dealing with Celeste. I did not want to risk damaging the alliance and directed the conversation in a different direction. "How did you get away from Garyck?" I asked.

"I left him with Sloane." Laria's innocent grin made me wary.

"Should I be worried?" I remembered the smaller female's propensity for being unpredictable when it came to dealing with my friend.

"Nah, I'm sure he'll be fine." She waved her hand dismissively, then focused her attention on Rick. "I remember you." The sound of her voice suggested the memories had not been pleasant.

"Was it you or the other guy who thought it would be a good idea to ram Trixie?" she asked.

"Who the draeck…" Awareness glinted in Rick's gaze, and he scoffed. "Are you kidding? You really gave that piece of junk a name?"

Red spread across Laria's cheeks, and she pursed her lips. "Don't you dare say anything bad about Trixie."

"Or what?" Rick sneered.

I could not believe Jardun had not already grabbed the male by the throat for speaking to his ketiorra in such a manner. Instead, he leaned against the wall with his arms crossed, seemingly entertained by Laria's behavior.

"Or…" Laria drew out the word as she slipped her blade from its sheath, then slowly tapped it against her palm. "I can show you how skilled I am at carving a male's private parts." Her glare lowered to Rick's lap.

I did not understand why Celeste's friends persisted in threatening that part of the male anatomy, but in this case, it seemed to be most effective. It was the first time during the questioning that Rick cringed and his face paled.

"Burke, you need to do something." Rick's plea sounded more like a whine. "You can't let her…"

Burke shrugged. "I can and I will if you continue to insult her. I can vouch for her expertise with a blade and suggest you tell her everything she wants to know."

Zaedon tipped his head toward Jardun and murmured, "I did not know your female had such a devious nature."

Mischief flickered in the look Laria gave Zaedon. "You have no idea." She turned her attention back to Rick. "Why did you attack my transport?"

"We were after that little bitch Carl, I mean Cara."

We had all been around the humans long enough to recognize the reference and knew its insulting meaning. Jardun grabbed Zaedon's arm when he growled and pushed away from the wall to go after the male. Zaedon was an intimidating male when he was angry. Seeing Rick frantically tugging at his restraints gave me a small amount of gratification. I'd been clenching my fists and resisting the temptation to pummel the male myself for going after Celeste.

"Cara is my friend, and if you call her that again, I will turn you over to the ketaurran." Laria's harsh tone made more of an impression than Logan had earlier with his fist. "Now tell me why you were after her."

"Anyone who crosses Doyle doesn't live very long. And Cara deceived him for weeks by pretending to be a guy." Rick's gaze never left Laria's blade. "She caused a lot of damage before she left, and Doyle wants her real bad. He's willing to pay a lot of cradassons to get her back."

"Logan, he's all yours." With a disgusted sigh, Laria turned and left the room, with Jardun following behind her.

No one said anything after they left, but we all knew what had to be done. Rick and the other male could not be released or allowed to return to Doyle. If the merc was determined to find Cara, then many lives were at risk, not just hers.

CHAPTER EIGHT

Celeste

How hard could it be to spend a few hours in the same room with Khyron? Yes, he'd grown more handsome over the years. Yes, my body, traitorous as it was, responded to his nearness with the same level of heat it always had. And yes, I wanted to run my fingers over his scales and feel his lips pressed against mine. But none of those things were going to happen.

I pushed the thoughts from my mind and reminded myself I was more than capable of dealing with Khyron. I'd dealt with danger before, handled deadly mercs, and fought my way out of far worse situations. Besides, it wasn't like he and I were going to be alone together. The vryndarr, my friends, and some of Burke's men were going to be attending. The place had ample room to move around, so keeping my distance shouldn't be a problem.

I wasn't happy that I'd had to fill the empty sheath on my hip with another knife. When I'd gone back later to retrieve my favorite blade from the tree, the one I'd thrown at Khyron, it was gone.

I usually wore my hair in a braid because it was easier

to manage and prevented distractions when I practiced throwing or ended up in a knife fight. For the first time in a long time, after I'd taken a bath, I left my hair draped loosely over my shoulders. Not because I knew Khyron liked it that way but because I wasn't in the mood to braid it, or so I kept telling myself.

Taking longer to get dressed and sifting through my clothes to find the perfect pair of pants and shirt that accentuated my curves had nothing to do with him either. It was about me. Or maybe it was about him just a little. Maybe I wanted to remind him what he'd given up when he hadn't kept his promise to come back for me.

I reached for my newest pair of boots, the ones I bartered for in the city market to replace the pair I'd ruined during the trip to the wastelands. I had one boot on and was pulling on the other when my bedroom door swung open.

"Are you about ready to go?" Sloane didn't bother knocking before strolling into my room. "Normally, you're the first one dressed and... Whoa, one look at you and Khyron's tail is going to end up in knots."

I blew out an exasperated sigh. "I don't care what he does with his tail or any other part of his body." My statement was the opposite of the truth, but I refused to admit it to my friend.

"You keep telling yourself that." Sloane wrapped her hand around my wrist and tugged me toward the door.

"Is she ready?" Laria was waiting for us in the gathering room, and I could tell by the way she was pacing, she was anxious to see Jardun.

She stopped moving long enough to check out my outfit, then smiled. "I guess so."

I held up my hand. "Not another word... From either of you." I aimed my glare at one, then the other. "I'm only going because you said I had to."

"Uh-huh," they both said at the same time.

"Err, let's go." Uninterested in getting anymore

unwanted comments or advice, I didn't bother waiting for them and headed for the door.

As soon as we'd reached Burke's place, my friends abandoned me. Laria immediately joined Jardun and slipped into his open arms. Sloane started a conversation with Logan and Vince, which quickly led to irritating Garyck. I stayed near the door, searching the room for a certain pair of crystal-blue eyes, and was interrupted before I found them.

"Zyrdena." I turned at the sound of Zaedon's voice and found him standing near the wall on my right, holding a half-empty glass of Nayea's ale.

"Zaedon," I said, noting that his normally happy smile seemed strained. I took the empty space next to him hoping to find out what was bothering him.

He took another swallow of his drink, then tipped his head closer to mine. "I should be angry with you for not telling me you were leaving, or that you planned to take Cara with you."

Should be. Did that mean he was or wasn't mad at me? Regardless of what he meant, I still couldn't get past feeling guilty. "I'm sorry for misleading you. I didn't ask Cara to come with me. She volunteered because she didn't want me to travel by myself."

"I see." He pondered my comment by scratching his chin. A few seconds passed, then he smiled. "Then I will forgive you."

Could the real reason he'd been upset have more to do with Cara leaving than with me being untruthful? Cara was a good friend, but could the reason she wanted to leave have anything to do with Zaedon's interest in her? Until one of them wanted to talk about it, I figured it was none of my business, and nudged his shoulder. "Thanks."

"I am curious," he said.

"About what?"

"Why did you not tell me about Khyron, that he and you…"

"There is no him and me. Hasn't been for a very long time." I glanced at his drink, wishing I had one of my own. "I didn't find out that Khyron was the drezdarr until yesterday. And since you're friends with both of us, I didn't want to put you in the middle of a bad situation."

"You consider me your friend?" Zaedon was a dangerous warrior, yet he flashed a boyish grin and swished his tail as if he were a puppy.

"Unbelievable... Of course, I consider you a friend." I shook my head and smacked the pale blue scales on his thick-muscled arm. "I really need a drink." Maybe two or three. I headed toward the counter containing several empty glasses and numerous pitchers of the thought numbing liquid. No sooner had I poured a drink and turned to say something to Zaedon, than I spotted Khyron. He was on the other side of the large room, speaking with Burke, but his gaze was leveled at me.

The room suddenly seemed warmer. My stomach fluttered. I wasn't sure what to expect, how he would react after our encounter earlier today. He smiled, tipping his head to acknowledge my presence, then looked away to answer something Burke had said.

Zaedon glanced between Khyron and me, then lowered his voice. "Yes, I can see there is definitely nothing between you."

"Not another word." I pinned Zaedon with a narrow-eyed glare, downed the contents in my glass, and quickly refilled it. I realized two or three drinks wasn't going to be enough if I planned to make it through the rest of the evening.

***

Khyron

Celeste had made it clear she wanted nothing to do with me. I was certain she would not make an appearance when I had been informed all the females would be attending the meal and the discussion I had planned afterward. When I saw her enter the room, it took every bit of my willpower not to walk away from my conversation with Burke and go to her.

It was hard not to appreciate the way her pants and shirt accentuated each of her curves perfectly. It was her dark flowing locks that drew my attention the most. Had she remembered my preference to see her hair worn loose, not bound in a braid? Was it an unconscious choice or deliberately meant to torture me, to remind me of what I'd lost? I deserved the latter and did not care if it was her motivation as long as she remained where I could see her.

Her laughter, caused by something Zaedon said, had me seething. I was certain his interests lay elsewhere, that he considered Celeste no more than a friend, but he was receiving the attention I wished she would bestow on me. The knowledge that he would never do anything to jeopardize my relationship with her, or current lack of one, did not prevent my jealous reaction or the urge to pull him away from her.

Shortly after filling a glass with ale, she glanced in my direction, noticing my presence for the first time. Her flushed cheeks and the way she held my gaze gave me hope that she was not as unaffected by me as she pretended.

My conversation with Burke about the topics we planned to discuss later shifted direction now that Sloane, Thrayn, and Garyck had joined us.

"I suppose I could give you a chance to win it back… If you're willing to make another bet." Sloane caressed the hilt of Thrayn's blade, now sheathed on her hip.

The male had not taken losing the knife well, even after I assured him there was nothing I could have done differently with Celeste to change the outcome.

Thrayn smiled, ready to agree to Sloane's new terms, until Garyck, who was standing behind her, shook his head.

Thrayn slumped his shoulders. "Female... I mean, Sloane," he corrected when she raised a threatening brow. "I have decided it is unwise to make wagers with you."

"Huh, can't imagine where you got that idea." Sloane turned her head and glared at Garyck, then strolled to the counter on the other side of the room to refill her glass with ale.

Not long after that, Vince announced the meal was ready, and our group moved into the room used for meeting and dining. There were fifteen people in attendance. All the members of my group were present. Burke had asked Vince, Logan, and Marcus, the male responsible for overseeing the teams that monitored the outlying areas surrounding the settlement, to join us.

Besides Celeste and her friends, Harper and Nayea were the only other females who had been asked to attend. They were an integral part of the community. After the human male's attempt to abduct the young one, Harper insisted that she be included in the group. She might not have the skills of a warrior, but she was respected by the settlement's inhabitants. To have her support would help greatly with building trust between the humans and the ketaurrans.

As much as I wanted to sit next to Celeste, even if she ignored me throughout the meal, the best I could do was a seat directly across from her at the long rectangular table. I got the impression I had unsolicited allies in Laria and Sloane when I noticed them keeping anyone from sitting in the chair and encouraged a grumbling Thrayn to sit elsewhere.

We were halfway through a meal made up of freshly hunted meats, courtesy of Garyck, and a variety of vegetables grown on the nearby farms when Burke said, "Besides wanting you all to meet our guests" —he waved his hand at my friends and me—"there's a reason I asked you to attend this get-together."

"Which is?" Logan's disdain wasn't quite as harsh as when we had arrived, but there was still a rough quality to his tone.

Burke frowned at his second-in-command. "You all know that I've set up teams to patrol the perimeter areas to protect our community from bandits and mercs. What you might not be aware of are the rumors and speculations we've been getting from the other settlements about the possibility of Sarus's supporters regrouping."

Burke ignored the gasps and murmurs. "I've spent quite a bit of time talking to Khyron and the other males in his group, and I think you should hear what he has to say."

Before my sire died, he had told me the arrival of the humans, coupled with the war, had changed many things. In order to be a good leader, the role of drezdarr needed to change with them. The success of his ideals, which became my goals, depended on getting everyone's support. Prior to the meeting, I had asked Burke not to use my title, but to introduce me by my name. I wanted everyone to be comfortable with my presence, to offer their support because they agreed with the objective for the future, not out of respect for or fear of my position.

I also believed it was not necessary, at least not at the moment, to reveal that Jardun, Zaedon, Garyck, and Thrayn were actually vryndarr and not just my personal bodyguards. Jardun had recently discovered, through an encounter with a group of luzardees, that bounties were being offered for the capture of any of the elite warriors. The bald males with beady black eyes and flat faces were worse than mercenaries when it came to greed and unethical dealings.

"Khyron, why don't you start by sharing the information you gave me and explaining your proposal," Burke said.

I remained seated and glanced at everyone around the table, noting eagerness on some faces and skepticism on others. I held Celeste's gaze, noting a brief glint of admiration before she masked her expression and reached for her ale.

As much as I wanted to devote all my attention on her, I needed to focus on the important matters facing us all. "I would like to propose a collaboration of sorts," I said to the group, then proceeded to outline the relevant details of what Jardun, the other vryndarr, and I had uncovered over the last few months.

During that time, I had not stayed in the city hidden within my dwelling as many believed. My friends and I had disguised ourselves as traders, traveled to various locations, gathering information. I wanted to see firsthand what life was really like for the inhabitants without them being aware of my presence or knowing they were being observed.

What saddened me most was seeing so many people struggling to survive after the damage my sire's brother had caused, and discovering the smaller ketaurran villages still dealt with random attacks by mercenary groups.

The ploy to hide our identities also worked well in obtaining information about the covert agendas of those who participated in criminal activities, mainly the mercs. It was rare not to find at least one business the humans referred to as bars, a place that served various forms of alcoholic brews, in the places we visited. It was even easier to learn what we wanted to know from the males who enjoyed imbibing.

There was also the possibility females were being abducted and transported to other locations to be used for sexual pleasure. I was disgusted when Jardun told me about the ketaurran soldiers manning the post near the Quaddrien and how they had attempted to take Sloane and Laria. Though I did not include it in the items I mentioned to the group, it was something else I added to the list of things I planned to investigate.

I shared what little knowledge we had acquired about

mercs, like Doyle and other Sarus supporters who might be banding together, then briefly mentioned my desire to disband them before they could start another war.

I omitted revealing the attempt on my life. Only those closest to me, along with those who had accompanied them to the Quaddrien, were aware of the threat and how close I had come to dying. Someone with the ability to get close to me was a traitor. Once Vurell had determined the source of my illness, Jardun, Zaedon, Garyck, and I had many lengthy discussions on the topic. None of which provided us with an answer.

Jardun had always believed that the report of Sarus's death had been false, possibly a way to lower our defenses. After Vurell had been abducted by Doyle, I had to consider that his theory might be correct. Without my leadership and the help of the vryndarr, there would be chaos. It would be easy for any remaining Sarus followers, or Sarus himself, if he was truly alive and in hiding, to take control and force the humans into slavery, or end their existence altogether.

"My team and I"—I acknowledged the vryndarr males with a tip of my head—"will continue the mission we started months ago. At times, what I am proposing will be dangerous, and requires commitment. I do not expect an answer tonight and will understand if you choose not to participate. All I ask is that you give it some thought before making a decision."

"I'm not sure if this is the best time to bring this up, but what did you guys learn during your interrogation?" Cara glanced between Burke and Logan.

Apparently, Laria had not had the opportunity to share the information Rick had provided about Doyle's plans with her friend.

"Seems Doyle isn't happy with you for infiltrating his compound, or the destruction you caused before we left. He put a price on your head. That's why Rick and Neil followed you from the city. They planned to take you back to Doyle."

"Really." Cara scoffed, seemingly unaffected by the news that the mercenary leader wished her harm.

Not unexpected after I had learned she volunteered to go to the wastelands alone and find out more about the rumors of laser blasters. From what I had heard, her fighting abilities—preferring to use her body as a weapon—rivaled those of a ketaurran male, even a vryndarr.

Zaedon was good at disguising his irritation. If he had not been seated on my left, I would not have noticed the way he tensed after hearing Cara's words. A muscle in his jaw twitched, and I was certain he wanted to throttle the female for her indifference to the situation.

"Cara, I'm sorry." Concern filled Celeste's dark eyes. "If you hadn't come with me…"

"Hey, Doyle might want me personally, but that's not going to stop his men from coming after any one of us. If I hadn't been with you, things could have gone a whole lot differently, and you know it." Cara fingered the edge of her glass. "At least this way, we know what he wants and can be prepared for the next time."

"Cara makes an excellent point. I think it would be unwise for anyone to travel alone." I held Celeste's gaze, unable to shake the tightness gripping my chest at the thought of what could have happened to her if she had been alone and the males had somehow managed to subdue her.

"It would kill me, but I can always find another transport," Laria said. "But you guys can't be replaced, and I'm glad nothing happened to either of you."

"On that note, and before you girls get too mushy, I say we move into the other room." Burke's comment elicited groans from the females.

"What does mushy mean?" Vurell asked. "I have not heard this human word before."

Burke got out of his chair and took a stiff step with his

injured leg. "Come on, I'll explain after I refill our glasses."

"I would be very interested to hear your explanation as well." Thrayn got to his feet and followed after them.

Now that the meal and discussions were over, many of us, myself included, returned to the main gathering room. I had just finished refilling my glass with ale when Celeste said my name. I turned and found her standing behind me.

"Did you mean it when you said you wanted to help the humans, to bridge the gap between your people and mine?"

She was so close, I couldn't stop myself from taking a sniff of her alluring scent. A hint of a smile touched her lips, and I had to restrain my tail from swishing or curling around the back of her legs. "I did, yes."

"Then I want you to know I will work with you, I mean the group, because I believe in what you're doing. But you and I... It's probably best if we keep our distance."

I was glad she would be a part of my team, which would keep her close, yet her words of rejection were a piercing blow to my heart.

"I understand. And, Celeste..." I wrapped my hand gently around her wrist when she started to leave. "Thank you."

"Sure," she said, then walked away after I reluctantly released her.

I spent the next hour participating in several conversations, only half listening to what was said. My thoughts and my gaze continually returned to Celeste. It wasn't long before the room began to empty.

I watched Thrayn interact with the females, worried by his persistence to offer them protection. He had relentlessly pressed, more like pestered, Harper until she finally agreed to let him escort her home.

I was not surprised when Jardun and Laria disappeared, no doubt in search of some time alone. Once again, I envied my friend and the happiness he shared with his ketiorra. Though the war had changed so many things, fighting was not a role a ketaurran female chose. The life of a warrior, mine included, was dangerous and made finding a female to share a lasting relationship with nearly impossible.

Choosing to be a vryndarr meant solitude and the occasional female to warm their bed. With the existence of the human female warriors, those capable of fighting by our sides, the future now held different possibilities. A future I fantasized about sharing with Celeste.

"Little one." Garyck's growl drew my attention to the other side of the room. He narrowed his gaze and stuck his hand, palm up, toward Sloane. "My band."

"What makes you think I have it?" Her blue eyes sparkled with mischief as she turned toward the door.

I tipped my head toward Zaedon. "Care to explain what is going on with those two?"

"Sloane has a unique talent for acquiring things. The jeweled band Garyck wears on his forearm seems to be her latest focus." Zaedon grinned. "Personally, I believe she does it to irritate him; otherwise, according to Celeste, she would not return it and he would never see it again."

Sloane barely made it two steps before Garyck lashed out his tail and caught her around the ankle. Most people would have lost their balance and fallen to the floor, but Sloane hopped on her other foot and remained standing as if she had been expecting the move.

"Hey, stop accosting me with your tail."

Garyck quirked a brow. "Would you rather I perform a body search?"

Sloane perused him from top to bottom, then sighed. "Tempting, but no." She lifted the back of her shirt and unhooked the band from the inside of her belt. After placing the band back on his arm, she leaned to the side and looked behind him. "Well, that's not good. I think I better take Celeste home before she falls off her chair."

Sloane strolled across the room and removed the glass from her friend's hand, then set it on the table. "Celeste, sweetie, how many of these have you had to drink?"

Celeste wiggled her fingers as if she was trying to use them to count. "Six." She slurred the word, then grinned. "Or maybe it was seven."

Her consumption had seemed a bit excessive throughout the evening, so I had been keeping a close watch on her movements for the last hour in case she needed assistance. I handed my glass to Zaedon and moved around Sloane. "Allow me." I carefully lifted Celeste out of the chair, expecting her to put up a fight. Instead, she wrapped her arms around my neck and laid her head on my shoulder.

Sloane grinned. "Okay, then. I guess I'll meet you at our place."

I nodded, then shifted Celeste's weight, pulling her closer to my chest.

"Khyron," she murmured.

"Yes, zadierra." I murmured the ketaurran version of treasured one, then sniffed her hair, taking a moment to enjoy her familiar scent before heading for the main door leading out of the building.

She lifted her head and poked my chest. "I am very, very mad at choo."

Even when inebriated, she was enchanting. I chuckled as I stepped out into the cool evening air. "I know, and I plan to do everything possible to change it." I doubted she'd remember this conversation later, but it did not stop me from uttering the words anyway.

I took my time carrying her home, savoring having her in my arms. Sadly, I reached my destination sooner than I wanted to and found Sloane standing in the doorway patiently waiting for me.

"Her room is this way." She turned and led me inside, then down a hallway to the first room on her right.

"Thank you," I said after Sloane opened the door and

stepped aside.

"Holler if you need any help. Not that I think you will." She winked and headed farther down the corridor.

Each step, each rub of Celeste's body against mine, had increased the uncomfortable state of my hardened shaft. By the time I placed her on the bed, my craving to caress every inch of her bare body, a pleasure I had yet to experience, had reached an unbearable level. With the little willpower I had left, I removed her boots and covered her with a blanket.

Celeste's eyes were closed, yet when I turned to leave, she gripped my wrist and mumbled, "Khyron, don't leave me."

I longed to lie next to her, to hold her in my arms, if only for a few short hours, but refused to take advantage of her weakened state. I knew she would not be pleased if she woke and found me in her bed in the morning. I would not risk making things between us worse, so I leaned forward, brushed my thumb across her cheek, and pressed a kiss to her forehead. "Sleep well, Celeste. I will never go far from you ever again." It was a promise I meant to keep, or give my life trying.

CHAPTER NINE

Celeste

When I woke with my mind in a hazy state, it took me a few moments to realize I was in my own bed with no idea how I'd gotten there. Or why I felt as if someone had smacked me in the head, then continued the abuse with a punch to my stomach. It was obviously still morning because sunlight filled the room. If it had been any later in the day, Sloane and Laria would have dragged me out of bed. Thinking about my friends brought vague memories of the meeting at Burke's, seeing Khyron, and drinking way too much.

Snippets of the previous evening's conversations and Khyron's proposed plan for collaboration popped in and out of the haze. Out of all the memories, the most vivid was when his blue eyes brightened with hope when I'd agreed to help him.

I groaned and rolled onto my side, then wished I hadn't when the throbbing got worse and the room started to spin. I closed my eyes and took several deep breaths before opening them again. This time, the room didn't move and my vision wasn't blurry. I also got a better look at the stand by my bed. Sitting next to the dish containing my stones was a small container filled with a fresh bouquet of chirayka blossoms and the blade I'd thrown at Khyron the day before. He'd obviously been in my room while I'd been sleeping. He was the only male I knew who'd be brave enough to give a female back a weapon after she'd thrown it at him.

I wasn't sure if I should be happy about his thoughtfulness or worried that something else had happened while he'd been here. Had I gotten so drunk at the gathering that I'd invited him home and into my bed? Denying that I wasn't still attracted to him would be moot, but sharing my body with him after I'd consumed too much alcohol and couldn't remember the experience was not something I wanted to think about.

Reflexively, I jerked the blanket off my body, relieved to find I was fully dressed. The only things missing were my boots and, after a quick glance around the room, I spotted them sitting out of the way next to the wall.

"From what I hear"—Laria appeared in the doorway holding a mug—"you were on your way to passing out last night when Khyron carried you home. In case you were wondering."

"You left early with Jardun, so how would you know what I did or didn't do?" I asked.

If Laria noticed the envy in my sarcastic tone, she ignored it. "Sloane stuck around to make sure you got home okay?"

I loved how I could always count on my friends to look out for me, especially if I did something that might get me into trouble. Though out of the three of us, Sloane was usually the one who excelled at causing problems.

Laria sauntered into the room and sat on the edge of the bed next to me. "You know drinking yourself into oblivion isn't going to help the situation with Khyron." She waited for me to finish sitting up, then held out a mug filled with steaming yellow liquid.

I didn't respond because she wasn't telling me anything I didn't already know. I took the cup, gave the contents a sniff, and wrinkled my nose. "What is this?"

"It's called creevea. Supposedly, it's a ketaurran version of a caffeinated drink. Only this one does wonders for body aches." She refused to take the cup when I tried handing it back to her. "I'm sure it will help your hangover too."

At this point, I'd try anything to get rid of the pounding in my head, and took a sip.

Laria giggled when I made a face. "The taste grows on you, I promise."

My stomach felt a little better, so I forced down another swallow. Even the throb in my head was now a bearable ache. "I wonder why Nayea hasn't brewed any of this for us before."

"Jardun said it's made from a special plant, but I don't think it grows around here."

Even the grogginess in my head was fading, and I felt like my brain was working better. "Did Khyron spend the night?" The assumption made sense since we had two extra bedrooms.

"No." Sloane peeked around the corner, then walked into the room. "He left right after he tucked you in. I was curious, so I checked."

I set the mug on the nightstand. "Then where did those come from?" I pointed at the flowers and my blade, bewildered how Khyron knew where to find the delicate flowers. The only place I'd found them growing was near a spring on the other side of Harper's place. He'd gone to a lot of effort and must have gotten up before sunrise to pick them.

"He left them when he came back early this morning to check on you," Sloane said.

"Is he still here?" I straightened and glanced at the hall outside my doorway.

"He left with Jardun," Laria said.

I should've been glad to hear that he'd gone, that he was respecting my wishes and keeping his distance. Instead, I was disappointed and miserable.

Laria placed a comforting hand on my arm. "I know you've never wanted to share the details about what happened between Khyron and you, but maybe it would help if you talked about it with us now?"

"There's not much more to tell," I said.

Laria crossed her arms and gave me one of her disbelieving looks. Sloane climbed on the opposite side of the bed, then sprawled on her stomach with her upper body braced on her elbows and stared at me expectantly.

I knew they weren't going to leave until I told them what they wanted to hear. "Okay, fine." I smacked my thighs and gave them the abbreviated version of my relationship with Khyron during the war. I included the part where he'd neglected to tell me he was the drezdarr's son and how he promised to return and never did.

When I was finished, Laria said, "Honestly, he seems too honorable to have abandoned you, and he did come all the way out here to find you."

"Not to mention he was willing to track you down on his own after we arrived, even after Laria and I both warned him there was a good chance you'd try to take off his head."

"Are you sure he didn't come after me because I refused to obey one of his directives?" The excuse sounded weak even to me.

"No way. You should have seen the way he reacted when he heard you'd left. He never said anything to us about punishing you, only that he needed to see you," Sloane said.

"In case you've forgotten, someone poisoned him, and, according to Jardun, it wasn't the first attempt on his life. Yet, he was willing to put himself in danger and travel all the way out here to find you," Laria said.

"Kind of says a lot about the guy, don't you think?"

Sloane added.

It did and was one more thing in his favor, which didn't help my confused emotional state. The fact that, no matter how much I wanted to hate him, I couldn't deny after all this time I was still in love with him.

"Do you think it's possible something happened to him when he left?" Laria asked.

"Like what?"

"Oh, I don't know, something that kept him from coming back for you." Laria tapped her chin. "Maybe something to do with the war, or maybe his father."

"You know, there are always two sides to every story." Sloane rolled into a sitting position with her legs crossed in front of her. "Maybe you should give him a chance to tell you his."

Before I could give their advice much thought, footsteps echoed in the hallway outside my room. A few seconds later, Cara appeared in the doorway. "Morning, everyone." She aimed her smirk directly at me. "I heard somebody had too much to drink and got an escort home by one very hot ketaurran male."

The bad thing about living in a place this size was how quickly information traveled. Nothing about anyone's personal life stayed a secret. I groaned, wishing I could crawl back into bed and forget about the night before. "I suppose everyone in the settlement has already heard about it."

"Nah, just us." Cara grinned. "And, of course, the handful of people who were still hanging around."

That didn't make me feel any better. If any of Burke's guys had been there, I could expect a lot of teasing over the next few days.

"Anyway, I wanted to let you know that I'll be heading out to my grandparents' place in a few days. I still need to visit the trader's market and see if I can find some backup parts for Trixie. If it's okay with you"—she spoke to Laria—"I'd like to take her with me and work on her in my shop out there. Hopefully, if I don't run into any problems with the repairs, it shouldn't take me more than a week to get her up and running again."

"After what Burke told us last night, are you sure you should be leaving at all?" A lot of strategic planning for the safety of the inhabitants had gone into the selection of the settlement's location as well as its layout. Burke's men did a great job of making sure everyone stayed protected. Even the outlying farming areas implemented precautions to keep the people who lived there safe. But those areas were spread out and harder to protect. If Doyle really wanted to get to Cara, her grandparents' farm would be the best place to do it.

"I've been gone too long and need to check in, make sure they're okay." Cara crossed her arms. "Besides, you know me. I'm not big on hiding out. If Doyle really wants me, it doesn't matter where I'm staying. At least if I'm out there, I can make sure my grandparents are safe."

It wasn't her family I was worried about, it was her. I understood Cara's concern for her only living relatives. If any members of my family were still alive, nothing would stop me from wanting to protect them.

"Before I head out, I thought you all might be interested in doing a little reconnaissance with me," Cara said.

"What kind of reconnaissance?" Laria asked. "Does it require leaving the settlement?"

There was no way Laria would leave without letting Jardun know first.

"No, I thought we might go check out the inside of the solarveyor we took when we escaped from Doyle."

"Why?" The last time I'd been in the vehicle was when we were fleeing across the Quaddrien. I didn't remember seeing anything inside that shouldn't have been there.

"Remember when Rick and Neil forced us to stop, then asked us to turn over what we stole from Doyle?"

"Yeah," I said.

"It just seemed odd and has been bothering me ever since." Cara's gaze turned speculative. "Why not just tell us they wanted the toxins back?"

I hadn't given it much thought. "Now that you mention it… You think there's something hidden in the transport, something they didn't want us to find, don't you?"

"Totally possible and worth checking out," Cara said.

"Sounds like you need to get your butt out of bed so we can go find out." Sloane grinned and yanked on my blanket.

"A shower probably wouldn't hurt either." Laria scooted off the bed before I could smack her with my pillow.

***

Now that I had bathed, changed, and was feeling better thanks to the creevea Laria had insisted I drink, I was able to think more clearly. I stood near the control panel in the solarveyor we'd stolen from Doyle, the conversation I'd had with Laria and Sloane about Khyron swirled through my mind. Khyron's actions, his plans for the future, his thoughtfulness when it came to me, did not correlate with the beliefs I had formed about the male I assumed had abandoned me.

Was it possible my friends were right? And, if they were, what did it say about me for judging him without giving him a chance to explain first? Had I been so consumed with guilt over my family's loss and the death of a sister I knew deep down I couldn't have prevented that I'd blamed Khyron to help ease the pain?

The click from Laria sealing the panel on one of the overhead units into place drew my attention back to what I was supposed to be doing, which was searching for something that shouldn't be in the transport. Something Cara was certain Doyle had hidden and wanted back.

"There's nothing out of the ordinary in any of these storage cabinets," Laria said.

"Nothing here either." Cara groaned, then realigned and secured the sheet of metal she'd removed from the interior wall. "I was sure we'd find something."

"Guys," Sloane called from the rear area of the vehicle. "I really think you need to see this."

Laria flashed Cara and me a quizzical look, then led the way to where Sloane knelt on the floor. She'd removed the contents in a lower storage, including the back panel.

I stared at the concealed area amazed at how easily she'd located it. "Do we want to know how you knew there'd be a hidden compartment in there?"

"Probably not." Sloane dismissed my inquiry with a shrug.

She never talked about her life after the crash or what she did during the years before the three of us found each other again after the war had started. We'd been close, almost inseparable on the *Starward Bounty*, but after the spaceship crashed on Ketaurrios, we'd ended up living in different locations.

Before finding Burke and being reunited, my friends and I all had to do things to survive. Things we weren't proud of. Things we didn't want to share with anyone. Sloane had developed an unusual talent for acquiring things, items that didn't belong to her. I'd often wondered if the past life she refused to talk about included spending some time working with thieves or bandits that raided transports.

Sloane reached inside and pulled out a large square container. "It looks like your intuition was right." She pried off the lid, exposing at least ten laser blasters.

"This *is not* what I'd expected." Cara crouched next to Sloane and picked up one of the weapons. "At least now we know what Rick and Neil were really after."

"Besides you, you mean," Sloane said.

"But why go after Trixie if the lasers were hidden on

this transport?" I asked.

"Maybe they were afraid of getting caught by Khyron's soldiers and were waiting for an opportunity to get inside without being noticed." Cara returned the weapon to the container.

"Or maybe when they spotted us leaving the city, they saw their chance to take Cara and possibly a way to get the lasers back," I said.

"At this point, all we can do is speculate." Laria headed toward the front of the transport.

"Where are you going?" Sloane asked.

Laria paused with her hand on the exit's frame. "To let the guys know what we found."

CHAPTER TEN

Khyron

I stood on the platform outside Burke's dwelling, watching the humans perform their daily activities. It was hard to concentrate on moving forward with the collaboration items I had discussed at the previous evening's meeting when all I could think about was Celeste. It had been several hours since I had returned to her home and left the chirayka blossoms along with her blade by her bed.

The ale she had consumed the evening before had ensured that she slept through my visit. While I was there, I noticed the small dish of glowing stones sitting on her bedside stand, similar to the one she told me helped keep her younger sister's nightmares away. Did Celeste now suffer the same malady and need the soft glow to prevent total darkness in her room?

Did losing her family and the experiences she had suffered in the past haunt her dreams? If so, was I partly to blame for her bad dreams? Were they a result of my inability to keep the promise I had made when I left?

"I heard you carried Celeste home last night." Jardun

appeared at my side, his grin most likely an aftereffect of his time with Laria. "Can I assume since your head is still attached to your body that things with her are progressing well?"

"We have not had a chance to discuss much of anything, so I do not think progressing well is an adequate description." I sighed and leaned back against the building. "She has agreed to join the team but wants nothing to do with me personally."

"You must realize that what happened was not your fault." Jardun placed his hand on my shoulder, a solemn expression settling on his face. "Celeste is an intelligent female, and I believe she will understand if you explain the events of the past."

I knew there was some truth to his words, but it did not relieve my guilt. My scars, especially the long one on my tail, were a constant reminder of my failure to protect the female I loved.

Laria appeared from behind the solarveyor we'd used to travel to the settlement, which was still sitting near the entrance to Burke's dwelling. The smile she flashed Jardun turned serious. "I hate to interrupt, but there's something you both need to see." She stepped up onto the platform, then reached for the door. "Just give me a second to get Burke. He'll want to see this too." She entered the building and returned a few minutes later with Burke and Logan following behind her.

"They're in here." She led us around the back side of the solarveyor and stopped near the open entryway.

"What's in here?" Burke ignored the step, then groaned as he grabbed the metal frame and hoisted himself inside.

As soon as the rest of us were standing next to him near the control area, Sloane and Celeste carried a large metal container from the back of the transport and set it on the floor near our feet. The blade I had returned was strapped to Celeste's hip, reminding me of the warrior she had become. It conflicted with my inherent nature to protect females, yet did not stop the proud tingle starting in my tail and surging through the rest of my body.

"Laser blasters." Cara lifted the container's lid. "Doyle might want the toxins back, but I think he also sent Rick and Neil to retrieve these."

With everyone crowding in the small space to observe the contents inside the container, I used the opportunity to move closer to Celeste. Even if my being near her was not her choice, it still had a calming and reassuring effect on my system. Not to mention one whiff of her scent and I was immediately and uncomfortably hard.

I forced my thoughts to return to the weapons and the ramifications of what possessing them meant.

"Where did you find them?" Burke leaned forward and ran his fingertips along the smooth edge of a blaster. "We've been in and out of here numerous times and never saw them."

"That's because Doyle did a good job of hiding them, and if it weren't for Cara we never would have thought to look for them," Sloane said.

Intrigued, I glanced at Cara. "What prompted you to start a search?"

Cara tucked a loose curl behind her ear. "It was the way Rick said he was after what we stole from Doyle that bothered me, so I thought it was worth checking out."

Celeste nudged her friend. "It was actually Sloane who found the hidden compartment behind one of the storage units."

Burke furrowed his brows. "Why doesn't that surprise me?"

Sloane grinned, her glance taking in the group, then returning to me. "No Garyck?"

It appeared the interest between the two was not one-sided. "He took Zaedon and Thrayn hunting with him."

"Finding the lasers makes sense." Logan scratched his chin. "I got the impression Rick was holding back when we questioned him. Now I know why."

It was good to know I was not the only one who had noticed Rick's aversion to answering some of the questions with more detail.

"This definitely changes things and might give us an advantage." Logan directed his remark at Burke.

"Khyron, I think these are too dangerous to leave sitting around. We should keep them locked up until we have a chance to discuss what we're going to do with them. We also need to make sure no one outside of our group finds out we have them."

I was certain Burke consulting me for advice on how to proceed was for Logan's benefit, a reaffirmation that he was committed to moving ahead with the collaboration and expected all the males under his command to comply. "I agree."

"Good, then we should get these secured before anyone sees them and starts asking questions." Burke took a step back so others could get out of the transport.

"Where?" Jardun lifted the container with ease.

"We can put them in the same room with the container Vurell had us lock up." Logan exited in front of Jardun.

Besides Celeste and me, Burke was the last to exit. He paused outside the entryway. "Khyron, once they get these taken care of, we can go on that tour we talked about…if you're still interested."

"That would be fine." I realized Celeste still hadn't made any effort to leave.

In my haste to turn, I banged the end of my tail on the doorway's metal frame.

The action did not go unnoticed by Celeste, who squinted sympathetically. "Khyron." Hearing her speak my name without a hint of anger made my heart race.

"Yes." My tail was one of the most sensitive parts on my body, and I tightened my jaw to keep from growling through the pain radiating along my scales.

"I wanted to thank you for making sure I got home safely last night, and for returning my knife."

I was glad she did not further my embarrassment by asking me if I was all right like a dam would a child. "You are welcome." I took a step closer but kept my hands fisted against my thighs. She was speaking rather than avoiding me, and I did not want to do anything to change it.

"I can't believe you remembered, or went to the trouble to pick them." She bit her lower lip.

Had the gesture somehow changed the fragile connection between us? If so, I would need to thank the Melissa later for her words of wisdom and for showing me where to find the blossoms. "It was my pleasure." I wanted to tell her I remembered everything about her, the details of every moment we ever shared.

"You are feeling better, then?"

"I am."

There were so many things I wanted to say, needed to ask, but with our friends hovering close by, this was not the place to have that discussion. "Laria gave you the creevea?"

Her gaze widened. "That was from you?"

I nodded, inching a little closer. "I carry a supply of the dried leaves with me. It does not have the best taste, but the healing properties are very useful."

"You're right about the taste." She released a nervous giggle. "That stuff is nasty, but it really helped the pounding in my head."

"I am glad." Only inches separated our bodies. I caressed her cheek, the urge to capture her lips with mine overwhelming. The need dissipated as soon as I heard a growl and felt a heavy weight trap my tail to the floor. Both actions were immediately followed the hysterical shrill of Melissa's voice. "Fuzzball, no."

I turned to find a furry creature with pink scales pawing and nipping at my scales as if my tail was an object meant for chewing. I snatched him off the ground and held him up so I could get a better look at him. He squirmed and playfully attacked my chin with the forked end of his orange tongue.

"Please don't hurt him." Melissa sobbed, a tear trickling down her face. "I'm sure he didn't mean to bite your tail."

"Oh, sweetie, don't cry." Celeste moved to kneel in front of the child, then brushed the moisture from her cheek. "Khyron would never let anything happen to Fuzzball." She glanced up at me. "Would you?"

"My ket…" An astonished gasp from Celeste had me correcting myself before I admitted out loud that she was my mate. "Celeste is right. I would never harm him. Though you might want to teach him tails should not be used to sharpen his teeth." Keeping the small creature clasped to my chest and doing my best to avoid his tongue, I crouched next to the young female. "Where did you find him?"

"Near the clearing where the boys practice with their blades," Melissa said.

"Chonderras are very rare. Were there others?" I asked.

"No, just Fuzzball." Melissa stuck out her lower lip, holding out her hands and wiggling her fingers.

After the animal happily went to the child, I got to my feet, then helped Celeste stand, glad she had not refused the gesture.

Melissa peered up at me, taking a step closer and speaking as if Celeste could not hear her. "Did you give her the chiraykas like I told you? Did she forgive you yet, or is she still mad?" She put a hand by the side of her mouth. "'Cuz if she is, I can help you find something else that might work."

I glanced at Celeste, who appeared amused and was doing her best not to smile. "I am not sure," I said to Melissa. "I am still working on it and will let you know if I need further assistance."

"Okay." She smiled at Celeste. "Well, I better get back so Harper doesn't worry." Without waiting for a response, she hurried off with Fuzzball bouncing in her little arms.

"Khyron," Jardun said as he walked around the back end of the transport, then stopped when he saw Celeste. "Burke and the others are ready to go."

I resisted the urge to glare at my friend for bringing an end to my time with Celeste. "One moment." I turned back to Celeste. "Perhaps we can continue our discussion after I return."

"Perhaps."

Her smile was all the encouragement I needed, a guarantee that I would seek her out later.

**

Garyck, Zaedon, and Thrayn had not returned from their hunt by the time we were ready to leave on our tour, so Jardun, Logan, Burke, and I were the only ones in attendance. I had not bothered to ask Vurell if he wanted to accompany us. He spent a lot of his time with Nayea, something I was grateful for, which meant he spent less time hovering over me and prodding my slowly healing body.

The trip I assumed would take no more than a few hours ended up lasting most of the day. Seeing the layout of the settlement and having Burke explain what he did to protect the humans was important. It did not, however, keep my thoughts from wandering to Celeste, or diminish my eagerness to spend more time with her.

We had taken one of the smaller transports and traveled on a narrow road that ran along the perimeter of the wooded area bordering one side of the settlement. Along the way, we stopped briefly to meet with Marcus and the three males on his team, who were alert, armed with blades, and appeared to be well-trained. Marcus must have briefed them about the prior evening's discussions, because the welcome Jardun and I received went better than I expected.

After answering their questions, we returned to the

transport and continued driving. I watched the landscape on the right side of the road gradually turn from sand to rock. Caves were not uncommon, and the occasional shadows I noticed on the upper ledges were most likely the openings to small caves, possibly larger caverns.

"What are they doing out here?" Logan ran his hand over the controls, bringing the vehicle to a stop.

I turned my attention from the side viewing pane to the one above the main operation control panel and spotted Garyck, Zaedon, and Thrayn walking toward us.

"I thought they were going hunting." Jardun opened the access door.

"So did I." I followed him outside, curious to find out why they were this far from the settlement. The meat Garyck had provided since our arrival had come from small animals living in or around the wooded area.

"Maybe they weren't having any luck," Burke said, walking up behind us with Logan.

"Garyck is very skilled and would have obtained his quarry long before now." There was another reason they were here. A reason I was certain I would not be pleased to hear.

"Not sure what you're doing clear out here, but there's room in the transport if you want a ride back." Logan's offer sounded sincere.

Zaedon grinned. "That would be appreciated, after we…"

Garyck pointed at the road and, with his usual abruptness, asked, "Is this the only way to access this area?"

"Yes, unless someone wants to spend a lot of time walking. This is the only ground level and smooth enough to accommodate a transport. Even the larger solarveyors have difficulty getting back this far," Logan said.

"Were you aware there was something living out here?" Zaedon directed his question at Burke.

A tightness crept into my chest. My first thought was

for the safety of Celeste and the young ones who frequented the wooded area.

"Over the last few years, we've only gotten glimpses of it and assumed it was a cave-dwelling creature. Our males have been warned to stay away from the rocks and, so far, we haven't had any problems with whatever it is," Burke said.

"I agree with the assessment, but I do not believe he is a creature." Zaedon ran his hand through his hair. "Garyck showed me the tracks he found. I believe what your males and you have seen is really a ketaurran male. I also believe if he wanted to hurt anyone, he would have done it by now."

"A male?" Logan shifted his gaze to the upper level of the rocks. "Why would anyone want to live out here alone?"

"He may be a loner, possibly a survivor of the war." I could only imagine the horrific things that must have happened to cause one of my people to seek solitude rather than the aid of his people.

"Should we go after him, take him back to the city with us?" Thrayn asked.

"No, we will allow him his privacy. He has to be aware there are others living nearby, and if he wanted to make his presence known, he would have done so already.

"There is something else." Garyck opened and reached inside the small pack he had strapped to his shoulder. He held out a long piece of dried skin. "I found it this morning."

Burke leaned closer to get a better look. "You're telling me you found a shedding from the scales of a luzardee out here?" He rubbed his nape. "That's impossible. In all the years we've been here, they've never ventured into this area."

I understood Burke's frustration. "As I stated last night, the war changed many things, survival for some is more difficult. We need to anticipate and be prepared for new possibilities."

"Do you think it is a coincidence or related to the attack on Jardun?" Burke asked.

Jardun had contacted a group of luzardees before sending Garyck and Zaedon to meet with Burke. After the luzardees gave Jardun the information he needed to find Vurell, they betrayed him, then turned around and arranged a payment from Burke for his release. It was during his rescue that Jardun learned large amounts of cradassons were being offered for the vryndarr.

"Is it possible the luzardee sent someone to follow Garyck and Zaedon to the settlement hoping to capture them for the bounties?" Thrayn asked.

"The shedding Garyck found is only a day or two old," Zaedon said. "If they had followed us, it would be a lot drier and would crumble to the touch."

Garyck grunted his agreement.

My tail twitched. This was something entirely different, though no less disturbing. Judging by their stiff stances and the frowns furrowing their brows, Burke and Logan were not happy to hear the news either.

"How the draeck did he get past our patrols?" Red rose along Burke's throat and cheeks.

"The luzardee have the ability to climb and move undetected." I swept my hand toward the wall of rock. "This border might deter humans but can easily be scaled by a luzardee. We will need to train your males on what to look for and alert everyone that one or more of the males may still be in the area."

CHAPTER ELEVEN

Celeste

My body had been rippling with tension ever since we'd found the laser blasters. Actually, finding the weapons had been upsetting, but the main source of my anxiety was Khyron. My emotions had been in turmoil ever since I'd walked into his sleeping quarters back in the city. They'd gotten even worse after I realized he'd been about to kiss me until Fuzzball pounced on his tail.

If I hadn't been frustrated about missing the kiss and distracted with thoughts of what would happen during our next meeting, I'd have been watching where I was going and not slammed into Vince's firm chest. Either he was more perceptive than I thought, or I'd been doing an awful job of disguising my stress. Whatever the reason, he'd asked me if I wanted to meet with him later to do a little sparring.

My friends and I never knew what kind of danger we'd encounter when we traveled, so training with the guys was a great way to stay in shape and keep our skills honed. Vince was a good fighter but nowhere near the challenge I got when I did hand-to-hand with Burke and Logan.

Those two were ruthless when it came to training. I'd end up wearing bruises for days every time I had a session with either one of them.

"Celeste." Vince's raised voice snapped me back to the present. "You need to focus. You should have blocked that move easily." He took a step back, bending his knees, preparing to come at me again.

Focus, right. Not so easy when all I could think about was Khyron. I remembered the desire in his eyes, could feel the warmth from his hand on my cheek. Deep down, I realized he was still the same person I'd known years ago. I'd watched him the night before, the way he handled himself with Burke and the other guys. The way he interacted with the vryndarr, the way he'd earned their respect. They weren't just his protectors, they were his friends.

He genuinely cared about what happened to my people. He'd demonstrated his concern more than once since he'd arrived. He might have been related to Sarus, but he was nothing like his uncle. He was a strong leader, honorable, determined to protect and unite all the races.

So if he was all those things, then why hadn't he kept his promise to return to me?

"I'm fine. Let's go again." Only I wasn't fine and continued to wonder if Sloane and Laria were right. Was I letting the guilt of not being able to save my family keep me from learning the truth about what happened after Khyron left?

"Does your lack of concentration have anything to do with the drezdarr?" Vince grinned, dodged to the side and avoided my punch. "You two couldn't keep your eyes off each other last night."

"I thought we were here to work out, not discuss things that are none of your business." I smiled with satisfaction when he grabbed for me, and the kick I planted in his side sent him sprawling on the floor.

"I know I'm not Laria or Sloane, but I grew up with

two older sisters." Vince rubbed his side after he got back on his feet. "If you ever need to talk, I'm a decent listener."

Vince was single and had left his family back on Earth to take a job working security on the *Starward Bounty*. He'd been assigned to Burke's team during the flight, and after the ship crashed had ended up in the same settlement with him. After the war started and Burke put together his band of rebels, Vince was one of the first to join.

"Thanks, I appreciate it." I held up my arms to fend off his next swing.

"Yep, the guy's really into you." He sidestepped to the right.

Vince might be a good listener but was also chatty and sometimes ignored boundaries. "What part of none of your business…" I mimicked his move, then threw a punch that missed his shoulder and grazed his arm.

He chuckled. "I think there's a good chance he thinks you're his ketiorra."

I gasped. "What makes you…" I didn't react fast enough to his next swing and ended up on the floor.

I quickly rolled to my feet, narrowing my gaze at his annoying grin.

"You know…his mate."

"I know what ketiorra means," I snapped, making the novice mistake of reacting with my emotions when I should have been using my brain. I realized too late that he'd been purposely baiting me, trying to mess with my concentration. My swing missed him entirely and I didn't get my arm up in time to prevent his elbow from connecting with the side of my head.

Vince was bigger and a lot stronger than I was. Luckily, he'd been holding back, or I would have ended up flat on my back and possibly unconscious. As it was, the blow had taken me to my knees.

"Damn, Celeste. I'm so sorry." Vince knelt next to me, his voice laced with regret.

I winced. "My. Fault," I managed after taking several deep breaths.

"Are you okay?" He gently cupped my chin and examined my face. "Do you want me to get Nayea?"

A loud male growl filled the room, followed by heavy footsteps. "Remove your hands from her at once." Khyron grabbed Vince's shoulder and yanked him away from me, then shoved him to the ground.

"Khyron, stop!" I yelled, launching myself at Khyron before his fist connected with Vince's jaw.

I caught him in the side with enough force to push him away and force him on his back. Before he had a chance to react, I straddled his midsection and pinned his wrists to the floor. "What do you think you're doing?"

"Zadierra, I…" Khyron could have easily tossed me aside, but he remained motionless, his blue gaze locked with mine, apologetic, yet expectant.

"Celeste?" Vince moved into a low crouch. He was prepared to attack but wouldn't interfere unless I asked him to.

"I'm okay." At the moment, I was more worried about Vince's safety. "You should go." I tipped my head toward the doorway.

"If you're sure."

I knew in my heart that Khyron would never hurt me. "Yeah, I'm sure."

Vince hesitated a few seconds longer, then got up, grabbed his boots and left the room. He cast one more concerned glance at me before disappearing down the hallway.

I shook my head and glared at Khyron. "If we're going to be working together, we need to have some rules."

"I agree." He was being too accommodating, and if I hadn't been so angry, I might have paid better attention.

"First of all, I want you to know that I can take care of myself." Since all ketaurran males were proud and had a thing about protecting females, I expected a snort, an argument, or some sort of disagreement. When he remained silent, I felt the need to explain. "Vince and I were training. He never would have gotten close enough to hit me if I hadn't been distracted."

He raised a brow. "Distracted by what?"

I held back a groan after realizing I'd revealed more than I should have. Khyron had always been exceedingly perceptive, sometimes to the point of being annoying. I was torn between telling him it was none of his business and having that long-overdue talk Laria and Sloane had insisted I needed. Finding out the truth about why he'd abandoned me and getting some much-needed closure, whether it was painful or not, won my internal struggle.

"You, all right? You're the distraction." I couldn't think clearly, not with him this close, and not with the warmth that started between my legs and was currently radiating through the rest of my body. I released his wrists and rolled off him, putting at least three feet between us. "You can wipe the smirk off your face. I didn't say it was a good thing."

**

Khyron

I did my best to hide the smirk Celeste was threatening to remove from my face. I never wanted her to suffer any pain because of me, but to hear her admit she was distracted by my presence was encouraging.

I had arrived in the training room seconds before Vince's elbow connected with Celeste's head. I was well aware that she could take care of herself and would never argue the point. Nor would I inform her, at least not at the moment, that my rage was a result of seeing the way Vince examined her face.

Celeste was my ketiorra, whether she wanted to be or not. Having another male touch her tenderly, when I had been denied the privilege for so long, had been unbearable. And so had been having her legs spread around my middle. She'd removed her boots, and the clothes she wore clung firmly to her body, exposing her arms and the soft skin around her middle. I'd barely resisted the urge to roll her on her back, to claim her, to show her how much I cared for her.

Once she rolled away, I knew it was time to make amends for the past, to tell her the truth, even if she hated me for it afterward. I pushed off the floor and stayed sitting where I was, ensuring she had adequate space so she did not change her mind about talking and decide to leave, then patiently waited for her to begin.

Celeste slid her palms along her thighs, then placed her hands in her lap. "When we first met, why didn't you tell me you were related to the drezdarr, that you would eventually *be* the drezdarr?"

It was not the question I expected her to start with, but it was one that needed to be answered. "You mean when you were threatening my life after you knocked me into the water?" I hoped my teasing would help make our discussion a little less stressful.

"No." Even though she rolled her eyes and huffed, there was a hint of a smile on her lips. "You know what I mean. You could've told me later."

"Times back then were difficult. My sire's brother was responsible for so much bloodshed, and many humans hated my people." I swallowed the lump rising in my throat. "I was afraid if you learned who I was, you would blame me for... That you would never consider me suitable." As it was, I had lost her anyway, thought she was dead, and, until a few days ago, had believed she was gone forever.

"You aren't your uncle. I never would have blamed you for what he did, or pushed you away." She fisted her hand as if she'd meant to touch me, then changed her mind.

"I realize that now, but it was not the only reason I did

not reveal the truth about my identity." I inched a little closer. "Until I met you, I had spent my life not knowing if a female cared about me for the person I was or if they returned my attentions because I was the son of one of the most powerful males on the planet." Several strands had pulled free from her braid, so I tucked them behind her ear. "You were different."

"How so?"

"You captured my heart from the moment you pushed me into the water. One sniff of your skin and I knew you were the only female I would ever care for, my ketiorra."

Though I had never told her about the connection we shared, she no longer seemed shocked by my admission.

"If I was your ketiorra, then why didn't you come back?" The disappointment and despair in her voice nearly crushed me.

I craved her nearness, knew it was the only thing that would relieve the tension rippling through me, ease my fear of losing her after my explanation. I scooted closer, stretching my legs on either side of her. "It was not common knowledge, but during the war, my sire fought with his soldiers to protect all his people, including the humans."

I had been proud of my sire. He was a good leader and a strong warrior. "The day I left he had sent word that a band of Sarus's males were nearby. I was supposed to meet him so we could battle Sarus together, to keep him from reaching any of the settlements, but we were ambushed." I fisted my hands, struggling to keep the vivid memories of that day out of my mind. "The attack had been brutal, many lives taken, including the life of my sire. If not for Jardun, I would have been one of the casualties."

She placed her hand over mine. "Oh, Khyron." The rasp in her voice sounded close to a sob.

I wanted no more secrets between us, wanted her to know everything. "I was unconscious for several days, and when I woke, my first thoughts were of getting back to you. I was not well enough to travel, so I sent soldiers to retrieve your family and you."

"You did?"

"Of course." I squeezed her hand. "I made you a promise and meant to keep it." Along with the admission came painful memories of the past. I swallowed hard and continued. "When the soldiers returned, I was told they found nothing but bodies, that your family along with others in the settlement who had not escaped before the attack were killed."

Saying the words out loud was the same as reliving the agonizing experience all over again. "I refused to believe I had lost you, so once I was healed, I returned to your home, or what was left of it after Sarus's males burned everything to the ground." Even after seeing all the devastation, I had not given up, and spent several more weeks searching for her. "With my sire dead, I was the new drezdarr, and our people needed a leader. I put my personal needs aside and did whatever was necessary to end the war."

I gave her a few moments to contemplate what I said before asking, "Unless it brings you too much pain, will you share what happened after I left…please?" I already knew most of it, but I needed to hear the words from her lips, hear what my prolonged absence had cost her. And hoped that sharing would lead to forgiveness.

I worried her lengthy silence meant she had no interest in closing the breach between us. When she finally raised her caring gaze to mine, I released the breath I'd been holding. "It was pretty much as you described. Two days after you left, Sarus's males attacked the settlement. My mother and father were scientists, not skilled fighters. They fought back, but their attempts were useless against males armed with blades."

Several tears streamed down her face. I wanted to pull her into my arms, to comfort her, but knew in order to heal, for us to have a chance, she needed to finish telling me everything.

"My parents made me take Maria into the wooded area behind our home and told us to hide. Not that it did any good. Maria got away from me and... One minute, she was screaming and running back toward our house; the next, she was facedown on the ground with a soldier's blade in her back."

Celeste swiped at the moisture on her face. "I knew I was too late, that there was nothing I could do for any of them, so I stayed hidden until the soldiers left. After that, I avoided all the access roads and made my way to the next settlement, where I was reunited with Laria and Sloane. Then we met Burke, and he helped us find a home and taught us how to fight."

I brushed my thumb along her jaw, wiping away the tear she had missed. "Is that how you became a warrior?"

She smiled. "I don't know if I would consider myself a warrior, but yes, learning to protect my friends and myself was a big motivator. After what happened to my family, I promised myself I would never be that helpless again."

"And now you work with Burke," I said.

"Yes, and sometimes what we do is dangerous, but it can't be helped if we want to survive." There was a defensiveness in her tone.

"I understand." I was not thrilled that what she did put her life at risk, but it was a part of who she was, and I did not want to change her. If not for her connection to Burke—something I greatly appreciated—I would never have found her again. "Is Burke the one who taught you how to wield a blade?"

"No, that was Logan." She absently place her hand on my leg.

"Is he as good as you?" I slid my tail across her lap, happy when she appeared amused but did not ask me to move it.

"Better, and way more lethal."

I had already determined it was best to have the male as

an ally rather than an enemy.

"Is what happened with your sire the reason you travel with the vryndarr now?" she asked.

"Yes. Other than Thrayn, who recently passed his training, I have fought side by side with the males and would trust them with my life." And had on many occasions.

"Is that how you got this?" She ran her fingertip along the scar on my tail. The caress made my scales tingle, spreading warmth through my entire body. It was all I could do not to pull her into my arms and show her the extent of my caring.

We were sitting too close for her not to notice the effect she was having on my shaft. I opened my vest in an effort to draw her attention elsewhere. "As well as this." I pulled the material farther apart to reveal my chest and the scar along my side, the one that had almost taken my life.

She did not glance away or appear repulsed by the jagged line running through my scales. I tipped her chin and held her gaze. "Celeste, I am so sorry I was not there for you, that I did not protect your family."

"Many awful things happened during the war, things that weren't your fault or mine." When she pulled away and got to her feet, I assumed she was going to leave, that this was the way things were always going to be between us, that I would never earn her forgiveness. Instead, she held out her hand. "I think it's time for both of us to heal, don't you?"

CHAPTER TWELVE

Celeste

Khyron didn't abandon me. The thought continually played through my mind as the heavy weight surrounding my heart lifted. It didn't erase the guilt I felt for doubting him. That would come with time.

He showed no reluctance when I suggested the best way to heal was to continue our conversation in his room. He pushed to his feet, not bothering to take my hand, then scooped me off the floor and carried me toward the door.

I wrapped my arms around his neck. "Are you afraid I'll change my mind?"

"I refuse to take any chances." He tightened his grip to emphasize his response.

Ketaurran males were generally taller and more muscular than human males. With me in his arms, he had to turn sideways to fit through the training room doorway. He wasted no time heading for the opposite end of Burke's dwelling. We had to pass through the kitchen to reach the hallway leading to the sleeping quarters.

Thrayn was sitting at the table and immediately jumped to his feet when we entered. After their arrival at the settlement, I'd noticed that at least one of the vryndarr stayed close to Khyron at all times. It must have been Thrayn's turn to act as bodyguard, since he was the only one I'd seen since we left the training room.

"Khyron, do you require assistance?" he asked, his pale green eyes narrowing with concern.

Thrayn's confusion was understandable. After I'd thrown my blade at the tree behind Khyron, the vryndarr had no reason to trust me.

"Not now, Thrayn. I must attend to the needs of my ketiorra."

Thrayn's eyes widened further, and I pressed my mouth against Khyron's shoulder to keep from giggling.

"Are you sure?" Thrayn scratched his head. "How is that possible?"

Khyron released an exasperated groan and stopped. "You are a grown male, but if you are unsure about the process, I am sure Jardun or Zaedon would be happy to provide you with the information. No more questions. I am busy and do not wish to be disturbed until tomorrow." He turned and started walking again.

"Tomorrow, huh?" I asked.

"I would have stated a longer time, but at some point, we will require food."

His wry smile and the darkened blue of his gaze hinted at the things he planned to do to occupy our time. My body responded with renewed warmth and anticipation.

As soon as we reached Khyron's room, he closed the door with his tail, then lowered me to my feet. He kept an arm wrapped around my waist and gently cupped my cheek. "I have missed you greatly, zadierra."

No matter how many times I heard it, the term of endearment warmed me to my core. "I missed you too." The words I spoke were true. My misconceived views about being abandoned had left me angry and hurt, but thinking I'd never see him again had caused me the most pain.

I pressed my palms against the scales on his chest. They weren't as smooth as I remembered, but over the past couple of days, I'd noticed some color returning to their dull blue hue. "I'm glad to see you're healing."

"If not for your friends and you, I would not be alive." He clasped a hand over mine. "I have many things to be thankful for, but the only one that truly matters right now is you." His lips covered mine, a gentle caress, almost a plea for acceptance.

The tenderness behind his kiss, coupled with my response, was quickly replaced by our overwhelming need to connect, to make up for what we'd lost. He slid his tongue along my lower lip, and with a moan, I granted him access. With each of his teasing and taunting movements, all painful hurts from the past dissolved until they were nothing but unpleasant memories. Memories I quickly shoved aside and replaced with the new ones we were currently making.

A growl rumbled from his chest, and his tail possessively skimmed the back of my thighs. When he finally pulled away to nuzzle my neck, we were both panting. "Celeste." He grazed the skin near my earlobe.

"Yes."

"You are my ketiorra, and there will never be another female for me, correct?"

"Uh-huh." My body responded to his touch the way it always had, my ability to think clearly—gone. I would be whatever he wanted as long as he didn't stop doing those wonderful things with his lips and tongue.

"Good." He slowly backed me toward the bed, then gave me a gentle push when we'd reached the edge.

I smiled at his show of dominance, his need to take control. Coming to his room might have been my idea, but he was still the drezdarr, an honorable yet powerful leader. Not someone other males trifled with when he was determined to have his way. It was a good thing I wasn't a male and would trifle with him all I wanted. "And what exactly does being your ketiorra entail?" I scooted to the middle of the bed.

"I plan to spend quite a bit of time showing you." He caught my ankle and pulled me toward him, my legs bent, knees hugging his hips.

I braced my upper body on my elbows and watched him start with my calves, skimming his hands appreciatively along my outer thighs until he reached my waist.

"It is too bad you were heavily influenced by ale the last time I placed you on a bed; otherwise…" He leaned forward and pressed several kisses along the strip of exposed skin along my abdomen.

His insinuation was clear. He'd already have taken care of the longing ache I'd been experiencing since his arrival. He slipped his fingers below the waistband of my pants, undid the fastening, then peeled back the fabric by slowly inching his way to my hips. With very little assistance from me, he removed my pants completely and tossed them on the floor.

For the moment, I was happy to let him lead, let him set the pace and finish undressing me.

Once he had removed all my clothes, he took a step back, his gaze taking in every inch of me. "You are more beautiful than anything I imagined."

I wasn't shy, and not many things embarrassed me, but his intense perusal made me shiver. A shiver that quickly turned to heat and the need to have him naked. I rose up on my knees and pushed his vest aside, slowly running my hands over scales and firm muscle before slipping the material over his broad shoulders.

When I slid my fingers beneath the edge of his pants, my fingertip grazing the tip of his hardened shaft, he groaned and clasped my hands, then took over by toeing off his boots and removing his pants.

"In a hurry?" My attempt at teasing ended with a gasp when I got my first glimpse of his naked body. Naturally curious, my gaze hovered below his midsection, appreciating the state and size of his erection.

He noticed the direction of my gaze and grinned. "It appears I am not the only one who longs to have our skin pressed together." He grabbed me around the waist, the words "arrogant male" never leaving my lips. With a quick spin, he turned and sat on the edge of the bed with me straddling his lap, his shaft pressed firmly against the place I wanted it most.

He studied me with a cherished gleam, as if having me close was fulfilling a longstanding fantasy, then shifted his attention to my braid. "Your hair…please."

I understood exactly what he wanted without him having to explain, and undid my braid, sifting my fingers through the tight twists. For added effect, I shook my head and watched the blue in his eyes darken when the loosened strands cascaded over my shoulders. "Better?"

"Much." He entwined his fingers in the hair at my nape, grabbing a handful and angling me backward so he could capture one of my breasts with his mouth. Using his tongue, he sucked and teased the nipple until it was a hardened nub and I was squirming. I moaned and gripped his shoulders when he gave my other breast the same tantalizing treatment.

Khyron didn't stop taunting my skin with his lips and tongue until he'd worked his way along my throat and stopped to sniff me. "I will never tire of your scent. It is unique and smells better than a chirayka blossom."

When I'd met Khyron for the first time, I'd noticed him doing the sniffing thing around me often. Back then, I hadn't known it was how the ketaurran males discovered the identity of their mates. I'd recently learned the information from Laria not long after Jardun claimed she was his ketiorra and had explained to her how he knew.

"It's nice to know I smell better than a flower, but I really need you to do more than sniff my neck." I wiggled my hips and rubbed against him.

"Your impatience and determination to have your way have not changed." He gathered me into his arms, then turned and placed me on the bed.

"You can't blame me for knowing what I want." I grabbed his wrist and tugged him on top of me.

"No, I cannot." He laughed, then lowered himself between my spread legs, the tip of his erection pressed against my opening. "If I had found you when I searched for you during the war, I would have claimed you and never let you go."

"Then claim me now." I pressed my heel into the back of his leg, urging him to thrust inside me. The stubborn male grinned, and even though I could see him straining not to comply, he refused to budge.

"Are you certain this is what you want, zadierra?"

Besides the vryndarr, Khyron was the most self-assured male I knew. He rarely expressed self-doubt, and I hated seeing a hint of it lingering on his handsome face. "Are *you* certain you wouldn't like me to give you another demonstration with my blade?"

"I suppose it is a good thing you are unable to reach my weapons." He chuckled, surged forward until he filled me completely, then had the audacity to continue taunting me by stopping.

"Khyron," I warned when no amount of bucking would make him move.

"Celeste," he replied with a nip to my chin. He curled his tail around my ankle, then slowly pulled out and plunged deep again. This time, he continued moving, slowly at first, then gradually increasing the speed of each thrust. It wasn't long before he pushed me over the edge, and every nerve in my body reacted by shuddering with pleasure.

He continued driving into me, drawing out my orgasm, then, with one final push, he called out my name and found his own release. Panting heavily, he collapsed on top of me, shifting his weight so I could breathe. We stayed like that for the longest time, enjoying the closeness and our reconnection. Khyron's tail absently caressing my leg was the only way I knew that he was still awake. I was exhausted, but now that I had him back in my life, I didn't want to sleep. "Khyron." I ran my fingertips along the scales on his back.

"Yes?" He lifted his head and smiled, his expression the most relaxed I'd seen since his arrival at the settlement.

"Do you suppose you could show me again what it means to be your ketiorra?"

***

Khyron

"Do you think if I check the hall, I'll find Thrayn standing guard outside?" Celeste snuggled against me with her chin braced near my shoulder.

It was still early and anyone who had a sleeping chamber connected with the outside corridor would have heard the male pacing for the last twenty minutes. With a sigh, I pulled her closer. "It is his job to protect me. And you are a dangerous female." I pressed a soft kiss to her forehead. "Though I will admit he takes his job a little too seriously. It is why I asked him to accompany the group. I am hoping if he spends more time here, he will learn how to interact better with your people."

Celeste grinned. "I assume you're talking about the females?"

"Most assuredly the females, specifically the ones with fighting skills. I am hoping he will learn to appreciate their abilities rather than be intimidated by them."

"And what about you?" She traced a line across the scales on my chest, sending heat to my groin. "Are you intimidated by my skills?"

We had not discussed the topic much before now, and I knew there was a deeper meaning behind the simple question she asked. The future of our relationship depended on whether or not I could accept the way she lived and the person she had become. "I recognized your strengths long before you became a warrior. It was one of many things that made you so appealing." I slipped my hand under the blanket. "The firmness of your backside was another. It has always fascinated me." The squeeze I gave a cheek elicited a squeal and a playful slap.

Unfortunately, being the drezdarr came with great responsibility, things I could not ignore. No matter how badly I wanted to stay in bed with Celeste, Thrayn's presence outside my room reminded me it would not be possible.

I brushed the hair off her cheek with the back of my hand. "There are some matters I need to address, and I am afraid I must leave you soon."

She stuck out her lower lip, her pout playful. "Are you sure? Because…" She traced a line down my chest, stopping at the blanket's edge and my already hardening shaft.

No. "Yes. Garyck found a luzardee shedding yesterday near the wooded area that runs along the perimeter." Maintaining the safety of others was not an easy responsibility, but I was committed to the task. This was Celeste's home, and I would do everything possible to keep her and the other inhabitants safe.

"Why would one of those slimy lizards be here? They've never bothered us before." Anger flared in her widened eyes. "Do you think it has anything to do with what happened with Laria and Jardun?"

"We are uncertain, which is why I want to investigate and have the area thoroughly searched."

"Oh no, the children… Someone needs to warn Harper." I held her in place with my tail when she tried to leave.

I remembered the close relationship Celeste had with her younger sister. When it came to the human younglings, she possessed the fierce protectiveness of a ketaurran female. During the time I spent with Melissa, I learned how much the children looked forward to her visits. She would make a wonderful dam, and I longed for the day when we could have a young one of our own.

It was too soon to consider the possibility of creating a family, the rekindled bond between us still fragile. Healing wounds and building trust could only be strengthened with time. "Jardun has already spoken to her. The area is being watched, and we are going to do another search this morning."

"Then I'm going with you." She reached back and caressed the end of my tail, a ploy to get me to release her. As soon as she was free, she rolled out of bed, ending my plans for any further lovemaking. "And don't even think about trying to stop me."

It was too hard to concentrate, or refuse her anything, when I was distracted by her naked body. All thoughts of what my argument would have been disappeared the minute she bent to snatch her clothes from the floor and presented me with a breathtaking view of her backside.

After tugging on her pants, she reached for her shirt. Keeping her from covering her lovely skin with clothing was incentive enough for me to get out of bed. "I would prefer to have you return with me to bed." I pulled her back against my chest and nuzzled the base of her neck.

She turned in my arms and slipped her hands along my shoulders. "I would prefer that too, but you know we can't. Not with a certain male hanging around and possibly listening."

I had forgotten all about Thrayn until she mentioned him. It would have been easy to blame him for missing out on more time spent with Celeste writhing beneath me, but I could not.

She kissed my cheek and gave me a shove so I landed on the bed. No doubt repayment for what I had done to her the night before. After slipping her shirt over her head, and disappointing me by covering her breasts, she started to leave the room.

"Zadierra, where are you going?"

She stopped with her hand on the partially opened door. "I need to shower and change."

Any thoughts I had about inviting her to bathe with me vanished when she said, "I'm also going to see if Laria and Sloane want to go along. We'll meet you back here."

It was obvious the years had not changed the stubborn side of the female, not that I would complain. I enjoyed and admired the independent side of her personality. I was exhilarated by the prospect of losing my heart all over again to the female she had become. "I look forward to your return." Agreeing was my only option since I knew there was nothing I could do to change my beautiful ketiorra's mind, or deter her lust for danger.

She hurried into the corridor. "Good morning, Thrayn." The overly sweet tone of her voice was a precursor to something devious and made me cringe. "Don't worry, I didn't hurt him too much."

Though I could not see him, I assumed when I heard him grumble something about troublesome females that he must be standing nearby. I was also prepared to intervene, more for Thrayn's protection than hers, until the sound of her giggles faded.

Thrayn's loyalty and dedication to his role as one of my protectors was beyond question. I also knew he would not leave unless ordered to do so. I grabbed a blanket from the bed and wrapped it around my waist. "Stop hovering in the hallway."

Thrayn stepped into the doorway, his skeptical gaze disappearing once he saw me. "All is well with your female?"

"Her name is Celeste." Human females were particular about the use of their name, and I worried that Thrayn would incur some kind of injury if he persisted in addressing them as females. "And yes, she is fine."

"Then I will wait outside until you are ready." Thrayn turned to leave.

Things between Celeste and me were going better than I had expected, and I wanted to keep it that way. Though our conversation about the past had eased some of my guilt, I regretted our missed time together. Now that she was back in my life, I planned to utilize every opportunity to make it up to her. "Actually, there is something I need you to do for me first."

CHAPTER THIRTEEN

Celeste

"What do you mean I can't go?" I slapped my hands on my hips and glared at Khyron, not caring that Vurell and Nayea were sitting at the kitchen table listening to our conversation. "I swear if you…" My irritation with him outweighed my disappointment at not being able to help track down the luzardee.

I didn't care if Khyron was the drezdarr. He wasn't going to get away with ordering me around or changing my plans because he wanted to protect me. If he expected to be a part of my life, he needed to understand I was quite capable of making my own decisions and taking care of myself. Both of those things would never change.

"Zadierra." His tone was low and placating.

"Celeste, the choice was not Khyron's," Vurell interrupted, his gaze dropping to my belt when he spoke. He must have thought my hand was too close to my knife and was afraid I might decide to use it. "Your friends decided it was best not to disturb you. Jardun, Laria, and Sloane went with Burke to meet with Marcus and discuss additional training for his males. Garyck and Zaedon left

132

to track the luzardee and hunt for the evening's meal."

"Oh." My anger subsided, and I gave Khyron an apologetic smile.

"I agreed with their decision. I have been concerned about Khyron's recovery and his need for rest," Vurell said. "I was glad to hear he was spending more time in bed."

I didn't have the heart to tell the doctor his patient probably expended more energy in one night with me than he had during the entire time he'd been here. Vurell might be a few years older than the rest of the ketaurran males, but I didn't believe he'd never had sex. Either he hadn't realized what he'd said or it had been some time since he'd spent the night with a female. Whatever the reason, I couldn't ever remember struggling so hard not to laugh.

Poor Nayea, who'd been quietly listening to our conversation, choked on her freegea. She glanced at Vurell as if there was something wrong with him. "You do realize…"

He held up his hand. "Yes, female, I am quite aware the drezdarr was demonstrating his prowess and exerting his strength to please his ketiorra. My concern was for his emotional health, which seems to have improved greatly." He wiggled his brows at me, then turned back to Nayea. "I would be happy to discuss the benefits of a sexual encounter with you further if…"

Khyron groaned. "I believe it is time to leave." He grabbed my hand and rushed to get me out of the building.

Vurell might be a little gruff, but I found his dry sense of humor amusing, and I really wanted to hear the rest of what he had to say.

I waited until we'd stepped off the end of the platform, then pulled Khyron to a stop. "Where are we going?"

With a smile, Khyron slipped his arms around my waist. "Since our plans have changed, I thought you might like to spend some time together, perhaps accompany me on a walk."

"And if I said no?" I let the challenge hang in the air.

He brushed my jaw with his thumb. "Do you want to say no?"

He'd always been good at using his charm to manipulate a situation to get what he wanted. Now that I knew he was the drezdarr, I wondered if it was a skill he'd learned from his father. I'd heard from quite a few people that the old leader ruled with diplomacy rather than brute strength. "I haven't decided yet."

"Until you do…" He took my hand and started walking. "If you don't mind, I would like to stop by Harper's place first."

"I don't mind, but why?" I tensed, worried something had happened to one of the children.

"You had expressed your concern for their welfare earlier, and I thought you might like to check on them."

"I would, thank you." His thoughtfulness was touching, but I sensed there was an ulterior motive for the visit. One he wasn't sharing.

A few minutes later, I felt prickles along my neck as if we were being followed. I glanced over my shoulder and saw Thrayn keeping pace about fifteen feet behind us. I hoped Khyron's idea of spending time together didn't include vryndarr supervision. "I see your bodyguard found us." I didn't bother to mask my annoyance.

"Do not worry, I am selfish where you are concerned. He will not be with us very long."

By the time we arrived at Harper's place, my curiosity had reached its maximum level. I stepped up on the platform and knocked on the door. When no one answered, I led Khyron and Thrayn inside. Since it was midmorning, finding the gathering room and adjoining dining area empty wasn't uncommon. The children enjoyed being outside. The older ones usually disappeared to hang out with friends from other families, the trader's market one of their usual hangouts. "Harper, are you here?"

Her voice echoed from the back of the house. "In the kitchen."

"Good morning." I found Harper sitting at the table sipping a cup of freegea. With taking care of the children, she rarely got any time to herself, and I hated intruding on her peaceful moment. Or at least I thought it was one of those moments until Draejill popped out from under the table.

"Rawr." He curled the ends of his fingers, then ran across the floor as fast as his little legs would carry him. When he reached Khyron, he plopped on the floor and grabbed his tail.

"Draejill, no," Harper scolded. "I'm so sorry." She shot Khyron a worried look as if she still wasn't sure how to act around the drezdarr. "We're trying to break him of the habit because he does it to Nayea all the time."

"It is all right." Khyron picked him up, holding him under both arms out in front of him to prevent Draejill from grabbing his hair. "You are very fierce for one so small."

Draejill growled and giggled. "Look. Same." He swished his own tail, then pointed at Khyron's.

"Yes, they are the same."

Thrayn remained in the entryway, staring suspiciously at Draejill as if he was a creature he'd never encountered before, one that planned to attack his drezdarr. Was it possible he'd never see any children from a human and ketaurran couple?

"Can I get you anything to drink?" Harper asked. "Thrayn, how about you?" She'd sensed his unease and used his name to draw his attention away from Draejill.

"I am fine, but thank you." His gaze never left Draejill, but some of his wariness lessened.

The door leading from the kitchen to the area behind the house burst open, and Ben, with Gabe following on his heels, rushed into the room. "Celeste!" he yelled, then stopped, causing Gabe to slam into his back. "Why is he here?" He huffed and gave Khyron a scathing glare. "Is he your boyfriend now?"

Khyron smirked and directed a curious glance in my direction. The arrogant male knew exactly what the word meant. "Something like that."

"Does that mean you're not going to use him for knife-throwing practice anymore?" Gabe snickered.

"What?" Harper asked, her face paling.

I should have known the two miscreants would eventually tell Harper what they'd seen. "It was a misunderstanding, and nobody got hurt." I glared first at the boys for saying anything, then at Khyron, whose smirk widened into a grin.

Thrayn pursed his lips. "It was not a misunderstanding. She…"

"Thrayn." Khyron's scowl made the younger male take a step backward.

"Okay, then." Harper got up from her seat. She'd had plenty of experience refereeing squabbles between the children and didn't have any problem stepping between the two males. "Why don't you guys go back outside and play?" She gave Ben and Gabe one of her insistent, no-arguing glares until they turned and raced from the room.

To Khyron, she said, "I have what you asked for ready to go." She motioned to a bag sitting on the counter behind her.

"Thank you, Harper. It is greatly appreciated." Khyron held Draejill out to Thrayn. "I need some time alone with my ketiorra and insist you stay here to protect Harper and the young ones."

Reluctantly, Thrayn took Draejill. I tried not to laugh at the way he wrinkled his nose and held the child away from his body.

The bag was large and bulky, but Khyron had no problem lifting it and slipping the strap over his shoulder. He reached for my hand. "Come, Zadierra. I believe I promised you a walk."

***

"Aren't you worried there might be a luzardee or two lurking around somewhere?" I asked when Khyron led me into the wooded area behind Harper's place.

"We are both armed, and I have you to protect me." He might have been teasing, but I'd battled luzardees before and wouldn't hesitate to fight one if it meant keeping Khyron alive.

Since Vurell had mentioned that Garyck and Zaedon were doing more tracking, I was a little more assured that we would be okay. I'd expected him to take me to the area where I trained with Ben and Gabe, but he took a different route, one I didn't normally use. One that ended in my favorite clearing, the place I came when I needed time to myself.

I stepped over a stream that emptied into a secluded pool of water. When I was troubled, staring at its lavender hue rippling across its translucent surface always had a calming effect. "How did you find this place?" The clearing was hidden from view, and I didn't think Khyron had just happened upon it the day he arrived.

He walked up behind me and pulled me back against his chest, then unhooked the bag Harper had given him and let it slide to the ground next to us. "I had help from a young female who is very wise."

Being this close to him always felt right, natural, perfect. I turned in his arms and asked, "Are you talking about Melissa?" She was the only young female I knew he'd interacted with when Fuzzball attacked his tail.

"I am." He pressed a kiss to my forehead.

"But how? When?"

"She found me in the clearing not long after you left. Since you were angry with me, she suggested I find a way to apologize and brought me here."

"Where you picked the chirayka you left on my nightstand." I glanced at the wild vines covering the boulders bordering one side of the pool. Each spiraling tendril contained numerous deep purple blossoms.

"Not until the next morning, but yes," he said.

He tucked some strands that had escaped my braid behind my ear. "Did you know Melissa hopes one day to be a great warrior like you?"

The warmth from his touch combined with the compliment sent heat surging through me. "I don't know about the great warrior part, but Melissa and I have talked about me teaching her how to handle a blade."

His smile faded. "With the uncertainty of her future, I believe it is a good idea." A hint of regret laced his words, and I sensed the burden of being responsible for the lives of so many weighed heavily on his mind.

Moments where he didn't have to worry about the problems we faced would be rare, and I wanted to make sure this was one of them. "So"—I nudged the bag near his feet with the tip of my boot—"are you going to tell me what's inside?" Khyron had always been resourceful, but I was curious when he'd found the time to coax Harper into helping him.

"I thought you might enjoy a picnic and had her prepare us a lunch." He bent down to pick up the bag, then clasped my hand and led me to a flat area underneath a group of thorny trees.

"Where did you learn about picnics?" I couldn't remember ever discussing the topic with him. It was possible that Laria and Sloane, with their devious tendencies, had something to do with our outing.

"From the history data books the human leaders gave my sire shortly after your ship arrived on Ketaurrios." He opened the bag and pulled out a blanket, then spread it on the ground. "Is a picnic not used as a human ritual to gain a female's affections?"

I'd never read any of the history books the exploration team had assembled for the trip from Earth. From conversations I'd had with other ketaurrans, I sometimes wondered if the information was a little outdated or if something got misconstrued during the translation.

I didn't want to spoil his surprise by telling him he didn't need to gain my affections because he already possessed my heart. If it took performing romantic gestures to ease his past guilt and bring us closer together, then I had no objections and would play along. "Are you trying to tell me you want to date?"

"I do not know what dating is, but if it assists with proving my worth as a mate, to keep you as my ketiorra, then yes, I wish to date you." He sat on the blanket and pulled me onto his lap so I straddled his legs.

Khyron had amazed me more than once in the last couple of days, and I was touched by the fierce ketaurran leader's attempt at romance. We'd both been hurt, suffered loss, and used blame to relieve the resulting pain. It would take time to reinforce the bond we'd shared before the war ripped it apart.

I'd been in several relationships, all of them before I'd met Khyron. None of them amounted to anything, and they certainly didn't involve any real dating. So the idea of seeing what creative things he came up with to win me over seemed very intriguing. "I guess if you put it that way, how can I resist?"

CHAPTER FOURTEEN

Khyron

Elated did not describe my exhilaration at having Celeste agree to the human tradition of dating. The harsh realities of my world prevented continual happiness for its inhabitants. I enjoyed seeing the rare and radiant smile on her face and decided I would give her more picnics and whatever else I could devise to keep it there. So far, Laria and Sloane had proved to be excellent allies. Perhaps a conversation with them would provide me with the additional information I needed.

My body's response to her sitting on my lap was immediate, and though we had already shared one night of passion, I knew I would never get enough of my ketiorra. I would have loved nothing more than to make love to her out here in the wilderness, but I had no idea where Garyck and Zaedon's hunt would lead them and did not want to risk them seeing her naked.

"Then I will do my best not to disappoint you." I slipped a hand behind her nape and urged her closer, then brushed my lips softly across hers. During the hours we'd spent pleasuring each other the night before, I discovered that gentleness was not something she desired. She took control of the kiss with an eagerness that had me moaning.

With great reluctance, I ended the kiss and reached for the bag. "Shall we see what Harper has packed for us?"

"You know most males like to take advantage of a female during a date." Celeste wiggled her hips, an action that made my erection even more uncomfortable. "Aren't you at least going to try?"

"Later, zadierra." I grabbed her hips to halt her movements. "When we are alone in my sleeping chambers, I plan to take advantage of you often."

"Promise."

"Of course." I opened the first container and found it filled with pyteinna.

"Harper is a great cook. I don't know what she uses to flavor her food, but the pancakes she makes always taste good." Celeste snagged one off the top, broke it in half, then held out a portion for me to sample.

I took a bite and had to admit the cakes were well prepared. "If I remember correctly, cooking was not a skill you had any interest in learning. Has that changed?"

"The best I can do is grill meat. Sloane is the cook in our group." She frowned and lowered her cake before taking another bite. "Why, were you looking for a female with home-keeping capabilities?"

"No, my preference is females who can wield very sharp blades, specifically a particular one who has a firm yet squeezable backside." I grinned and snatched the remainder of the cake from her hand, then quickly popped it into my mouth.

"Hey, this blade-wielding female with the nice backside wasn't done with that."

Celeste was not impressed when I chuckled, or with my attempt to keep the rest of the cakes away from her. I soon found myself shoved on my back with an annoyed female sitting astride my midsection. With a prideful sneer, she grabbed another cake from the container. "Never steal my food."

Before she could reach her mouth, I rolled her over, pinning her wrists above her head. "Or…"

"Or I will…" Concern filled her dark gaze and she jerked her head to the side, trying to see past the wall of blue-thorned trees.

"What is wrong?" I asked.

"I thought I heard something. I don't think we're alone."

All playful thoughts disappeared, replaced by the need to keep Celeste safe. I immediately helped her to her feet, then drew my blade, and strained to listen. The rustling coming from my left started off low and grew gradually stronger. Celeste slowly unsheathed her knife, then pointed at a gap in the trees. We left the blanket and bag in the clearing, then simultaneously moved in the direction she had designated.

We hadn't gone far when Melissa burst into view, hair pulled loose from her braids, dirt clinging to her tear-stained face. She stumbled to a stop when she saw us, then put her hands on her knees, panting to catch her breath.

"Sweetie, what are you doing out here?" Celeste's concerned tone lacked any harshness.

After Garyck found the luzardee skin, Harper had been cautioned to keep the children close to their home. Of course, young ones did not always follow instructions. And with the large number of children the female cared for, it was impossible to keep track of them every minute.

"Fuzzball got away, and I went to look for him." Fresh tears trickled down her cheeks.

Celeste returned her blade to its sheath, then squatted in front of Melissa and rubbed her arms. "So why are you crying?"

"Because, because"—Melissa gulped more air— "because of what happened to Fuzzball and the white guy."

"What white guy?" Celeste asked, then shot me a

questioning look.

I shrugged, also baffled by the child's reference.

"The white guy who lives in the rocks." Melissa sobbed, expressing her exasperation by stomping her foot.

"I assume she is talking about the ketaurran male who lives in the caverns along the perimeter of the settlement." With everything that had happened, I had not had a chance to tell Celeste about Garyck's other discovery.

"You mean what we always assumed was a harmless creature is really a male?" Celeste asked, then turned back to Melissa after I nodded. "Start from the beginning and tell us what happened."

"I know we're not supposed to go near the rocks, but it was Fuzzball's fault, and..." Melissa swiped a cheek with the back of her hand.

Celeste wiped her other cheek. "You're not in trouble, okay?"

"Okay." Melissa pushed out her lower lip. "Well, there was a man hiding in the rocks."

"Not the white guy, right?" Celeste asked for clarification.

"Uh-huh, and he was mean. He said I had to go with him, and when I told him no, he grabbed me...hard." She held up her arm and showed us the red marks on her skin, which would no doubt turn into bruises later.

I clenched my fists. If the male was not already dead, he soon would be.

"That's when the white guy showed up and told the mean guy to let me go or else." Melissa gasped a deep breath. "Then they got into a big fight. Only the mean guy didn't fight fair and tried to push the white guy into a big hole near the rocks." Melissa threw her hands in the air. "Then Fuzzball tried to help the white guy, and, and...they all fell into the hole."

"Hole?" Celeste asked, her confusion matching mine.

"Yeah, it was really deep. I looked over the edge and could see the white guy, but I think he got hurt, and it was too far for me to reach, so I ran and…" Melissa looked up at me with pleading brown eyes. "Please, Khyron, you have to help them."

"Melissa, can you take us to the hole?" Celeste asked as she got to her feet.

"Yes." She bobbed her head, then took my hand and tugged. "It's this way."

I hurried, but it was hard for Melissa's shorter legs to keep up with me, so I scooped her into my arms and continued in the direction she'd instructed. She seemed grateful for the assistance and wrapped her arms around my neck. I clutched her closer, hoping the reassurance would comfort her.

"It's over there." Melissa pointed toward a flat area near the base of a rock wall where a group of boulders formed a natural staircase. It was probably one of many ways the ketaurran male accessed the ledges above.

I lowered her to the ground. "Show us."

"Here." She moved ahead of us slowly and circled the mound of boulders.

Hidden from view was a gap that cut between the rock walls. A large crevice, which I assumed was Melissa's hole, ran alongside it. If Fuzzball and the males went over the edge as she stated, I feared what we would find at the bottom.

Celeste placed her hand on Melissa's shoulder to keep her from getting any closer. "Why don't you move back a little so Khyron and I can take a look?"

"Okay."

Staying by Celeste's side, I walked toward the ravine and peered over the edge. The midafternoon sun cast light into the shadows, making it less difficult to see the bottom as well as the narrow ledge directly below us. Fortunately, the ketaurran male Melissa mentioned had landed on the ledge and not the jagged rocks covering the base.

He was an albino, a rarity in our kind, and most definitely white, all the way from his silvery hair to the pearlescent sheen on his scales. He was sprawled on his back, his eyes closed, with one leg hanging over the edge. A dark stain, the result of an injury, spread across the fabric covering his thigh. His arm was wrapped around Fuzzball, who lay on the male's chest, whimpering.

The human male hadn't been so lucky, not that I cared. The drop had taken him all the way to the bottom, where his body sprawled at an odd angle, his wide, lifeless dark eyes staring skyward. If the male had survived, a more severe death would have been his fate for harming Melissa.

Celeste showed absolutely no remorse for the human, though I noticed a glint of recognition in her contempt-filled glare.

"Do you know him?" I asked.

"Yes, that's Travis, the guy who tried to take Draejill." She spoke through gritted teeth, disgust in her tone.

I knew some type of slavery, or worse, would have awaited Melissa if the ketaurran had not come along and rescued her. For the child's sake, I did not share my thoughts openly with Celeste.

***

Celeste

It might be harsh and uncaring, but all I felt was relieved when I saw Travis's broken body lying on the jagged rocks at the bottom of the crevice. Relieved that he hadn't been able to carry out his plan to abduct Melissa. Relieved Draejill would be safe.

Right now, my main concern was helping the ketaurran male who'd risked his life to save Melissa and Fuzzball.

Melissa had done as I'd asked and stayed back while Khyron and I checked out what had happened to the males. Her lower lip quivered, but at least she'd stopped crying. "I want you to go back to Harper's and tell her what happened."

"I don't want to leave, not without Fuzzball." Melissa crossed her arms defiantly. "Besides, I've seen dead guys before."

She was extremely intelligent and knew the real reason I didn't want her to stay was because of Travis. All the children had seen dead bodies before, but it didn't mean she needed to add one more nasty image to her memory. I didn't want her around when we finally pulled Travis's body out of the ravine.

Personally, I'd be fine if we left him there for the leezacorr, the hard-scaled creatures that lived in the smaller caves, to have for their next meal. "I know, sweetie, but you don't need to see this one." I caressed her cheek, knowing arguing was useless, that she wouldn't leave without her furry pet. "I tell you what, I'll let you stay if you go sit over there on one of those rocks and let Khyron and me get Fuzzball out of the hole."

"You have to promise to help the white guy too, 'cuz he saved me." She furrowed her brow, glancing from me to Khyron, looking for reassurance.

"You have my word, Melissa," Khyron said.

I was in awe of how easily the trust he'd earned from the child resulted in a half smile and a gaze filled with hero worship.

"Mine too. Now go." I jutted my chin to the right.

"Okay." She raced to the other side of the secluded area and climbed on the first rock she came to.

I peeked over the edge again, noting the distance to the ledge. I wasn't thrilled about going down there, not when I had a problem with heights. I judged the distance to be six feet, seven at the most, which shouldn't be too hard to reach. I placed my hand on Khyron's arm. "We need to get them out of there." With Melissa nearby, I refrained from saying *before the male bleeds to death*. "I'm pretty sure I can reach the ledge if you lower me."

Khyron's arm tensed. "It is not safe. I will go." He pulled me away from the edge, keeping his voice low so

Melissa couldn't overhear him. "What if you startle him and he attacks you?"

It was a valid point, one I quickly dismissed. "You and I both know if he was dangerous, he wouldn't have helped Melissa."

"There are also the creatures that live within the rocks to consider. It will not be long before the scent of his blood draws their attention. I still believe I should go."

I understood his concern, his instinctive need to keep me safe. He was the leader of an entire race, and judging by his contemplative gaze, he was trying to decide whether or not issuing an order—one he'd expect me to follow—would be a wise choice.

Since lives were at risk and we didn't have time to continue arguing, I tried a logical approach. "That's great, but how do you plan to get him and yourself back out? The ravine wall above the ledge is too smooth for you to climb. Even if I had a rope, I'm not strong enough to pull either of you out. It makes more sense for me to go down. I can hand you Fuzzball, then help him stand so you can pull him out first, then me."

I didn't give him the opportunity to respond. "Khyron, I'll be all right. I'm not the same female you remember." I patted the blade on my hip. "I can take care of myself."

His intense gaze softened, and he placed his hands on my hips. "I am aware, but it does not make this any easier for me. I do not wish to lose you now that I have found you."

"I don't want to lose you either, but survival on this planet comes with many risks. If you want to unite our people, we need to work together, to trust one another." I cupped his cheek. "That also applies to our relationship."

"For goodness' sakes, are you going to help Fuzzball and the white guy or not?" Melissa raised her voice at the same time Fuzzball's whimpers turned into pleading growls.

Khyron groaned. "Leave it to a young one… Fine, I

will lower you."

I waited for him to get down on his knees, then knelt beside him. After swinging my legs over the edge, he clasped my hands, then lowered me to the ledge, the pale blue scales covering his muscles rippling from the exertion.

Dangling in the air was not my idea of a good time. At least I didn't have the same level of anxiety I'd had when our group had to scale a rocky cliff on the back of a chaugwai, the lizard-like creatures we'd used to enter the wastelands when we rescued Vurell. Thinking about Lou, the name I'd given my ride, helped override some of my fear so I could concentrate on finding the ledge.

After scraping the uneven rocky surface with the toe of my boots, it took me a few seconds to feel comfortable with my footing. "Okay, you can let go." I raised my voice more from anxiety than from wanting to make sure Khyron could hear me.

He released one hand, giving me time to brace it against the wall in front of me, then waited for me to find my balance before letting go of the other. I'd ended up on the end of the ledge nearest to the male's injured leg. His eyes were closed, but his chest moved, alleviating my concern that we'd arrived too late.

As soon as Fuzzball saw me, he made happy whimpers and wagged his tail. Normally, he'd come right to me, but since he didn't squirm or try to get closer, I assumed he didn't like high places either. "Hang on, boy. I'm going to get you out of here."

With my back near the wall, I eased closer and took note of the male's injuries and his appearance. His vest, pants, and boots appeared to be made from animal hides, suggesting he made his own clothes. The craftsmanship showed the same level of expertise I'd found at the trader's market. Even the empty sheath and belt strapped to his waist were quite impressive. I didn't see his blade anywhere close by and wondered if it ended up underneath him or went over the side with Travis.

I wasn't a medical expert, but nothing appeared to be broken. There were several small cuts on his chest, but the wound on his leg seemed to be the worst. Through a large tear in his pants, I could see a nasty gash. The area surrounding it, including the material covering his leg, was soaked with blood. It looked as if the bleeding had stopped, at least for now.

"What is the male's condition?" Khyron lay on the ground, waiting to lend assistance.

"He's still alive."

"Is he conscious?" Khyron asked.

"Not at the moment. Give me a minute. I'm going to get Fuzzball first."

There was just enough room between the male and the wall for me to crouch next to him. "Can you hear me?" I asked, concerned he might wake up, be startled when he found a strange female hovering over him, and accidentally knock me off the ledge.

When all he did was moan, I slowly moved the arm wrapped around Fuzzball. "Come on, little guy. Let's get you out of here." Fuzzball swished his tail faster the instant I gathered him into my arms. After checking to make sure he wasn't hurt, I lifted Fuzzball over my head and waited until I was sure Khyron had a good grasp on him before letting go.

I hoped my next attempt to wake the male worked, because the thought of staying on this ledge until Khyron could get help was unsettling. I turned to crouch next to him again, then froze when I found a pair of reddish-pink eyes staring at me. "Please don't be scared. I'm here to help."

"I am not afraid." He tried to rise into a sitting position and grimaced.

"Here, let me help you, but be careful. Your leg is badly injured, so try not to move it too much." The last thing I wanted was for it to start bleeding again. I held out my hand and pulled him forward.

"You are the female who teaches the young human males how to handle their blades. The one they call Celeste." He sounded matter-of-fact. "And the male who is assisting you"—he gave Khyron a quick glance—"is the drezdarr, is he not?"

Had he been spying on us? And if he had, why hadn't I ever sensed his presence? "He is, but how did you come by that information?"

"I hunt in the wooded lands and have observed you with the young ones many times. I have also been watching all the males since their arrival."

I thought about asking him why he never let us know he was nearby, then realized he must have had his reasons. "You know you don't have to live out here. You're welcome to live in the settlement."

"I am…different, even for a ketaurran." He averted his gaze as if discussing his uniqueness troubled him.

Had he been shunned by his own people? I planned to ask Khyron later if being an albino was considered a bad thing in his culture, because I refused to let it be a problem in mine.

"What is your name?" I asked.

"Rygael."

"Okay, Rygael, before we move you, I'd like to make sure your wound doesn't open again. Would it be all right if I secure my belt around your leg?"

He gave me a brief nod.

"Good, and once I'm done with that, I'll help you stand so Khyron can pull you out." I unfastened my belt, then removed the sheath and slid it, along with my blade, into the back of my pants.

He braced his arms behind him, then bent his knee, lifting his leg enough for me to slide the belt underneath it.

"I'm sorry, but this is going to hurt."

"I understand."

I positioned the leather as gently as I could, doing my best not to touch the wound, but Rygael still winced and ground his teeth. I'd barely finished cinching the belt when a snarly hissing noise echoed in the distance.

"Celeste, you must hurry." Khyron must have heard the noise too. Up until now, he hadn't said much, but the entire time I'd been on the ledge, I'd sensed his presence and didn't need to look up to know he hadn't moved and was keeping a protective watch over me.

"On it." I got to my feet and held out my hand. "Let's get you out of here." Rygael was a big guy. His frame rivaled Khyron's, and getting him to his feet wasn't an easy task. Rygael's stance was a little wobbly, so I wrapped my arm around his waist and took some of his weight. I'd barely gotten him positioned beneath Khyron when the noise I'd heard sounded louder and a lot closer.

"Female, you must go first," Rygael said.

"Celeste," I corrected, although my need to get the draeck off the ledge outweighed my annoyance at being called a female. "And you're in no condition to fight, or do anything else. Now go."

"Rygael, it will do you no good to argue with her, so give me your hand." Khyron extended his arms and wiggled his fingers, anxious to get Rygael out of the ravine.

I didn't know if Rygael's compliance was motivated by fear of what would happen to him if he disobeyed his drezdarr or the angry glare I leveled at him. The fact that he grabbed Khyron's hand and was being hoisted off the ledge was all that mattered.

Rygael was halfway up the wall when I heard growling below me. I reached behind my back and slid my blade from its sheath, then peered over the edge to see what was making the noise.

There were two leezacorr, both about the size of small dogs, with scaly black skin and translucent green eyes, ravaging Travis's body. Their appearance wasn't nearly as disgusting as the snakkrils that lived in the Quaddrien, but they were just as vicious. Seeing them shred his clothes and tear apart his body was nauseating, something I preferred not to keep watching. I also didn't want to draw their attention and slowly backed away from the edge.

"Celeste." Khyron had finished helping Rygael and had his arm outstretched for me.

I wasn't about to put my blade away, not with the creatures so close. With my free hand, I reached for Khyron. My fingertips brushed against his when he called out, "Behind you."

I'd never actually seen a leezacorr climb a rock wall until one hoisted itself onto the ledge a few feet away from me. So much for Travis's body keeping them busy until I was out of here.

As far as I knew, they preferred dark places, wouldn't attack unless provoked, and never ventured into the wooded area. Obviously, the information I'd been given lacked an important detail—Khyron was right about the carnivorous creatures being attracted to the scent of blood. And since a large amount of Rygael's blood had seeped onto the ground near my feet, it wouldn't be long before more leezacorrs found their way up here.

I was standing in the middle of the ledge. The distance to either end couldn't be more than five or six feet. I held my position, too afraid I wouldn't have enough room to maneuver if I moved. The creature snarled and snapped, slowly advancing toward me. When it was about a foot away, it reared up on its hind legs and took a swipe at me. I didn't react quickly enough to keep its claws from catching my arm above my wrist. Pain burned across my skin, and blood oozed from three long cuts. I'd been injured before, and, other than the pain, this one didn't look too bad.

A well-placed kick to the leezacorr's midsection would knock it off the ledge. I wasn't willing to risk ending up with more gashes or have it dig its claws in at the last minute and take me with it. Fortunately, I'd gotten in a slice of my own, catching it near the shoulder. It growled and paced, acting wary, but keeping its distance.

It wasn't until another creature appeared on the

opposite side of the ledge that the first one got more aggressive, and started inching closer. Both creatures snarled and hissed in a back-and-forth banter as if they were communicating with each other. Simultaneously, they rose onto their hind quarters, and I knew what was coming next. My heart pulsed, and I gripped my blade tighter. "Khyron, if you have any suggestions, now would be the time to share."

"Aim for the throat," Khyron said, just before he dropped through the air and landed on the ledge next to me.

With a precise and graceful swipe of his sword, he took off the leezacorr's head. The second the dead creature hit the ground, the other one released a guttural noise similar to a high-pitched scream. While the creature's attention was focused on the downed leezacorr, I sliced with my blade. The cut wasn't as clean as Khyron's sword, but it ended the creature's life, which, along with getting off this ledge, was all I cared about.

Khyron leaned forward and glanced over the edge, then returned his focus to me.

He opened his mouth to speak, but I cut him off. "If you're going to tell me you told me so, don't."

"I would never..." His expression might appear innocent, but his smug tone said otherwise.

"Uh-huh."

"I was going to say we should leave before more leezacorr arrive."

"And how exactly did you plan on doing that?" I was grateful he'd shown up when he did, but he was also my only way to the top. Now we were both stuck here with the possibility of having to fight more of the disgusting creatures.

"Zyrdena." I glanced up at Zaedon's voice and saw him peering over the ledge, grinning.

"Zaedon." Shocked, then massively relieved, I smiled back at him.

"I see you have found a way to get into trouble again. Apparently, the drezdarr and you have quite a lot in common."

"Take Zaedon's hand." I wasn't sure if Khyron's brusque tone and frown were because of Zaedon's remark or because he'd called me little princess rather than use my name. He didn't give me a chance to act on my own. He grabbed me around the waist and lifted me, making it easy for Zaedon to pull me out of the ravine.

"How did you know where we were?" I asked Zaedon once my feet were back on solid ground.

"Garyck and I came across the chonderra's trail, the creature you call Fuzzball, along with that of a child. We were concerned there might be a problem when the tracks headed in this direction and decided to follow." He reached back over the edge, then tossed the two leezacorr carcasses on the ground next to me.

My instinctive need to protect myself by slicing first and worrying about what I killed later or, in this case, swinging and jumping back about a foot, had Zaedon laughing and me ready to smack him. "Not funny." I slid my blade into its sheath, then tucked it into the back of my pants.

When Khyron reached the surface, I asked, "Why didn't you leave those disgusting things down there?"

"Their meat is excellent and good for eating. Garyck would be angry if he learned we had wasted them."

An image of the grumpy ketaurran grunting his displeasure popped into my mind, but when I glanced around to see if he was listening, I didn't see him or the others. "Where did everyone go?"

"Garyck took Rygael and Melissa back to Harper's place so Vurell and Nayea can take care of his wound," Zaedon said.

"I am glad you are unharmed." Khyron pulled me into a tight hug, then slowly released me. He noticed the claw marks on my arm, and his smile quickly faded. "Zadierra, why did you not tell me you were injured?" He took my wrist and examined the cuts with more scrutiny.

I'd been so busy trying not to get killed that I'd forgotten all about the cuts on my arm or how much they still throbbed. "Khyron, it's not that bad." The bleeding had stopped, but not before coating my skin and making the injury look a lot worse than it was.

"It is, and I will not risk you getting an infection. I have seen what happens when an animal wound does not receive immediate medical care, the illness it can cause, the result sometimes fatal."

The next thing I knew, he swept me off the ground and carried me in the direction of Harper's place. Khyron might have grown up on the planet and be more knowledgeable about the creatures living here than I was, but I still thought he was overreacting. "Khyron, I *can* walk."

"No." He tightened his grip.

With tension rippling through his body, I decided now might not be a good time to argue with him.

Zaedon had grabbed the bodies of the leezacorrs and had no problem keeping up with Khyron's pace. Over the last couple of weeks, Zaedon and I had gotten to know each other fairly well. He knew I wasn't thrilled about being toted around like a child's precious toy. His smirk implied he was enjoying my displeasure way too much and irritated me even more. I decided to show him how much I didn't appreciate his smug attitude once I got Khyron to put me down.

CHAPTER FIFTEEN

Khyron

When Celeste tensed in my arms, I was certain she planned to continue arguing with me for overreacting to her injury and carrying her all the way to Harper's place. At the moment, I did not care. I was angry at how close she had come to being severely injured by the two leezacorrs. Had Zaedon not arrived when he did, she could have been hurt a lot worse. Her going down to help Rygael had been the right choice, and, if I was thinking logically like a drezdarr rather than emotionally like a mate, I would not be acting this overprotective.

It did not help that Zaedon had used every opportunity possible since entering the wooded area to taunt me about my reaction to the situation. His teasing annoyed Celeste immensely, if her tight grip on my nape was any indication. I feared what would happen to my friend once I released her and she decided to reach for her blade.

Because of my quick strides, we reached Garyck and Rygael shortly before they arrived at Harper's place. Rygael, his arm draped over Garyck's shoulder, was limping, using his uninjured leg to support the majority of his weight.

The door at the rear of the building swung open, and Harper burst outside, then froze when she saw us. "Melissa said a white guy saved her from…" Her gaze locked with Rygael's, and she gasped. "Oh, I'm…"

Harper's shock did not last long once she noticed the belt secured around Rygael's leg and the dark stain beneath it. "Garyck, follow me. You can put him in my room."

Harper pointed at the leezacorrs in Zaedon's hand. "Those things can stay out here until you've skinned them or whatever it is you do before they can be cooked." She held the door open until everyone was inside. "It's this way. I already sent Ben down to Burke's to get Nayea. She should be here any minute." She hurried ahead of Garyck and Rygael, then led them down a hallway to my left.

"I think it's safe to put me down now." Celeste wiggled her hips when I did not comply immediately.

I kept my hands on her waist even after I lowered her feet to the ground. Keeping her close reminded me that she was alive and minimized my stress. I was not sure if I would ever reach a point where the painful thought of losing her all over again did not continually hover in the back of my mind.

Thankfully, she left her knife tucked safely in the back of her pants, but the glare she leveled at Zaedon was almost as deadly as the blade's sharp edge. "If you don't stop teasing Khyron, I'll tell Cara why you're always sniffing her."

I did not think Zaedon's eyes could get so wide. "You would not dare."

The ability to detect the unique scent belonging to our ketiorra was not information readily known by the humans. Celeste was aware of it because I had shared the information with her.

"Wouldn't I?" Challenge sparkled in her dark-cinnamon eyes.

I could fight my own battles, yet I straightened my

shoulders, proud my ketiorra cared enough to come to my defense. Maybe my overprotectiveness did not bother her as much as I thought.

"And you…" She poked me in the chest. "Just because I'm defending you doesn't mean we aren't going to have a discussion later about your bossy behavior."

I had never heard anyone use the word bossy before, but by her annoyed expression, I assumed it was not good. I also did not think now was the time to have her explain its meaning, and decided to wait until we were alone, preferably near a bed in case I needed to seek seductive means to temper her anger.

Zaedon chuckled, seemingly unconcerned by Celeste's previous threat. Or at least he was until she jerked her head and narrowed her eyes in his direction.

Before I could insist that Celeste let me take care of her wound, Ben raced into the room from the front of the dwelling, with Melissa and Fuzzball jogging closely behind him. Both children skidded to a stop as soon as they saw us.

"Hey, guys," Celeste said to the young ones. If she heard Zaedon's overly loud sigh at being spared her wrath, she did not mention it.

Melissa smiled at me, then anxiously glanced around the room. "Where's the white guy?"

"His name is Rygael, and he is in the sleeping chamber at the end of the hall," I said.

"Great, thanks." Melissa motioned for Ben to follow her, then took off running again.

Laughter echoed from the corridor, and a few seconds later, Garyck appeared, frowning more than usual. "I will collect the leezacorrs and prepare them for eating." He stopped when he reached Celeste and me, then grunted. "Are you aware your female is injured?"

"Yes, I am aware." And had there not been so many interruptions, I would have taken care of it already. "I will have Nayea look at it once she arrives."

"Good," Garyck mumbled, then, without saying another word, he headed for the door leading back outside. I was not insulted by or worried about Garyck's quick exit. In all the years I had known him, being social was not something at which he exceled. The things he had endured during the war made it worse, and being around a lot of people made him uncomfortable.

"I'm pretty sure I can take care of it myself," Celeste said, trying to pull from my grasp. My intent to assist her was delayed by Nayea and Vurell's arrival.

"Who is in need of our assistance?" Vurell huffed. "It is hard to understand the young ones when they are excited."

Nayea shook her head at Vurell. "I had no problem understanding them. Perhaps if you cannot communicate with children, you are too old to be administering medical care."

Harper walked into the room with her arms crossed. "The patient is the ketaurran male who lives in the caverns outside the settlement. His name is Rygael, and you two can finish arguing once you've taken care of his wound."

It appeared there was more to Harper's temperament than I imagined. The female wielded her tongue the same way a warrior would their blade. She also had an underlying sense of humor and flashed Celeste a wink, one that Vurell did not see.

"My apologies, Harper." Vurell somberly bowed his head. "Please direct me to this male."

"Nayea." I stopped her by touching her arm. "Before you attend to the male, would you mind taking care of Celeste's injury?"

"I will be in to assist you shortly," Nayea said to Vurell before he entered the hallway.

He adjusted the large bag strapped across his shoulder. "I do not require assistance, but you are more than welcome to observe."

Nayea snorted, then lifted Celeste's wrist for a closer

look. The blood had crusted, but the skin around the cuts had swollen and appeared redder than the last time I examined them.

Celeste rolled her eyes at me. "It's nothing."

"These look like claw marks. What did this?" Nayea asked.

"A leezacorr. Why?" Celeste asked.

"Because the risk of infection from this kind of injury is *serious*. Why did you not wash the wound immediately?" Nayea's tight-lipped glare started with Celeste, then ended with me. "Never mind." She dismissed any answer either of us would have given with a wave of her hand. "Follow me into the cooking area so I can clean the cuts and apply some healing salve." She placed her hand on Celeste's shoulder and urged her from the room.

Even if it meant losing some of the ground I had gained with Celeste's forgiveness, I should have insisted she let me tend her wound. Weighted with guilt for not taking better care of my ketiorra, I followed the females.

After Celeste and I took a seat at the table, it did not take Nayea long to clean and apply a salve to her cuts, then wrap them with a sealing cloth to protect the wound. "She needs to rest tonight and must not exert any energy." Nayea stared at me when she spoke, her insinuation that I refrain from undressing Celeste when I shared my bed with her later quite clear.

"Brew this and make sure she drinks an entire cup before going to bed." Nayea handed me a packet containing dried plant leaves. "It has healing properties to prevent infection, but will also make her sleep."

"Thank you, Nayea." Celeste stood and gave her a hug.

Had I missed something? Was there a reason Celeste chose to argue with me but not the older female? Until I could determine the reason, I thought it wise to follow Celeste's example. "I am grateful as well."

"Now, if you will excuse me, I must ensure that Vurell has not damaged Rygael." Her gaze glistening with mischief, Nayea exited the room.

Celeste giggled. "Vurell has no idea what he's in for."

"You may be right, but it will do him good." I pushed thoughts of the cantankerous male out of my mind and welcomed Celeste into my arms.

"And what would do *you* good?" She slipped her arms around my neck, then playfully nipped my chin.

I grinned, content that she was no longer angry with me. "I can think of many things, but for now, a kiss will have to do."

***

Celeste

Harper had been more than a little overprotective of Rygael and didn't want to leave him unattended, so I'd convinced her to let us gather at her place and help out by cooking the evening meal for the children. Her sleeping chamber was on the opposite end of the building, so hopefully, any noise we made wouldn't disturb Rygael.

Besides Laria, Sloane, and me, Khyron and the vryndarr had also agreed to help out. Burke and his males had other things to do and couldn't make it. Cara had delayed her trip to see her grandparents because she'd been spending time at the trader's market searching for additional transport parts, but had declined the invitation. Zaedon was also absent, and, if I had to guess, had followed Cara and was doing his best to irritate her.

I had no idea where Vurell and Nayea went after they'd taken care of Rygael. Other than the children and Fuzzball, Vurell and Nayea had been the only other people who'd been allowed into the room to see Rygael. I knew Khyron wanted to speak with the male, to learn more about what happened with Travis and personally thank him for rescuing Melissa. He'd decided to wait until Vurell and Nayea were finished, which had taken longer than we'd expected. No doubt because they'd been arguing about the best way to treat Rygael's wounds.

When they finally emerged from the room, Nayea told us the injury on Rygael's leg had been bad and required sealing. She also informed us he had been given the same healing drink she'd insisted I take later and would not wake until morning.

Now that we were all seated at the long dining table and the meal had been served, it took me a few minutes to push the images of the leezacorrs out of my mind in order to take a bite of the meat Garyck had prepared. "I had my doubts about whether or not I'd be able to eat this, but I have to admit, it does taste delicious."

Garyck, seated across the table from me, responded with one of his usual noises. I thought for sure the compliment would elicit a hint of a smile, but so far, Sloane was the only one who'd been able to change his somber demeanor. Sometimes it was hard to tell if there was a mutual attraction between them or if he enjoyed sparring with her.

"I don't know why he should get all the credit." Only Sloane would be brave enough to tease Garyck about his cooking, then snatch a piece of meat off his plate. "You would have burnt it if I hadn't helped."

"Little one." Garyck wrapped a protective arm around his plate.

"What?" She triumphantly held the piece of meat in the air. "You need to learn how to share."

Either I was getting used to his growls, or they didn't sound as menacing as they did when we'd first met. Melissa, who was sitting on Garyck's other side, giggled. It seemed the gruff ketaurran didn't intimidate her either.

Laria sat to my left and nudged me with her arm. "Yeah, I think he'll make someone a good wife, I mean mate, someday."

She and I both stared at Sloane and grinned. Red spread across our friend's cheeks. She started choking and reached for her drink, then glared in our direction, which I understood meant we could expect future retribution.

After the laughter died and everyone settled back into finishing their meals, I turned to Khyron, who balanced a sleeping Draejill on his lap while he ate. It was adorable to see the massive warrior with the little guy's tail wrapped possessively around his leg. "Are you sure you don't want me to take him?"

"He is fine." Khyron looked down at Draejill and smiled. "Should he awaken and find interest in pulling my hair again, then I will gladly let you have him."

I heard a familiar whimper and knew if I looked under the table, I'd find Fuzzball sitting near my feet, hoping I'd sneak him a scrap. Since Harper wasn't around to scold me, I didn't have a problem slipping him a bite, though I'd wait until Garyck wasn't looking to do it.

Ben and Gabe had been thrilled when they found out Khyron and his friends would be joining them to eat. They'd had plenty of questions, mostly about how good the vryndarr were at throwing blades. Now that the boys had emptied the plates they'd heaped with food twice, they were ready for more conversation.

Ben looked at Khyron. "I heard you helped Celeste kill the leezacorrs." He folded his arms across his chest, then glanced at Melissa as if he didn't believe she'd been telling him the truth.

"Yeah, me too," Gabe chimed in. "How did you do it?" He swept his arm through the air, mimicking the swipe of the sword.

"Yes, I did assist with their demise." Khyron's answer had all three children expectantly leaning on the table and waiting to hear his explanation.

I suspected Khyron's proud grin meant he had no problem explaining what happened in great detail. Too bad I heard footsteps coming from the hallway, figured it was Harper, and knew she wouldn't be happy to hear what I was sure would be a gory rendition of killing the leezacorrs. "I think telling them about it can wait until later." I placed my hand on Khyron's arm and, with a small shake of my head, directed my gaze across the room.

"Tell them what?" Harper seemed more exhausted than usual. Even her normally brisk walk had slowed.

"Oh, nothing," Ben said.

"Uh-huh." Harper scrutinized each of the children in turn. "Why don't you three clean up the dishes and stop pestering the drezdarr?" She tucked a few loose crimson strands behind her ear. "And when you're done with that, it's time to get ready for bed."

All three children groaned and slowly got up from the table. They continued to display their displeasure by haphazardly stacking the dirty plates into piles before loading them into their arms and shuffling from the room.

"Harper, why don't you sit down and have something to eat?" Laria scooted closer to Jardun to make room between us on the bench.

I didn't think she'd appreciate it if I added *before you fall down*. After she took a seat and grabbed a clean plate off the stack in the middle of the table, I reached for the platter with the remaining slices of leezacorr meat.

None of us had a chance to talk about the incident with Travis, and I was certain everyone wanted to know how he'd gotten past Marcus's men. Now that the children were out of the room, it seemed an appropriate time for a discussion. "Garyck, did Rygael say anything to you about Travis when you brought him here?"

"No," Garyck said.

I'd hoped for more of an explanation, and rather than ask Sloane to coax more information out of him, I turned to Harper since she'd spent the most time with Rygael. "How about you?"

"He didn't really say much to me other than to thank me for my help." Harper placed a few slices of meat and some plant cakes on her plate.

"It might be a coincidence, but it seems odd we found

proof of the presence of a luzardee at the same time Travis arrived." Jardun leaned forward with his elbows on the table.

"Is it possible they were working together?" Laria asked.

"The thought had occurred to me," Khyron said. "Rygael might be able to supply us with more information. He had to have seen the transport arrive and been watching Travis. Otherwise, how would he have known Melissa needed help?" He adjusted Draejill to keep him from sliding sideways. "In the morning, Celeste and I will go alone to speak with him. He is used to a solitary life, and I do not wish to overwhelm him."

"Your safety is still a concern, and I recommend you allow one of us to accompany you." Jardun shared a knowing look with Garyck.

After the incident with Travis and the presence of a luzardee, I knew it wasn't a request. Jardun was politely informing his drezdarr that he would have a bodyguard whether he wanted one or not.

I'd expected a quick response from Thrayn and glanced at the far end of the table where he'd taken a seat so he'd stayed as far away from the children as possible. His attention perked, then faded when he realized we'd be coming back here in the morning.

Since he didn't volunteer, I decided to press the issue. "I think we should bring Thrayn with us." Normally, Sloane was the one with the wicked side, but I knew the children made Thrayn nervous, and I couldn't resist tormenting the arrogant male just a little.

As I'd expected, his shoulders tensed, and a muscle along his jaw twitched. "It would be my honor." His tone lacked enthusiasm, reminding me of the way Gabe, Ben, and Melissa acted when they were assigned chores.

Khyron realized what I was doing and smirked. "Do not worry, Thrayn, I will protect you from the children."

***

Khyron

Once the meal was over and the young ones had been sent to bed, I accompanied Celeste to her home since it was closer to Harper's place than Burke's. She was not happy about having sleep induced by the healing drink and preferred to use her own quarters.

After she went to her room to settle into bed, I headed into the kitchen and prepared the brew from the packet Nayea had given me. On my return to her room, I ran into Sloane on her way to her sleeping chambers. Jardun and Laria spent their evenings at Burke's place, so I assumed she was the only other person in the dwelling.

She stopped to sniff the mug's contents, then made a face at the unpleasant smell. "Does Celeste really have to drink that?"

"Yes, if she does not want her arm to become infected," I said.

"I'm glad it's her and not me."

I chuckled. "On that we both agree."

"I guess I'll say good night, then." She turned to leave.

I was a male who had been trained to handle any situation, to be confident in my decisions. When it came to Celeste and our reuniting, I found myself questioning my actions before proceeding. "Sloane, before you return to your room, would you mind answering a question for me?"

"Not at all," she answered with a wry smile.

"What does bossy mean?"

"Depends on who said it, or if it was aimed at someone specifically."

"It was Celeste who made the reference." I preferred not sharing the circumstance that elicited the word's use. It was bad enough I had admitted my ketiorra had assigned the human term to me.

"Ooh." Sloane tapped her chin. Her blue eyes sparked with interest. "And I'm guessing she was talking about you when she said it."

Annoyed by her perception, I nodded.

"Pretty basically it means an arrogant, overbearing person with control issues." Sloane placed a comforting hand on my arm. "If that's the worst thing she's called you, I'd say you're probably doing okay." She headed for her room, pausing in the doorway. "Oh, and good luck."

I was a ruler, a warrior who depended on skill, not luck, when making decisions and going into battle. But if luck was what I needed to keep Celeste, then I hoped for an exceedingly large amount of it as I entered her room.

She'd turned on the solar glow emitters, their soft light casting shadows in the corners. Celeste sat in her bed beneath a blanket, propped on a pillow she'd braced against the wooden headboard. She appeared more beautiful than ever, with her dark, silky hair draped across her bare shoulders, the blanket barely covering her breasts.

She was a tempting vision, one which was difficult to resist and made me hard. I focused on the healing brew, the necessity that would keep me from indulging in a night of pleasure with her.

"Everything okay?" she asked.

"Everything is fine." I sat on the edge of the bed next to her and handed her the mug. "You must drink all of it."

She took a sniff and made the same face Sloane had. After a few reluctant seconds, she finally took a sip. "This is nasty. Do I really have to drink all of it?" She tried to hand the cup back to me. "I won't tell Nayea if you don't."

If her health was not an issue, I would have relented to her request. I maintained a stern resolve and shook my head. "I will not be telling Nayea anything because there won't be anything to tell her. Now, please finish it."

Celeste's harrumph led to an adorable pout. "Fine." She bravely downed the liquid, then handed the empty mug back to me. "Happy?"

"Yes." I got off the bed and patted the space next to her. "You should lie down. It will not take long for the drug to take effect."

"Aren't you going to join me?" She scooted farther under the blanket, turning on her side and smiling at me. "I believe you promised to take advantage of me."

"It distresses me greatly not to feel your body beneath me, but your health is far more important to me." I leaned forward and pressed a kiss on her cheek. We had spent the day together, but had not discussed whether or not I would be sharing her bed. Now that I knew what bossy meant, I did not want to make any presumptions. It would pain me to sleep apart from her, but I would return to my room at Burke's place if it was what she wished. "Now sleep. I will check on you in the morning."

She grabbed my wrist when I turned to leave. "Where do you think you're going?"

"I assumed…"

"Well, don't assume." She lifted the edge of the blanket invitingly. "The least you can do after making me drink that horrible stuff is curl up next to me and let me use your naked body as a pillow."

CHAPTER SIXTEEN

Khyron

The night spent with Celeste in my arms was the most restful one I had experienced in the last year. It had been torment at first to feel her soft skin pressed against mine and not be able to give her pleasure, but once I finally relaxed and enjoyed her nearness, sleep had not evaded me. When I woke, I was refreshed and mentally ready to address whatever issues arose from my conversation with Rygael.

When Celeste, Thrayn, and I arrived at Harper's home, she was leaving the kitchen with a tray of food with Melissa following close behind her. Jardun and the others had agreed to wait at Burke's place for a report once we finished our visit.

"Is Rygael awake? We would like to speak with him," I said.

"Come on back. We were just taking him his breakfast." Harper walked into the room ahead of us, then spoke to Rygael. "I wasn't sure what you'd like to eat, so I made a few different things."

Rygael's gaze never left Harper as he watched her walk

across the room and place the tray on the stand next to the bed. His chest was bare, the dirt wiped from his white scales and skin, his cuts cleaned and sealed with a light coat of healing salve. The material of his pants covering his injured leg had been cut down the front all the way to the end, exposing the wrap Vurell had applied to his wound.

"Here let me help you with that." Harper moved closer to the bed and adjusted the pillow so Rygael could lean back comfortably.

There was a softness in the male's reddish pink eyes when he looked at her. He also used the opportunity to sniff her with a subtleness that went unnoticed by the female. Celeste, ever observant, had not missed his actions either. She gave my arm a slight nudge and lifted an inquiring brow in Rygael's direction.

"The sweet cakes were my idea," Melissa said proudly, then plopped on the edge of the bed, careful to avoid Rygael's injured leg. "You know…to say thank you for saving Fuzzball and me from the bad guy."

"Thank you, Melissa." Rygael stared at the meal as if it were a treasured gift, something he had never received before. I wondered what unpleasant event or combination of events had driven the male into living a solitary life. I hoped one day to discover what had happened in his past, and determine if there was anything I could do to lure him into moving his home into the settlement.

"Good morning, Rygael. I assume you are doing better." I took Celeste's hand and urged her into the room with me.

"Yes, drezdarr." Rygael bowed his head, acknowledging my title.

"Please, call me Khyron. You have already met Celeste, and this is Thrayn." I tipped my head toward the doorway.

I was glad I had asked the others to remain behind. As it was, Rygael eyed Thrayn warily, exposed muscles tensing.

Celeste must have noticed the male's discomfort as

well. "Hey, Rygael," she said, taking a step forward. "You look a lot better than the last time I saw you."

Rygael's gaze focused on the wrapping on Celeste's arm, and he frowned. "I am sorry you were injured after helping me."

"It's nothing." She refrained from glancing in my direction but squeezed my hand, urging me not to disagree. "And the least I could do after you helped Melissa and Fuzzball."

After hearing the furry creature's name, I instinctively surveyed the floor. Melissa saw me and giggled. "He's outside with Ben and Gabe, so your tail is safe."

Rolling my eyes at the child only encouraged more laughter, which I ignored by returning my attention to Rygael. "Please do not let us intrude on your meal. I only have a few questions, then we will be on our way."

"Here." Harped picked up the tray. "It will be easier to eat if I set this on your lap."

Rygael moved his hands out of the way so she could situate the tray. He did not tense or seem bothered when she perched on the edge of the bed next to him.

"What would you like to know?" Rygael asked.

"Can you…" I was interrupted by a loud commotion coming from the hallway and did not get the chance to ask Harper if it would be best not to have Melissa overhear my questions.

It seemed young ones were quite adept at knowing when visitors entered their dwelling. It was not long before Gabe and Ben arrived, then pushed their way past Thrayn. Fuzzball rushed through the gap in his legs and ran straight for Melissa and not my tail.

"How's it going, Rygael?" Gabe waved at the male, then stood next to Ben at the foot of the bed.

Rygael smiled at the two young males. It was apparent by the male's reaction that the three children had been spending quite a bit of time visiting with him.

"How come he gets sweet cakes and we don't?" Ben

whined.

Melissa scooped Fuzzball off the floor and returned to her spot on the bed. "'Cuz he's a hero, that's how come."

"Okay, everybody out so Khyron and Celeste can talk to Rygael." Harper got to her feet and ushered the young ones toward the hallway. She tapped Thrayn's arm on her way out. "Come on, Thrayn. I'll fix you a nice cup of freegea while you wait."

"I do not suppose there are additional sweet cakes available, are there?" Thrayn asked eagerly.

"I'm sure I can scrounge up one or two." Harper disappeared into the corridor.

"In that case…" Thrayn grinned and followed after her.

Once Thrayn was gone, I released a disbelieving sigh. "The male is worse than the young ones."

Celeste clasped a hand over her mouth, trying to hide her laughter.

Even Rygael grinned as he bit into a piece of meat. Once he finished swallowing, he asked, "What were your questions?"

"How did you know the human male was trying to abduct Melissa?" I asked.

"I saw him leave his transport and followed him." Rygael took a bite of a sweet cake, then made an appreciative moan. "I have never had anything this delicious before."

I wanted to ask him how long he had lived in the caverns, but decided the question might bring up personal things he did not wish to discuss and decided to save it for another time. "Where did you see the transport?" If Travis found a way to get past Burke's males, then others would be able to as well.

"There is a passageway in the rocks near the ravine where you found me. It can be used to access the other side of the rock formations. That is where the human left his transport. I can take you there if you like."

"Oh, no, you won't." Harper had reappeared in the doorway and looked as if she would tackle him if he tried to get out of bed, which would have been amusing to watch considering how much larger he was than her. "Vurell and Nayea said you can't put any pressure on that leg for several days."

"I appreciate the offer, but it is best to follow Vurell's instructions. You need to get more rest so you can heal properly." I received an appreciative smile from Harper. "I am sure we can find it without any difficulty." I stood and motioned for Celeste to follow me. "We will be back to check on you later. In the meantime, if you need anything, please let Harper know."

"Drezdarr, I mean, Khyron," Rygael muttered.

I stopped and turned. "Yes?"

"Thank you… Thank you both."

***

Celeste

After returning to Burke's place and relaying what Rygael had told Khyron and me to the group, which included Jardun, Laria, Sloane, and Garyck, we decided to take a trip to find the transport. Cara had gone with Burke to the trader's market to talk to the handful of people who came from the outlying areas to sell on a regular basis. Many of them would know Joe. If Cara and Burke were lucky, they'd find someone who knew Travis and might be able to tell them how he'd acquired Joe's transport.

Personally, after my run-in with Travis at Harper's place, I was pretty sure he'd killed Joe and stolen his vehicle. I also had a feeling Travis had been working with some mercs to steal children, and wanted to have my suspicions confirmed one way or another. If mercs were involved, there was a good possibility that others would try to find a way to snatch the children, which presented another problem for Khyron and Burke to address.

After a discussion, which lasted well over an hour, we decided to travel as a group and try to locate Travis's transport. Not long after we entered the wooded area behind Harper's place, an unsettling dread wound its way through my system. I couldn't shake the feeling we were missing something. Something important. Something menacing that had me fingering the hilt of my sword, the secure feel of metal against my skin reassuring.

The mood of the group grew solemn the second we left Burke's place, reminding me of our trip to the Quaddrien. The vryndarr males were a powerful team that worked well together and, without Jardun saying a word, had all taken positions to ensure Khyron stayed protected. Garyck and Zaedon had taken the lead. Sloane, Khyron, and I ended up in the middle with Thrayn following behind us, and Laria and Jardun a few more feet farther back.

"Zadierra, is everything all right?" Khyron pressed his hand to the small of my back.

How did I tell him something wasn't right when nothing in the surrounding area seemed out of place? "Just a feeling, but it's probably nothing." I forced a smile, hoping it would remove the concerned frown from his face.

"What kind of feeling?" Sloane, who'd been walking on my other side, asked.

"Not sure." I searched for the right words, but Zaedon spared me an explanation.

Zaedon stopped, his focus on something Garyck had found on the ground. "Khyron, Jardun, you need to see this."

The rest of us quickly joined them.

"These tracks were made by a luzardee male. He took off his boots, no doubt so he could climb through the trees and remain undetected. The ravine and passage Rygael specified are not far from here." Garyck pointed to the left of the direction we'd been traveling. "These tracks head away from us, back into the wooded area."

"Can you tell if it is the same luzardee from the other day?" Khyron asked.

Garyck squatted to get a closer look. "Uncertain."

Khyron rubbed his nape. "You and Zaedon follow the tracks and see if you can find the male. The rest of us will continue on to the transport."

Out of all the vryndarr, I'd learned that Garyck and Zaedon were excellent trackers and the best choice for finding the luzardee.

"And when we find him?" The smile Zaedon usually wore had faded, revealing the dangerous warrior I knew him to be.

"Alive, if possible. I wish to know why he is here and if there are more. But protecting the settlement's inhabitants is the priority."

"Understood." Zaedon paused long enough to answer, then trailed after Garyck, who was already following the tracks.

"I think I should head back to Harper's and make sure everyone there is okay." Leaving Khyron was the last thing I wanted to do, but Rygael was in no condition to fight. If the children were the target, I wanted to make sure they were well protected.

"You stay here. I'll go." Sloane, perceptive as always, glanced at Khyron, then back to me, letting me know she thought I should stay by his side.

"You be careful," Laria said.

With a grin, she drew the blade she'd won from Thrayn and headed back the way we came. "Always," Sloane replied as she ducked between two thorny blue trees and disappeared.

"Do you think it was wise to let her go alone?" Thrayn asked.

Jardun held out his hand to Laria. "You can go after her and tell her otherwise if you wish."

"Yeah, I'm sure that will go over well." Sarcasm laced Laria's comment.

"Come on, Thrayn." I jerked my head, urging him to follow Khyron and me. "Laria and I wouldn't have let her go if we thought she couldn't handle herself."

"If you are certain." Thrayn glanced in the direction Sloane had gone one more time, then hurried to catch up with us.

About fifteen minutes later, we reached the area where the trees ended and the rocky surface began. I pointed in the general direction of the ravine. "The passageway Rygael mentioned is on the other side of those boulders."

Laria walked to the rocky edge and peered below. "That ledge isn't very wide. Rygael's lucky he didn't miss it when he fell."

Jardun leaned forward to get a glimpse. "I do not think we need to worry about retrieving Travis's body. It does not look like the leezacorrs left much."

"Knowing how you feel about heights, Celeste, I still can't believe you went down there," Laria said.

"It wasn't nearly as scary as that rock wall I scaled on Lou's back."

"Who is this male you are referring to, and why were you on his back?" Khyron released a jealous growl, and swished his tail rapidly.

"Easy there, drezdarr." I giggled and placed my palms on his chest. "Lou's the name I gave my chaugwas."

He wrapped his arms around my waist, his tail curling around the back of my legs, then softly murmured into my ear, "That is a good thing, zadierra. I do not wish to share your affections and was afraid I would have to order another male's death."

I couldn't tell if he was teasing or being earnest, though I suspected it was the latter. "Sharing will never be something you need to worry about." I swept my fingertips along the part of his tail I could reach and thrilled at the power I had to make him shudder.

Laria cleared her throat. "Um, guys, you're embarrassing Thrayn."

"Female." Thrayn sputtered, his cheeks flushing a dark green. "I *am not* embarrassed."

"Thrayn, my ketiorra was teasing. You must learn to lighten down," Jardun said.

Laria laughed harder than I did, then corrected him. "I believe the human phrase you're looking for is lighten up."

***

Khyron

Reluctantly, and with my tail still tingling with the aftereffects of Celeste's caress, I released her. As much as I enjoyed the others' playful banter and the tension-relieving distraction it provided, it did not resolve the critical issues we needed to address. "Laria is correct. We should continue. I do not wish to be out here after dark." Though we had not found any evidence of more than one luzardee, I did not voice my concern that the males rarely traveled alone and there might be more than one of them in the area.

I headed for the gap in the rock wall I had noticed the day before.

"I will go first." Jardun, with Laria in tow, moved ahead of me, amazing me once more with how in sync they had become in the short time they had known each other.

Prior to leaving Burke's place, I had attached a small glow emitter to my belt in case visibility in the tunnellike pass became difficult. So far, there were enough overhead gaps between the rock walls for the sun's rays to provide ample light, leaving only small portions of the walkway harder to see.

"This is pretty awesome." Laria paused to brush her fingertips along the wall's smooth surface. "It would also explain how Rygael gets around and we've never see him."

"You have to wonder if there are more of these passages that we don't know about," Celeste said, mimicking her friend's movements.

"It is a question I will address with Rygael. If there are more, then Marcus's team will need to monitor them." Discussing the various ways to access Rygael's home would require substantial diplomacy. I did not want the male to view us as a threat and hoped he would be forthcoming with the information.

Had I not been watching Celeste and seen the shower of tiny pebbles falling near her shoulder, I might not have looked up in time to see the avalanche of rocks toppling over the upper ledge of the rock wall behind her.

"Look out!" I yelled, then grabbed Celeste around the waist, yanking her backward and colliding with Thrayn. In my periphery, I saw Jardun lunge for Laria in time to keep the largest of the rocks from landing on top of her.

Though I did my best to take the brunt of the fall, Celeste and I hit the ground hard. I helped her into a sitting position, then pushed some stray strands off her face. "Are you all right?"

"I think so." She rubbed the back of her head.

Thrayn had been knocked farther back and out of my immediate line of sight. "Thrayn." I glanced behind us to make sure the male had not been injured during the fall.

He was already on his feet and dusting off his pants. "I am unharmed."

"Oh no." Celeste pushed to her feet, then rushed toward the impassable wall the loosened rocks had created. "Laria, can you hear me?" She coughed from the dust filling the air.

For Celeste, losing Laria would be like losing another sister, and I hated seeing the panic-stricken look on her face.

"We're okay." Laria's voice echoed through the small gap at the top of the pile. "What about you guys?"

"A few bruises, but no injuries." The rigid line of

Celeste's shoulders relaxed.

Jardun spoke next. "Khyron."

"Yes." I moved closer to Celeste.

"There are too many rocks and no way for us to reach you."

Unease skittered across my skin, my instincts blaring that the fallen rocks had not dislodged themselves. So far, everyone was safe, and I wanted to keep them that way. "Take Laria and continue on to the transport, then use it to return to the settlement." If Travis had planned to leave before being detected, there was a good chance he'd kept the vehicle's solars charged.

"What about you?" I could hear the frustration in my friend's voice and knew he was worried about my safety.

I reached for Celeste's hand. "We will head back the way we came and find Garyck and Zaedon." The sooner we were out of the narrow passageway, the better I would feel.

Thrayn flanked my other side, easily matching my strides. "I do not believe those rocks fell by themselves." The male might lack experience when dealing with humans, but he was intelligent, with good instincts when it came to assessing dangers.

"Neither do I." Celeste's tone reflected her anger as she warily surveyed the area ahead of us.

No sooner had we made it into the clearing outside the passage when three luzardees appeared around us. One clung to the rock wall behind us; the other two were on the ground in front of us and blocking the path leading back to the wooded area. The males were dressed in similar vests and pants, but because climbing required the use of the claws on their feet, they had shed their boots.

Tan scales covered the majority of their body, including their bald heads. Their beady black eyes lacked pupils, their faces flatter than a ketaurran's, with larger nostrils.

"Hello, drezdarr." One of the two luzardee standing in front of us took a step forward. "Are you aware that someone is willing to pay a large sum for you? And they do not care if you are dead."

The male standing behind him snickered. "Being crushed by rocks would have been less painful than what we will do to you now."

It was unclear until the male issued his threat whether or not they had meant to separate us or bury us under an avalanche of rocks.

"Spare the female," the luzardee standing closest said to the other two. "I know a buyer who will pay quite well to have a human female share his bed."

"You will not touch her." My growl, loud and guttural, ripped through the air.

"You will have no say what we do to her once you are dead." The male flexed his hands.

Luzardees didn't need blades to injure or kill. They could extend and retract razor-sharp talons from their long fingers.

With the ravine on our right and a wall of rock on our left, maneuvering during a fight would be difficult but not impossible. All that mattered was protecting Celeste, and I would risk my life if it meant keeping her safe.

"We shall see," I said as I withdrew my sword.

***

Celeste

Hearing what the luzardees had planned for me didn't bother me nearly as much as hearing what they had planned for Khyron. "Draecking slimy lizards," I muttered under my breath and withdrew my blade. Now that Khyron was back in my life, I planned to do everything possible to make sure he stayed there.

Thrayn had also drawn his weapon and positioned himself between Khyron and the edge of the ravine. The young vryndarr had taken a vow to protect the drezdarr, but I hoped he wouldn't have to give his life to keep the male I loved safe.

My presence and the luzardee's threat had Khyron reacting emotionally, not rationally. If we were going to work together, he needed to view me as one of the team on our missions and not as his ketiorra. It was something we'd be discussing later, but right now, I needed him to calm down and focus.

My options were limited, so I used the one thing I could rely on—the ego of the luzardee male who'd done all the talking, the one who was most likely their leader. "I have to admit, it was really clever using the human male to gain access to the settlement."

When Khyron raised a curious brow in my direction, I hoped it wouldn't take him long to realize what I was doing, and why.

"It wasss easy to let him believe our main goal wasss stealing the children." The luzardee's forked tongue popped out of his mouth every time he hissed his words. "He never would have agreed to help if we told him it was the drezdarr we were after. The other ketaurran male saved us the trouble of killing him later."

"If you weren't going to sell the children, why bother taking them?" I asked.

"Oh, pretty one, your assumption is incorrect. There are definitely buyersss for human children, especially the half-breedsss."

Thinking about what would've happened to Melissa if Travis had turned her over to these males had me gripping my hilt even tighter. I steadied my breathing, reminding myself why I'd started the disgusting conversation.

"Zadierra, do not waste your breath on this male. He is no better than chaugwas dung." Khyron followed up his insult with a wink, letting me know he understood what I'd been trying to do and was back to thinking clearly.

"I totally agree," I said with a sneer. This wasn't the first time I'd dealt with luzardees, and when the leader scowled, then glanced above my head, I knew what was coming next. I spun around and sidestepped, placing myself between the luzardee clinging to the rock wall and Khyron and Thrayn.

Launching themselves through the air to attack was their favorite ploy, and the male didn't disappoint me. He might have been ordered not to kill me, but it wouldn't keep him from causing pain to subdue me.

Unfortunately for him, I was prepared and ducked before his claws could connect with my flesh. As soon as he landed on the ground and turned, I drove my blade into the center of his chest. His heart might not be in the same place as a human's, but the injury I'd caused was still fatal. With a shriek that turned into a gurgle, he clutched his chest and dropped to his knees before landing face-first in the dirt.

Not bothering to wipe off the green blood coating my blade, I turned to help Khyron and Thrayn. Both males had moved and were engaged in battle with the other two luzardees. They wielded their blades with agile grace and precision, deflecting claw swipes to defeat their opponents.

Luzardees could move fast, and it was hard to keep track of their actions. Letting them get close, risking injury from their claws, was the only way to kill one. It was either that or throwing a knife from a distance and hoping your aim was accurate and they didn't move at the last second.

I was about to jump into the fight when movement overhead caught my attention. Another luzardee had climbed over the rocky ledge and was slithering down the wall in Thrayn's direction. He stopped in an area too high for me to reach with my blade without throwing it. I assumed the reason he hadn't attacked yet had something to do with Thrayn's nearness to the ravine. If the luzardee miscalculated or Thrayn decided to move after he'd launched, the male's death would be extremely unpleasant.

"Surrender now, drezdarr, and I promise your death will be quick." The lead luzardee took another swipe.

Khyron snorted his disbelief, then executed the same technique I'd seen him use on the leezacorr by leveling his sword and taking off the lead luzardee's head. The other male, after seeing his friend's head roll on the ground, released a furious roar. He dodged a blow from Thrayn and launched a vicious attack at Khyron. Thrayn turned to assist, the move taking him away from the ravine's edge and giving the male creeping down the wall the advantage he was waiting for.

"Thrayn, look out!" My warning came too late to stop the male from landing on Thrayn's back, knocking him on his knees, and digging claws into his shoulders.

Thrayn snarled, dropping his sword, then reaching behind his back, trying to remove the male.

The luzardee easily dodged his efforts and, in a deep, malicious tone, said, "You cannot help the drezdarr if you are dead, vryndarr."

When the luzardee freed one hand to strike, I threw my knife. The blade sailed through the air, then sank into the luzardee's side below his ribs seconds before his swipe would have ripped out Thrayn's throat.

Between the male's struggle to reach my knife and Thrayn's forceful shrug, he lost his balance and fell sideways. His midsection caught the edge of the ravine, and he toppled over the side.

As I'd expected, Khyron had been quick to end the other luzardee's life and joined me in helping Thrayn off the ground.

"Are your injuries bad? Do they need tending before we return to the settlement?" Khyron asked.

"They would have been far worse…" Thrayn smiled at me, nothing but respect gleaming in his pale green eyes. "I will gladly fight by your side anytime, Celeste."

It was nice to hear his humble praise, and the fact that he'd used my name rather than call me female was also a plus.

"As will I." Khyron slipped his arm behind my back.

I glanced into the ravine to make sure the luzardee was dead. Ironically, he'd landed several feet from what was left of Travis after the leezacorrs had made a meal out of him. "What a waste."

Confused, Thrayn wrinkled his nose. "You mourn for the male?"

"No, I'm talking about the blade." I leaned my head against Khyron's shoulder and sighed. "It was my favorite."

CHAPTER SEVENTEEN

Celeste

Several days had passed since the luzardees' attack without any further problems, attempted abductions, or bloodshed. How long our peaceful existence would last, I didn't know. Because of the world my friends and I lived in, there would always be more unexpected situations and dangers we'd have to deal with. It didn't mean we wouldn't try to get the most enjoyment we could out of the quiet moments in between.

During that time, we'd learned the male Garyck and Zaedon had been tracking before we'd been ambushed was the one that ended up in the ravine with my knife in his chest. None of the regular traders Cara and Burke spoke to knew Travis and they hadn't seen Joe in weeks, so my theory about his death was probably accurate.

Khyron had also arranged for two more dates. The first was another picnic, which started out on a romantic note with a lot of kissing, then ended with an unexpected visit from Fuzzball and Melissa. Thankfully, the furry little creature was after food and had ignored Khyron's tail.

The second was supposed to be a quiet night at my

place, which turned into a meal with our friends, complete with Garyck grilling meat and Sloane offering her unsolicited critiquing. I didn't mind the camaraderie, not when the evening ended with Khyron giving me another one of his wonderful lessons on what it meant to be his ketiorra.

Khyron led me from the shade of the wooded area out into the early afternoon sun to a section of the rocky perimeter bordering the settlement that I'd never seen before, then headed toward some flat rocks that resembled a set of stairs.

"Where are we going?" I asked.

"I already told you it is a surprise."

He'd been annoyingly secretive about the location of our next date and wouldn't let me peek into the large bag he had strapped over his shoulder. Since we didn't have a bodyguard—namely Thrayn—accompanying us, I wondered if Khyron had bothered to tell anyone else where he was taking me.

At the top of the naturally formed staircase was the entrance to a cave. We didn't need a portable glow emitter to see inside. A large hole had formed in the center of the ceiling, letting in plenty of sunlight. I'd barely taken a few steps when I heard the soft splash of water and noticed a rocky basin filled with water from a miniature waterfall. The surface shimmered the same lavender hue as the pool in my favorite clearing. The overflow of water had formed a groove about a foot wide in the rock and flowed across the floor to disappear into a small opening at the base of one wall.

"Khyron, this is beautiful." I skimmed the water's surface with my fingertips. "Is this why you wouldn't let me come with you to speak with Rygael this morning?"

He slipped the bag off his shoulder and set it on the ground. "It is." He turned me around and pulled me into his arms. "I wished to give you a date with no interruptions."

"Well, unless we were followed, I'd say you did a good job." I placed my hands on his shoulders.

His grin faded, and the gaze holding mine turned serious. "Before we begin our date, there are several things I wish to discuss."

The queasy flutter in my stomach came close to making me nauseated. I hoped whatever he wanted to say didn't end with him telling me he was leaving again. "Okay."

"Celeste, I love you deeply, will give my life to protect you, and wish to have you by my side always. But..." He cleared his throat. "I am also the drezdarr, trained to lead, not to have my orders questioned. There will be times when I will be difficult to deal with, especially when it concerns your safety."

His gaze softened. "I realize you are quite capable of taking care of yourself. All I ask is that you understand my struggle and know that I will do my best not to be...what was it you called me? Oh yes, bossy."

"Khyron, I..."

"Wait." He placed his finger against my lips. "I am not finished." He got down on one knee and took my hand, the blue in his eyes darkening.

"What are you doing?"

"I do not wish to spend another day without knowing that you will allow me to fully claim you as my ketiorra, that I will always be the only male in your life." He held my hands in his. "The ketaurrans do not have an elaborate celebration when we join with our mates. There is simply an acknowledgment of the bond and commitment to each other. I learned from the history data books that humans perform a ceremony. I believe it is called a wedding."

"Are you...proposing?" Shocked and elated all at once, I could hardly manage the last word.

He furrowed his brows. "Am I not doing it correctly? Is proposing not part of your mating ritual?"

"Yes, proposing is part of the ritual."

"Good." He got to his feet. "Then I wish to make our

joining official, to bond with you in the tradition of your people, and to make you my drezdarrina in the tradition of mine."

Drezdarrina. The realization of what he was asking, the responsibility that came with the title, tightened my chest and sent a surge of warmth rippling to my core. Not only did he want me to marry him, but he wanted me to be the female equivalent of a ketaurran leader. He was offering me a commitment that translated into forever...and I couldn't be happier.

He squeezed my hands when I took too long to answer. "According to the rules of human courtship, you are now supposed to respond with an affirmative answer."

He was so adorable, I didn't have the heart to tell him that negative answers were also allowed. "Yes, I agree to your proposal." I barely had a chance to wrap my arms around his neck before he lifted me off the floor and his lips found mine.

When he finally released me from the most amazing kiss we'd ever shared, he picked up the bag and led me to a flat boulder, then motioned for me to sit next to him.

He reached inside the bag and pulled out a long rectangular object wrapped in leather and placed it on my lap. "I know it is not the traditional gift of your people, but I had a local craftsman make this for you."

After unwrapping the leather, all I could do was stare at the handcrafted knife with a shiny blue-black blade, the hilt adorned with several small zapharite stones.

"It is to replace the one you lost."

"Khyron, this is perfect." I grinned and picked it up, then laid it across my palm to test its balance. "Sloane is going to be so jealous."

I loved hearing him laugh and vowed in the days to come to make sure he did it more often.

After he placed the knife back in the bag, he took my hands again. "There is still a lot of work to be done to ensure a better future for your people and mine. It will require many missions, traveling with the vryndarr and, of course, your friends. So I would like to settle the issue of where we will live."

It was a topic I'd thought about often since the night we'd shared a bed together. Up until now, it was something neither one of us had discussed.

The end of his tail snaked around my ankle. "I know how much you enjoy being around the young ones and teaching the males to wield a blade. Please know I would never do anything to change your relationship with them. If it is acceptable to you, I would like to make the settlement our home. Though there will be times when certain matters will require us to return to the city."

Even though his tone was sincere, I still needed reassurance. "You'd really give up your home in the city to live here with me?"

"Zadierra, my residence in the city is only a dwelling. My home is, and always will be, wherever you are."

ABOUT THE AUTHOR

Rayna Tyler is an author of paranormal and sci-fi romance. She loves writing about strong sexy heroes and the sassy heroines who turn their lives upside down. Whether it's in outer space or in a supernatural world here on Earth, there's always a story filled with adventure.

Printed in Great Britain
by Amazon

17354449R00112

THE BEST OF PETER EGAN

Inspiring | Educating | Creating | Entertaining

Brimming with creative inspiration, how-to projects, and useful information to enrich your everyday life, Quarto Knows is a favorite destination for those pursuing their interests and passions. Visit our site and dig deeper with our books into your area of interest: Quarto Creates, Quarto Cooks, Quarto Homes, Quarto Lives, Quarto Drives, Quarto Explores, Quarto Gifts, or Quarto Kids.

First published in 2018 by Motorbooks, an imprint of The Quarto Group,
401 Second Avenue North, Suite 310, Minneapolis, MN 55401 USA. T (612) 344-8100
F (612) 344-8692 www.QuartoKnows.com

Motorbooks titles are also available at discount for retail, wholesale, promotional, and bulk purchase. For details, contact the Special Sales Manager by email at specialsales@quarto.com or by mail at The Quarto Group, Attn: Special Sales Manager, 401 Second Avenue North, Suite 310, Minneapolis, MN 55401 USA.

10 9 8 7 6 5 4 3 2 1

ISBN: 978-0-7603-6379-9

Library of Congress Cataloging-in-Publication Data

Names: Egan, Peter, 1948- author.
Title: The best of Peter Egan : four decades of motorcycle tales and musings
   from the pages of Cycle World / Peter Egan.
Other titles: Cycle world.
Description: Minneapolis, MN : Motorbooks, 2018.
Identifiers: LCCN 2018019222 | ISBN 9780760363799 (hc w/jacket)
Subjects: LCSH: Motorcycling--United States. | Motorcycles. | United
   States--Description and travel.
Classification: LCC GV1059.52 .E47 2018 | DDC 796.7--dc23

Acquiring Editor: Zack Miller
Project Manager: Nyle Vialet
Art Director: Brad Springer
Interior Design and Layout: Laura Shaw Design

On the front cover: photo courtesy of Peter Egan
On the back cover: Illustration by Hector Cademartori
On the title page: photo courtesy of Cycle World
Interior Illustrations by Hector Cademartori and Mick Ofield (page 268-271)
Photo credits: Tim Gainey/Alamy Stock Photo (page 10-11); Jeff Gilbert/Alamy Stock Photo (page 56-57); Ron Kimball/Kimball Stock (page 241-242); Science History Images/ Alamy Stock Photo (page 243); AF Archive/ Alamy Stock Photo (page 244); Everett Collection Historical/ Alamy Stock Photo (page 246); Nick Berard/ TNT Creative LLC (page 263-264); All photographs are from the author's collection and courtesy of Cycle World

Printed in China

THE BEST OF
PETER EGAN

PETER EGAN
FOREWORD BY JAY LENO

// CONTENTS //

FOREWORD // JAY LENO

It was an honor to be asked to write this foreword because I was a fan of Peter Egan long before I was a friend. Motorcycles are emotional machines, and finding people who can write about them without being overly effusive or ridiculously introverted are hard to find. The two best pieces of motorcycle journalism I've ever read are *The Mint*—T. E. Lawrence's account of his days in the RAF with his Brough Superior motorcycle—and anything written by Peter Egan.

One never gets the feeling that Peter thinks he is a better rider than you. He makes you feel like he *is* you. His pieces are never about the fastest or the best, but about the journey. If your spouse can't understand why sitting in your garage amongst your machines can give you solitary peace, give them this book. What is it about old, leaky, hard-to-start British machinery that we find irresistible? It's all in here. What is it that guitars and motorcycles have in common? Is it that they are both singularly solitary pursuits that we can never quite truly master?

I am not a meditation-type guy, yet when I ride a motorcycle I understand how meditation works. Reading this book, I feel like motorcycles are Peter's meditation and his thoughts and feelings are revealed in these pages. His are the only travel pieces that I read. That's because I'm one of those people who believe that what I'm riding is way more important than where I'm going, but in Peter's writing the motorcycle is never just the conveyance, it's the companion. Plus, I love the fact that he has written about motorcycles for more than fifty years without ever once using the word "bro."

J Leno

INTRODUCTION

A Summing Up

The novelist D. H. Lawrence once said, "It's better to be born lucky than rich," and I have to agree. I've never had a chance to check out the "rich" side of that equation, but I certainly got lucky back in 1977, when the Editor of *Cycle World*, Allan Girdler, bought my first freelance story, which was about a Norton breaking down in Montana while my wife, Barb, and I were heading for the West Coast.

At the time, I was a UW Journalism school graduate and Vietnam vet, working as a foreign-car mechanic in Madison, Wisconsin. The shop, Foreign Car Specialists, was a hotbed of road racing activity, and I spent most of the seventies there, racing a couple of sports cars as well as a Honda CB400F in WERA's 400 Box Stock class. I loved the racing life at FCS, but I was also spending a lot of my spare time trying to vindicate my lost student years by writing books and magazine articles, and I had a huge stack of rejection slips to prove it.

So Editor Girdler's acceptance of my touring story was very good news indeed. After that, I managed to sell *CW* four more touring stories and was then offered a full-time job at the magazine in 1980. Barb and I sold our house in Madison and moved to Newport Beach, California, and at the ripe old age of thirty-two I had my first journalism job.

As an introduction to magazine world, it would be hard to beat having Allan Girdler as your first editor. He was (and still is) funny, fair, and a colorful writer, with a veteran newspaperman's conviction that the reader—and the truth—always comes first. It was also a golden era for the motorcycle industry and the magazine business, with an endless stream of new, exciting motorcycles to test and a huge Baby Boomer audience to buy and read about them. Good times.

And when Allan retired from *CW*, l was invited to join the staff of our sister publication, Road & Track. The new *Cycle World* editor, David Edwards, then asked if I could also contribute a monthly column and an occasional feature story to *CW*, so I suddenly found myself actually paid to participate in my two favorite activities. Proof, I guess, that "luck" is just fortuitous timing that can never be repeated.

In 1990, Barb and I moved back to Wisconsin and bought a place out in the country, partly to escape the Southern California traffic and partly so I could build a large heated workshop to restore old cars and bikes, which I am still doing twenty-eight years later—while also working as a freelance contributor to both magazines.

And during the years since we moved back, I've been able to enjoy a lot of motorcycle traveling with David Edwards and the editor who succeeded him, Mark Hoyer, both good friends and great traveling companions. And that's been, perhaps, the best part of this job—to develop a fascination with parts of the world and then concoct a plan to go there, preferably on a motorcycle with which you are also fascinated. These trips, often with Barb along, have taken us to the Alps, New Zealand, the Isle of Man, Ireland, England, and all over Europe, Mexico, Canada, and the US.

The American travel stories, some readers may notice, often have something to do with music. I'm a Blues fan and I play the guitar—as best I can—in a garage band that shares a floor space with my car and bike projects. So naturally my first long road trip for CW was a late-seventies musical odyssey on my Honda 400F down Highway 61 through Memphis and the Mississippi Delta to New Orleans. Two years ago, I repeated parts of this trip with editor Mark Hoyer—another hardcore music buff and guitar player—when we rode a couple of new Indians from Memphis to the Big Easy. Can't stay away from that part of the country. I guess it's the music, the food, and the aroma of French roast coffee at Café du Monde.

But perhaps the best part of this lifetime of riding bikes has just been the people. Barb and I threw a big party for my 70th birthday a few months ago and realized that about 70 percent of our friends on the guest list had some connection with motorcycling, without which we probably would never have met. There were some car racers, musicians, and airplane pilots (our other vice) in there as well, but bikes were the glue that seemed to hold it all together. I have a self-aggrandizing theory that a simple willingness to get on a motorcycle and head out into the world separates us from that part of the population that is … how shall we say it? … just a little too careful.

Of course, the best stroke of luck I've had in motorcycling was meeting Barbara, who had a Wards-Riverside Benelli 125 when I met her in college. A little story here:

I quit school in the middle of my junior year and joined the army. When I came home from Vietnam, married Barbara, and I went back to the UW to finish my last three semesters. I'd sold my Honda CB160 while I was overseas, so I had no motorcycle. Couldn't afford it; the GI Bill, it seemed, didn't pay for motorcycles. Barb took a loan out from the credit union at the hospital where she worked as a physical therapist and bought me a brand-new Honda CB350 as a birthday surprise. I was speechless, for once. And back on the road.

So, if I had to pick just one story or column to put in this book, that would be it.

And it's in here, along with some other good memories. Motorcycling is one of those rare sports where you can look back on your life and say, literally, it's been a great ride.

SECTION

1

THE FREELANCE STORIES: 1977–1980

DATELINE MISSOULA

" GUESS IT'S BETTER to bend a valve in Missoula than to lose your mind in Bozeman," my wife said, patting my hand as if to console me. I winced and wondered if Phaedrus ever took the bus.

Our bus was rolling across the South Dakota night, late enough for all the reading lights to be out. Just across the aisle sat a nun beside a shrunken old man who reeked of some refreshment from a brown paper bag. The nun slept the sleep of the just—nearly upright, a ghost of a smile on her ivory face—while her companion snored in a kind of death rattle and was gradually toppling into the aisle. I feared that one of those wide ladies in polka dots would barge past on her way to the privy and break the poor fellow's neck.

We were riding back to Madison, Wisconsin, via Greyhound, returning to a city full of prophets honored in their own time. Everyone had told me not to ride my old British Twin to Seattle. Howard was the first.

An old friend and first-generation Honda mechanic, Howard had grown up among Super Hawks, Benlys, and Dreams, having little patience with things that leaked oil, blacked out, or had to be kicked. With just the lightest touch of derision, he had named my venerable motorcycle "the Manxton Contaminator Twin."

I told him, "Next month Barb and I are riding the bike out to Seattle." He looked at me exactly as my mother had when I told her I'd quit college to join the army: wearily, quietly incredulous.

"Take a car," he said.

"What?"

"Take a car. Turn on the radio. Chew gum. Put one foot on the dash. You can steer with one finger and look around at the scenery. Write postcards while you drive. Read the *Wall Street Journal*, roll your windows up or roll them down— anything. But don't take your motorcycle."

"Why not?"

"Because on that bike, you can't get there from here."

Howard had a racer's bias against touring. He campaigned, sometimes successfully, a highly tuned Honda 350 Four against droves of "off-brand ring-dings" on Midwest road circuits. He thought touring a tedious penance for some unspecified sin committed in an earlier life. He also feared and distrusted venerable British Twins.

Howard's last word of advice was that I send a Honda Gold Wing to the post office in Council Bluffs, Iowa, and then pray that I made it that far, so I could change horses en route. No thanks, I said. I'd ridden a Gold Wing. Too easy. Like taking a tram up the Eiger, instead of climbing the face.

Anybody could get to Seattle on a Gold Wing. Farrah, for-God's-sake, Fawcett-Majors could get there on a Gold Wing. It was adventure I was after, not trip insurance.

The next day, I visited my friendly Suzuki-BMW dealer, who had the last shop in town with antique British parts moldering on its back shelves. On the side of the building the names of three extinct motorcycles had all but faded away, like those Mail Pouch Tobacco signs on old barns. It was a shop with a glorious past.

Yes, incredibly, they had both the throttle and clutch cables I wanted as spares. Jeff, the head BMW/ex–British Twin mechanic, stepped outside to look at my bike, wiping his hands on a rag. I told him about my trip and asked if there was anything special I should do, outside of regular maintenance, to prepare the bike for a 4,000-mile trip.

"If I were you," Jeff said, "I'd change my oil, adjust my chain, set the valves, and then, just before I left, I'd trade it in on a BMW."

Skeptics, heretics, and hooters were everywhere, like some chorus in a Greek tragedy, portending ill for their flawed and heedless hero. I finally quit telling people about the trip and made plans with my wife in the privacy of our own living room.

We would travel light and simply. No fairings, trailers, or saddlebags on the old bike. A strong luggage rack on the back, to hold an army duffel-bagful of stuff, and a tank bag to hold the rest. For shelter from the storm we had Big Pink, a formerly red two-child Sears pup tent leftover from my child-hood (the replacement aluminum poles were too short, causing the tent, when erected, to look like a failed soufflé), and a double sleeping bag whose lining was printed with branding irons and cowboys. My wife had a modern, fully enclosed helmet, while I clung to my cork-lined Everoak Clubman—a piece of Geoff Duke–era headgear that resembles a polo helmet—and my split-lens goggles. There was some rain gear, minimum clothes, and a care-fully chosen tool kit. No compass, snakebite kit, or spare shoelaces. Traveling light on a motorcycle demands ruthless restraint, a fine sense of asceticism, and a big wad of colorful plastic credit cards. We left before sunup on a Saturday morning.

Two hours of ghostly predawn gloom swirled past, and then at 7:00 a.m. the Twin delivered us to the crest of the palisades above the Mississippi River Valley. The air was cool, but the first rays of the sun warmed our backs and began to burn away the mist. Only the towers of the bridges below rose out of the fog.

The hills on the opposite bank were golden green in the morning sun. "Not bad!" I shouted over my shoulder.

"What?" my wife replied. We were to have many such conversations in the miles ahead.

An hour later we were having breakfast in one of the famous EAT chain of fine restaurants on the edge of an Iowa farm town that was just opening for the morning, sipping coffee with the local merchants. They looked at us, and then at our motorcycle out in front of the café. Since we weren't dressed as pirates and were keeping a low profile, there was no hostility, just mild interest. It was OK. Talking and clatter resumed.

Iowa's rolling eastern hills stopped rolling, the trees dried up, and corn country arrived. The roads ran as straight as the crop rows, and the midsummer corn held down a hot blanket of humid air that defied even a 55-mph chill factor. No breeze blew; the heat was stifling. Corn plants, I noted, breathe and perspire just as we do. Maybe more.

The Contaminator Twin loved it. The engine had not missed a beat crossing one and one-half states—nearly the length of, say, England. Gas-station checks revealed no loose bolts or unnatural oil loss; the headlight still burned. I began to think that a little Loctite and silicone sealer might have changed the fate of British motorcycling.

As Iowa is firmly Middle West, South Dakota, for me, is the beginning of the West. The True West, of course, begins at the Missouri River Valley, which comes upon you as a startling strip of bluish-green washes and shorn, rounded hills. The road is wonderful, a quintessential cyclist's road of smooth, sweeping curves through a fantasy landscape of dwarfed trees on billiard-cloth hillsides—a land that might have nurtured tiny horses and reptilian birds. Like the Badlands, it has that quiet, dawn-of-time feel. "Lovely," I said to myself, making an expansive sweep of my arm over the view. My wife repeated the motion, knowing what I meant. One of the ten great gestures of motorcycle wind language, that sweep of the arm.

By evening we were in Winner, South Dakota, camped just outside of town. After a truck-stop dinner, we rode into town to see what there was to see. There are two theaters in Winner—the Pix and the Ritz, and they face each other on the main street. The Pix was closed, and the Ritz was showing *Flesh Gordon*, the Buster Crabbe–goes-hedonist remake. The popcorn stand was closed, the glass-covered poster case was empty, and nine people sat through the film. We emerged, not feeling terribly uplifted, onto a main street lined with pickup trucks and flashing bar signs. There was not a soul on the sidewalks. A wind had come up, and a lot of dust was blowing through the streets. "When I was a kid," Barb said as we climbed on the bike, "going to the movies was— different . . ." We rode back to the campground and a stormy night in Big Pink,

the Two-Child Tent, which affords about as much rain protection as a tree with quite a few leaves. In the morning we were awakened by a rooster that actually said "cock-a-doodle-do," as if reading the word.

My dislike of Interstates and love of secondary roads found us the following day on a clay and gravel goat path south of the Badlands. The road wound through some butte and gully country with dozens of pastel shades of rock and dust muting the strong sunlight. The dust, in fact, was worrisome.

We were trailing a wide plume of the stuff, and I wondered what deleterious effects it was having on Manxton chain, bearings, and cylinder walls. I hoped the air filters were keeping the inside of the engine cleaner than the outside. The Twin was never intended for Baja. After a few hours, I began to feel like a courier in the Afrika Korps and decided it would be best to avoid dotted-line roads and stick to the red ones in the future.

We rose over a ridge, where the road dropped straight across a wide sunken plain. Far on the horizon we saw a second cloud of dust, pushing a small dot along the road. Another motorcycle. I decided to pursue. The other bike was wasting no time, and it took us an hour to reel him in. Though the Contaminator is capable of quite respectable speeds, I was loath to push its thirteen-year-old engine to its limits for any distance, being no stranger to the Last Straw Theory of engine failure.

The other motorcycle stopped with us at a highway intersection. The bike was a Honda 550 carrying Tom, a friendly, slightly overheated-looking eighteen-year-old who happened to be from our home state. He looked at the Contaminator Twin with amazement. His 550 was clean and dry, while our Twin was covered with a thick layer of chalky dust that clung to all the oil that had sweated through the bike's mated surfaces. It looked like the ghost motor-cycle of the Plains. "You guys are a long way from home with that thing," he said. I didn't much care for the awe in his voice. It made me nervous.

We rode and camped with Tom for the next two days. He had left Wisconsin with $65, two weeks of vacation, and absolutely no plans except to go "out West." It was nice to ride with another bike, and the two machines made an interesting pair. The 550 whirred along silken and revvy, while the Twin sort of pulsed, and at a much lower note. The Twin had gearing leftover from the age of 70-mph freeways and turned less than 4,000 rpm at that speed (in theory, of course), producing all kinds of torque right down to the 2,000-rpm shudder barrier. Critics of British Twins have complained much about their vibration, yet that problem has never bothered me, since the vibration is more of a throbbing phenomenon than the sort of hectic, buzzing condition that drives feet off footpegs and hands from handlebars. With tall gearing, it is a one-pulse-every-telephone-pole vibration that merely assures the rider he is on a motorcycle and that his engine is still running.

On what was to be, it turned out, the last night of our cycle trip, we were turned back from Yellowstone Park by a "Yellowstone Full" sign on the entrance gate (now that folks can drive their houses out West, camping is more popular than ever), so we backtracked to a very pleasant campground in the Shoshone National Forest. Just before sundown, a group of chopper aficionados with mamas rode into camp, set up tents, then raced off to nearby Pahaska Teepee Lodge Bar. They returned at closing time, cycles blazing. After riding around their own tents until a couple of their bikes tipped over, they settled down to about 15 minutes of shouting "Yahoo!" and "Krrriii!" and punching each other in the shoulder before building a 5 billion BTU log-and-tree-stump fire. Someone got out a guitar and they all sang "Dead Skunk in the Middle of the Road" until passing out at 3:00 a.m.

"That's pretty good," Barb said at one point during the party. "Listen to them sing. They all know the words. When was the last time you heard twenty people who all knew the words to the same song, singing together like that?"

"Church?" I suggested "Or maybe the army . . ."

She listened for a while, then shook her head. "No, that's not the same."

The Twin started hard (i.e., not at all) in the morning. The weather was cool, and the 50-weight oil about as viscous as 3 quarts of Smuckers topping. Each time I jumped on the kick-starter, the engine went "tuff" and moved through half a stroke. Our friend Tom turned on his gas, set the choke, hit the starter button, and then walked away to brush his teeth while the Honda quietly purred and warmed itself up. Something was not right with the Contaminator. Usually two kicks, no matter how slow, were enough to make it fire. That morning, we finally pushed it downhill while I popped the clutch. It started reluctantly and ran less smoothly.

"Bad gas," I said. "It's that dishwater they're selling as premium now."

Tom said goodbye and turned south toward the Tetons, while we pushed north into Montana. If ever a license-plate blurb carried a grain of truth, it is Montana's "Big Sky Country." There is no other place in the world where you are eternally surrounded by mountains that are forever 50 miles away. We rode up the Madison River Valley into the first rainstorm of the trip, invincible in our rubber rain suits. By noon, a cool wind dried the pavement, and we were on the dreaded Interstate—our only choice—near Butte, headed for a night with some friends in Moscow, Idaho. After 1,400 miles and five days on the road, the Manxton Contaminator Twin still lived, running better than it had any right to. I began to suspect that we would not only reach Seattle but possibly even make it home again. I felt guilty, however, pushing this old sporting machine over endless miles of Interstate, even for one afternoon. It was like some interminable torture test, with the engine hovering at one constant, dull, unvarying pitch. Finally, the Twin decided it had endured enough.

About 25 miles from Missoula, the engine gave out a raucous mechanical clatter and stopped running on one cylinder. We pulled over, removed the rocker covers, and found three hundred thousandths of rocker clearance on the right-hand exhaust valve. It was not returning all the way. Bent, as it were. The right cylinder had just enough compression to blow one very faint smoke ring. I adjusted the tappet to cut down some of the clatter and tried to restart the bike. Oddly enough, it started and ran. We were on our way, albeit not too swiftly or silently. For 25 miles, the (now) Contaminator Single pulled us across the country, up- and downhill, at 45 mph.

I listened to the engine for sounds of further disaster, waiting for the worst. The bike kept on, lugging its 300-pound burden of passengers and gear on one tired cylinder. My emotions vacillated wildly; I couldn't decide whether to heap abuse or praise on the machine. But it was a painful ride for us, like forcing a crippled horse to run. We were exhausted from tension by the time we reached the first motel Missoula had.

Some quick telephone calls confirmed the worst. No shop in town had parts for, or could fix, the old Manxton. No one knew where to get parts, or anyone who even had such a bike. Someone at a Yamaha shop said one guy in town might be able to fix it if he had the parts, which he didn't, but he was on vacation.

The next morning, on Missoula's Annual Hottest Day of the Year, we pushed the Twin 2 miles across town to a Bekins freight office. The proud Manxton, which had conquered the Bighorns with impunity, now had me trembling at the sight of Missoula's manhole covers. As we pushed, swarms of children on banana-seat bicycles encircled us and asked clever questions or made witty remarks. Why, I asked myself, aren't these children working in coal mines or textile mills, where they belong? By the time we finished pushing I'd made a mental note to refrain from having any children, and had, at the same time, found new respect for the latent energy in a cup of gasoline. We filled out all the forms and mailed the bike home.

The trip to Moscow, Idaho, and then to Seattle was made by bus and train. We took the Greyhound home. Riding in the bus, I thought about the trip and about the motorcycle. When the Twin arrived home, I would fix the valve, clean the engine, polish the chrome, and keep the bike for special occasions like Sunday rides, the way one uses an MG TC or a Piper Cub. It deserves care, rest, and respect, as do all things that carry their age with grace. I had, unfairly, asked too much of the motorcycle. My fault.

Everyone had warned me what might, or surely would, happen. My own instincts had warned me. I knew the trip to be an undertaking whose outcome was uncertain. There was plenty of good advice to that effect. On any of a dozen other motorcycles our finishing the trip would have been a foregone conclusion. Maybe, in the end, that was why we took a thirteen-year-old British Twin. It's not so terrible, just two weeks out of the year, to not know what's going to happen next.

As the South Dakota night slipped by, I looked out the bus window and fell to aimless reverie. Could a Honda 50, I found myself wondering, make it all the way from Madison to Mexico City . . .

BECAUSE IT'S SMALL

With Its Faithful 10-Speed Companion, Stella, a 50cc Step-Through Honda Tackles Pikes Peak (Well, No, Not That Pikes Peak)

LIKE SO MANY GOOD THINGS, the trip began over drinks in an air-conditioned bar. My friend John was drinking unusually large amounts of Tequila Sunrise, not only because it "doesn't taste like booze" but because his Madison City League slow-pitch softball team, the Stupor Starz, had just taken a dreadful 28–3 drubbing from the West Side Ophthalmology Assistants. I was drinking along in sympathy.

"I've decided to take a motorcycle trip," I said, after a decent change-of-subject silence.

"Another one?"

"This is different. I'm taking my Honda 50."

John eyed me warily. "You serious?"

"Sure, why not? I've been riding the 50 to work all summer, and it runs perfectly. Now I have a hankering to hit the open road. It would be sort of a low-key 35-mph odyssey. Something to soothe the mind, instead of another mad dash across the continent. All I lack is a destination. It's not enough merely to ride; I need a goal, a mecca, a terminus worthy of the inherent rigors . . ."

John furrowed his brows and concentrated on the problem, as best he could. I sat watching an idle *Pong* game construct mindless labyrinthine patterns on a gray TV screen, apparently entertaining itself. I loved my Honda 50. It was a 1964 step-through, C100, two-tone blue, with 6,000 miles on the odometer. I bought it from a doctor who was cleaning his garage and wasn't sure if anyone would want the little thing, but took a chance on throwing an ad in the paper. His doubts were understandable. Who, after all, would want a used $75 machine that takes almost no maintenance, is reliable as a stone (though slightly faster), and takes the owner to work and back all week for 37¢? The day I drove out to look at the machine it was sitting in the doctor's driveway, and even as I drove up I could see that the bike was in mint condition. It nearly brought tears to my eyes. My Volkswagen was still dieseling as I wrote out the check.

A year later, the 50 still ran flawlessly, though I sensed it needed a good road run; something to blow out the cobwebs and decarbonize the head. In short, the bike needed a good tour. I knew the 50 could go the distance. After all, my old college roommate had a friend who heard about a guy whose brother rode a step-through from Wisconsin to Los Angeles and back . . . twice. But L.A. was a little more distance than I could handle in the few days of vacation I had available.

"I've got it," John said suddenly, halting his glass in mid-arc. "Pikes Peak!"

I let out a low whistle. "Boy, I don't know. Colorado and back is a long way to go in less than a week."

"Not Pikes Peak, Colorado, dummy. Pikes Peak, *IOWA!*"

"Never heard of it."

"It's a state park, just across the border, about 150 miles from here. I camped there once with my girlfriend on a geology field trip. Fine place. Excellent." He took a sip of his Sunrise. "Best place I ever camped. Lord, it was great . . ."

I entertained the notion for a few moments. The more I thought about it, the better I liked it. It wasn't terribly far. The country between Madison and the Iowa border is green and hilly, full of curving secondary roads. And as destinations went, the place had a nice ring to it. I grinned at John. "Sort of a 50cc Pikes Peak, right?"

"Exactly."

Later that evening, John confessed to a nostalgic attachment to the peak and asked if he could come along with me on his bicycle. Sure, I said. What the hell. John is an accomplished bicycle racer and has arms and legs that look like those bundles of steel cable that support the Golden Gate Bridge—certainly a match for the little Honda and its film-canister piston. It might be fun, a bicycle and a 50, though I wondered if John would have to wait for me at the bottoms of hills. Or at the tops.

That very week, I prepared the Honda for touring. Cycle shops, I discovered, don't carry a lot of Honda 50 accessories anymore. The beardless young salesman blinked and looked at me oddly when I asked about a luggage rack for a 50. I might as well have asked if he knew any Ray Charles tunes. Honda can still find you any part for the bike in just a few days, he said, through their computerized central supply system, but the aftermarket goodies have all but dried up. Unavailability being the mother of invention, I managed to adapt an old Bridgestone 50 rack I'd been hoarding in a box of keepsakes these many years. With a few tweaks and bends, I made it fit.

A trip to the Army Surplus store yielded a matched combo of touring luggage—all olive drab. I found a pair of genuine US Cavalry saddlebags (circa Pancho Villa) with the legend "1909, Cambridge Armory" stamped on the backs and a small rucksack for camera equipment, which I planned to hang over the handlebars. In addition, I had an old army duffel bag I'd used on other trips. Strapped to the bike, it all fit together perfectly, giving the 50 the vague aura of a frontier supply mule, clashing a bit oddly with that mid-sixties Petula Clark perkiness the Honda exudes so well.

For advice on mechanical preparation, I contacted my old friend Howard, the aging Honda mechanic. "What should I do to get this thing ready for a 300-mile tour?" I asked.

"Nothing," he said, savoring the word. "Well, almost nothing. Just make sure the oil is clean and your valves are adjusted. You can check your points and the plug if you want to, but there won't be anything wrong with them. Oil the chain and check the tire pressure. That's it. You won't have any problems. I know a guy who rode his 50 to the coast and back, twice. After the second trip he lapped his valves, just out of guilt, but the bike was running fine."

I nodded and wondered if this was the same guy I'd heard about.

I changed my oil—"Above 15 deg. C. (60 deg. F.) SAE #30," as it said on the crankcase—and oiled and adjusted my drive chain. My Honda 50 owner's manual said to adjust the valves to 0.002 for normal use and 0.004 "heard running" (Japanese translations into English have come a long way since 1964). I checked the plugs, points, and timing, and Howard was right; they were fine. The tires got 31 and 28 pounds, respectively, for heavy load conditions.

The load was quite heavy. John declined to compromise the purity of his Stella/Campagnolo racing bicycle by having it laden with earthly goods, so the Honda took it all: sleeping bags, clothes, tools, rain gear, cameras, pharmaceuticals, and Big Pink, my touring tent (originally red) since childhood, a piece of equipment so lacking in both size and water repellency that it builds incredible character on every trip. The whole load weighed 65 pounds That, added to my 175, I surmised, would keep those 50 cc's hopping during the final assault on Pikes Peak. In all fairness, John did carry the maps, his warmup jacket, and one wrench in a small handlebar pack. Big deal.

Labor Day weekend was chosen for the trip, more for its length than out of love for the other five billion people who would be on the road for the holiday. We both managed to wriggle out of work on Friday, giving us a four-day weekend.

Friday morning was dark and threatening rain as we escaped the city through Madison's beautiful Arboretum Drive. With all of our planning, John and I had not once tried riding the bicycle and the Honda side by side, to see how compatibly they would tour. Many bets had been made regarding the ability of the Honda to speed up- and downhill and of the bicycle to hold its pace on the level. ("Level," John claims, "is a mythical state. It does not exist.") It all worked out quite well. On moderate terrain John could cruise at about 22 mph, which put the Honda just above lugging speed in top gear. On mild hills, second gear for the Honda was matched by comfortable work for the bicycle, and killer hills demanded low gear from both, leaving engine and rider sucking wind.

Only two flaws reared their ugly heads. The main one was John's choice of gears. He'd elected to use his road-racing rear cluster, rather than his lower-range touring set. These gears were fine in the morning, but by afternoon his legs were aching for sprockets with more teeth; revs, rather than raw torque, were needed. The only other problem, and a very small one, was the Honda's gaping hole between first and second gears, complicated by a neutral slot in the middle. The bike almost rolled backward when downshifting on steep hills and all but stopped rolling forward on upshifts. The engine had to be wound into a scream-ing frenzy in first, followed by two clubby upshifts to reach second, which, by then, would not pull the bike. So back into first. And so on. The only answer, I discovered, was to be At One with very, very slow speeds; to enjoy the birds and the trees and the sky as the Honda churned along in first gear, a tiny mechanical juggernaut devouring hills as inexorably and relentlessly as a glacier.

Our route was lifted straight off the dotted red lines of a bicycle touring map of southwestern Wisconsin, and the roads were well chosen. Even on Labor Day, traffic was virtually nonexistent except when we chanced into larger towns or when one of our country roads crossed a major highway. At the main artery crossroads, we were treated to a vision of vacationing Americans acting out some sort of lemming nightmare, crawling along bumper to bumper with their boats and motorhomes and trailers. And yes, there were even some motorcycles in there, poor devils, all going . . . somewhere. But minutes later we would be back on the country roads with curves and fields, farms and old stone houses. No cars.

A few hours into the trip we rolled into a small glen that sheltered a cluster of buildings called Postville: a general store with gas pumps, a real blacksmith shop across the street, five houses, and a mobile home. On the corner, right in front of the blacksmith shop, stood an old Triumph Bonneville. The bike was that rarest of aged Bonnies, the complete, original, unchopped, and fairly clean variety (these defenseless motorcycles seem to attract more than their share of vandal-owners). It was parked at the corner of the lot in such a way as to suggest it might be for sale. I looked for a fallen sign, but found none. The blacksmith shop was closed. The general store was closed. The gas pumps were locked. Not one thing moved in the village. I knocked at all five houses and the mobile home to ask about the bike, but no one answered. Wind chimes on someone's porch made brittle, random music in the light breeze. It was all quite eerie, and I found myself humming the theme from *On the Beach* and scanning the village for Rod

Serling. I took a last, longing look at the beautiful, restorable old Bonneville. Restoring vehicles is a disease with me, and this one cried to be taken home and made to run again (the plug wires were missing). Then we got on our bikes and left.

By evening we were in Mineral Point, an old Cornish lead-mining town with many of its old stone miners' cottages restored to landmark condition. John and I dined at the Red Rooster Café on Cornish Pastys (*sic*), a delicious sort of meat and vegetable pie. After dinner, we decided to get our nightmares over early and see *Exorcist II* at the local theater. I can't resist movies in small-town theaters when I'm touring, and I'll go to see anything the industry can throw at me—as John discovered to his dismay. We came out onto a late-night square full of prowling muscle cars and chubby girls who shouted things at them from the street corners. We rode just out of town to our campground-by-the-highway, where we were lulled to sleep by the music of many semis upshifting their way past our tent and off into the night.

I awoke before John in the morning and crawled out of the tent to find that the last two feet of his sleeping bag were sticking out of Big Pink like a blue tongue (John is 6 foot 4 and the tent is 4 by 4), and that a brief night shower had soaked the end of his bag. Not only that, a huge orange cat had nested in a pocket of sodden goose down between his feet. Nothing disturbs the sleep of the touring bicyclist. On our trip John slept so hard that he actually frowned from the effort.

My first gas stop, on the second morning, revealed that the Honda had guzzled no less than half a gallon during the 80 miles we'd covered the previous day, at a cost of 32¢. That was 160 mpg. John was numb. "Thirty-two cents? That's crazy! Hell, I spent over a dollar on granola bars yesterday, just so I'd have enough energy to pedal this bike." He stared at the Honda with a troubled frown, as if trying to grasp some searing new truth. "That's plain madness. You can't make a gas tank leak that slowly, much less run a vehicle . . ."

That same day, we hit our highest mutual speed of the trip while racing down a long hill (one of those inclines so evil that a sign at the top says "HILL" and shows a truck perched on a steep triangle). We reached 46 mph, wheel to wheel, just as the road bottomed onto a one-lane bridge whose ramp-like apron nearly tossed us off our bikes. We got into the low 40s a few times after that, but never again broke the magic 46. Uphills were less speedy that day, when a strong wind shifted into our faces. The Honda was unbothered by the wind at low speeds, but the bicycle's progress took a quantum leap downward, and John appeared to be pedaling in a slow-motion bionic frenzy.

We had a late lunch at a small café in Lancaster, a small city whose skyline is dominated by two landmarks: an intricate green glass dome on the Grant County Courthouse and one of those space-age water towers that look like giant turquoise golf balls. "Some day," I told John as we rode into town, "God, with his enraged sense of aesthetics, will descend from heaven with a giant fiery Gary Player–autographed driver and tee off on all those water towers and then we won't have to see them anymore." John nodded grimly, sweat running off his nose. He loved to joke while pedaling into the wind.

We ate at Bud's, where the waitress, seeing our bikes outside, asked if we were in some kind of contest. John looked up suddenly and in a hoarse, distracted voice said, "Huh?" Proof that fatigue was setting in.

Toward evening we were blessed by the long descent into the Mississippi River Valley at Prairie du Chien. The town was crawling with Labor Day tourists, and our hopes of finding a motel (and a shower for John, who was beginning to smell like the Chicago Bears) were soon dashed. We ended up at a commercial campground right next to the river. As we were about to register, the manager asked if we had a pup tent. We nodded. He closed the registration book and pointed to a sign that said "No Pup Tents."

"Can't allow them anymore," he said sadly. "Last year a motorhome backed over a pup tent with two campers in it, and now the insurance company won't allow any tent that isn't tall enough to be seen in truck mirrors." John and I turned to each other, incredulous. A campground that doesn't allow pup tents? Crazy. I looked around at the gleaming row of campers, trailers, and motorhomes. I suddenly felt like I'd drifted into camp from another era, some kind of Dust Bowl Okie, with my miserable little canvas tent and only a sleeping bag to put in it. John looked so forlorn at the prospect of more pedaling and searching that the camp manager was moved. "I'll tell you what. I've got a Jeep camper by the house. You can sleep in that." We gladly accepted. He apologized for the rules several times. He didn't like it any more than we did, but it was the insurance.

Living well being the best revenge, we got even for our lack of motel that night by eating steak and lobster at the Blue Heaven Supper Club, a place with tiny blinking lights embedded in the blue ceiling and cherubs on the walls. Later, we saw *Joyride* at the theater on Main Street. John's resistance to the nightly movie was building, I sensed. When we came out the street was almost violently alive with drunks, more muscle cars, big motorcycles, shouting youth, cruising squad cars, and roving bands of cowboys in town for a rodeo. Sundown on Labor Day. By the time we returned to the campground, it seemed like a very good place. It was soothingly peaceful, dotted with campfires, Japanese lanterns, and murmuring circles of friends. John went right to sleep in the truck, and I walked down to the willows at the edge of the river and sat on the shore, enjoying the quiet and smoking a corncob pipe I'd bought off a cardboard display at a café—something I'd wanted to do ever since I read *Tom Sawyer* at the age of ten. The Mississippi, when you sit next to it at night, is a dark and powerful thing.

Prairie du Chien was our final camp in the assault on Pikes Peak. On a bright Sunday morning we rolled across the Mississippi bridge into Iowa and began the climb out of the town of McGregor. It was strictly low gear for Honda and Stella, but after a 15-minute ascent, we wheezed into Pikes Peak State Park. We had a man take our picture at the gate, then went directly to the highest spot on the peak (which is really a bluff overlooking the Mississippi) and planted a tiny Wisconsin State Flag to commemorate our conquest. We savored the magnificent view of the junction of the Wisconsin and Mississippi Rivers in the valley far below, and read a tourist leaflet explaining that Zebulon Pike had picked this spot for a US fort during an exploration trip in 1805, but that the government, always seeking the lower ground, had eventually built the fort next to the river, in Prairie du Chien.

At the park concession stand, we bought postcards, T-shirts, ice cream, and a corncob pipe with "Pikes Peak" burned into the stem. Mailing all those cards telling people we'd made it was a glorious moment.

We coasted back across the river into Wisconsin and turned up the Wisconsin River Valley to head for home. That night we finally found indoor lodging. An ancient hotel in Muscoda (pronounced Mus-kah-day) took us in for $11. The place had beautiful old woodwork, a lobby with a potted fern, spotlessly clean rooms that looked like something from *Gunsmoke*, and, best of all, a bathroom with a shower at the end of the hall. John returned from the shower reborn. We dined on catfish at the Blackhawk Supper Club to celebrate his cleanliness. After dinner, John refused to take in *Sinbad and the Eye of the Tiger* at the local Bijou, so we went to the hotel bar and I called my wife, who was much relieved to hear that we still existed. That night, John and I discovered that Muscoda had the world's highest per-capita population of Harley-Davidsons with straight pipes. All of them patronized the bar across the street from our hotel window, taking turns doing demonstration burn-outs on Main Street for a throng of cheering drag fans.

In the morning we had breakfast at the Chieftain's Teepee, feeling a little out of place as the only customers not wearing Muscoda Gun Club jackets. We loaded our bikes with gear in front of the hotel and met two other guests, a couple in their fifties who were touring by bicycle. They wore safety-orange vests, safety bike helmets, safety flags on fiberglass poles, safety reflector stripes on their packs, pedals, and spokes, and little rearview mirrors attached to their helmets. Nice folks, but a little too safe for my tastes.

A few hours up the river we found Taliesin, the beautiful home of the Frank Lloyd Wright Foundation, just outside of Spring Green. We stopped to visit Bill Logue, an old friend of mine who works for the foundation, and he gave us a tour of the buildings and grounds, showing us some of the new architectural works-in-progress, the most spectacular being a mountaintop home for the daughter of the

Shah of Iran. We had lunch at the Spring Green, a Wright-designed restaurant overlooking the Wisconsin River, then left on our last leg of the trip, the 30 miles home to Madison. We were home just at sundown.

We cleaned up and went out for a celebratory pizza, rehashing our trip and doing some calculations. The ride had been exactly 303 miles long, over four days. The Honda used 1.8 gallons of leaded regular or premium, depending on what was available, which is 168.3 mpg, at a cost of $1.13. With over 6,000 miles on the original engine, the Honda used no discernible amount of oil—the dipstick level was constant throughout the trip. John ate about $4 worth of granola bars while riding, plus a peach and three apples. There were no malfunctions of any kind on either machine.

In fifteen years of riding and touring on all kinds of bikes, this was my favorite trip. It was a microcosm tour, measured in time rather than distance. Two days from home, the Mississippi River felt as far away from home as Denver or Montréal had on other trips with faster motorcycles. The pace was slow and enjoyable, largely over roads and through towns we had never seen before, though all were within a one-day drive by car. The natives spoke English, or some dialect thereof, and our currency was accepted everywhere. Best of all, we beat our postcards home, thus receiving news of our progress while it was still fresh and exciting.

THE FRENCH QUARTER CONNECTION

A Sense of Adventure, a Honda 400, and a Search for Cheap Chicory Coffee

I **STARED AT THE TOP OF THE COFFEE CAN IN DISBELIEF.** "Five sixty-nine for a pound of Louisiana French Roast Coffee? That's ridiculous!" I exclaimed to my wife, who agreed. "Three months ago it was $2.95." I couldn't believe it. My favorite blend of chicory coffee—which everyone tells me tastes like kerosene—had nearly doubled in price. I put the can back on the shelf. "I won't pay it!" I said, loudly enough to be overheard by the assistant manager of the supermarket, who was hovering nearby with a clipboard and a matching shirt and tie. "In fact," I added, "I think I'll run down to New Orleans to buy my coffee."

It was a pretty flimsy excuse for a 3,000-mile motorcycle odyssey that would take me the full length of the Mississippi, all the way to the Gulf and back to Wisconsin, but it was just what I was looking for.

Ever since I was a kid I'd wanted to take a raft trip down the Mississippi—maybe start in Minnesota near the headwaters and drift down to New Orleans, watching the famous old river towns and the green shoreline slip past while I sat back on a pile of provisions and smoked a pipe.

Then one summer I worked on a Burlington Railroad section crew along the Mississippi and I saw the river in action. Whole oak trees floated by, only to disappear in sudden, mysterious undercurrents; hydroelectric towers and dams swallowed millions of gallons of water from greenish whirlpools of their own making; and tugs pushed half a mile of unwieldy barges around blind river bends. It was all a far cry from Huck Finn's sleepy river, and no place for a novice—especially a novice with an unnatural fear of Indifferent Nature, as manifested in the force of fast-moving water.

It suddenly dawned on me that a motorcycle trip down the Great River Road might be a pleasant, relatively nonlethal, alternative to rafting. I could still visit those famous cities and towns and keep an eye on the river itself. "And," I asked myself, "what twentieth-century vehicle lives more in the spirit of Huck Finn's raft than a motorcycle?"

"Why, none," I answered.

The prospect of a river trip, together with a chance to score a can of cheap French Roast coffee, was too much. I opened the attic closet and got out My Things.

My Things, it turned out, were all wrong for the trip. I realized that nearly all of my cycle gear was intended for cold or cool-weather riding, which is the rule rather than the exception in Wisconsin. Since I was heading south in the middle of August, I would have to leave it all behind: my leather jacket, my Belstaff suit, gauntlet-style gloves, down bag, and riding boots. It was strictly tennis-shoe and T-shirt weather. I took a denim jacket for early-morning and late-evening riding, an old army blanket to sleep on rather than in, half a gallon of Cutter mosquito repellent, and Big Pink—a faded red pup tent from childhood, so shopworn that I can gaze at stars through the fabric at night.

The motorcycle would be my latest pride and joy, a 1975 fire-engine-red Honda 400F Super Sport. There are those who would (and several who did) point out that the 400F is a rather precise instrument to use in the bludgeoning of 3,000 miles of open highway; a waste, in effect, of a machine whose forte is 410 Production racing or the Sunday-morning ride on twisty blacktop. They are right, of course. It was for that kind of sport that I bought the bike. Even as it sat in my garage, the 400 was on the brink of being converted into a 410 Production racer. All of the racing parts were laid out in neat array on my workbench. I had a set of Konis, some flashy orange S&W 70-110 progressive springs, two new K-81s, three plastic number panels, a set of Racer-1 clubman bars, 4 quarts of Castrol GP 50-weight, and a roll of safety wire. But my first race was five weeks away, and I was up for a good road trip.

And, purist considerations aside, the 400 does make a fine road bike. It is utterly reliable, handles legal and extra-legal highway speeds easily, is not awkward to maneuver in tight places (no embarrassing assumption of the beached-whale position while a whole campground looks on), and looks and sounds good. Also, I prefer the short, straight bars so I can lean into the wind while I ride, as opposed to the more popular dumping-a-wheelbarrow-full-of-concrete riding style. With a light luggage load—I took only an Eclipse tank bag and a duffel bag on the rear seat—the bike handles almost as well as the unladen item and makes riding on curving roads a genuine pleasure. Nothing is more annoying than to be stuck with half a ton of mechanical corpulence when the riding gets fun.

At 7:00 on a Friday morning I kissed my wife goodbye, patted our three cats on the head, and rode off into a hot and gloriously sunny morning. Just outside of town I stopped to install some earplugs I'd bought to ward off total deafness on the long trip. After five minutes, I had to stop and take them out. They worked too well; I couldn't hear a thing. They made riding surreal, and eerily quiet. For all I knew, my exhaust header had fallen off, and a broken rod was

hammering my block to pieces. I began to fantasize engine and chassis noises, much the way someone wearing stereo headphones constantly imagines that the phone and doorbell are ringing. Like those early airline pilots who objected to enclosed cockpits, I preferred to hear the wind in the wires and ignore the instruments.

The first leg of my trip did not take me south toward New Orleans, but 500 miles north to the Minnesota resort town of Brainerd. I wanted to make a proper river trip out of it and start near the headwaters of the Mississippi. The true source of the river is Lake Itasca, northwest of Brainerd, from which the river flows in none-too-impressive volume through Bemidji and southward through many small lakes, gathering strength. I went to Brainerd because I have good friends, Tom and Lynn Dettman, who have a farm and cabin near the town. I also wanted to scout around Brainerd International Raceway for an upcoming road race—and another chance to unleash *Lola the Vicious Underdog*, my battle-scarred and outdated Formula Ford racing car. (Lively, these little towns in the North Woods.)

I rode into Brainerd after ten hours on the bike and after dark, equipped with a copy of a copy of a hand-drawn map purporting to show the way to the Dettmans' cabin, some 20 miles from town. Three hours later, on a mosquito-clouded back road in the dark forest, I gave up searching for the imaginary landmarks on my map, switched my tank to reserve, and prayed I'd make it back to town. I rolled into a gas station and café in Brainerd at 1:00 in the morning, my engine sputtering.

"Is there any place around here I can lie down and sleep?" I asked the waitress over a cup of coffee in the restaurant. "I must have sleep. I've been on my motorcycle for thirteen hours."

"There's some old railroad cars down by the river. You could sleep in those," she offered.

"Perfect," I said. As I left the café, the cook at the grill shouted, "You bed down in one of them railroad cars and you just might wake up in North Dakota!" She cackled and flipped a hamburger. I didn't care. I had to lie down.

In the morning I awoke on a bench in a vandalized caboose car and found myself lying in a bed of cigarette butts, crushed Dixie Cups, and spent lime vodka bottles, all features I'd overlooked while stumbling in from the night fog. I brushed myself off and looked out the train window. I was still in Minnesota— or what the mosquitos had left of me was still in Minnesota. The mosquitos in that state are so large that they lack the usual high-pitched whine and drum their wings at a much lower frequency, like quail taking off from a thicket.

With the aid of sunlight and friendly natives I managed to find the Dettmans' place, a remote cabin on a beautiful lake, which they share only with a Bible camp. Tom showed me around the town and the racetrack. We spent the evening visiting, and my second night on the road, sleeping in their cabin on the lake, was considerably more pleasant than the first—though Tom persisted in addressing me as "Boxcar Egan." They fixed me a good breakfast for a sendoff down the river.

South of Brainerd the Mississippi develops into a solid, respectable little river that winds easily through flat Minnesota farmland, widening here and there to water the marshlands of wild rice and cattails. It passes through Little Falls, where Charles Lindbergh lived before he had the good sense to move to Madison, Wisconsin—where he attended the university before he had the good sense to quit school and take up flying. South of St. Cloud, the river gets lost in the fast-growing suburbs and the downtown(s) of the Twin Cities. The Falls of St. Anthony, once a landmark and barrier to upper river navigation, are now caught between two dams and circumvented by a lock system. Modern cities have a way of overwhelming the physical features that once determined their locations, until those features are lost and unimportant. I spent part of my youth in St. Paul and never heard anyone mention the Falls, nor did I ever see them.

At Prescott, Wisconsin, the St. Croix River joins its crystal-clear waters to the already Muddy, if not very Big, Mississippi. I decided to follow Highway 61 down the Minnesota side, having seen too much of the Wisconsin side when I worked on the railroad and literally shoveled my way from Prescott to Bluff Siding.

Highway 61, from Hastings to La Crosse, Wisconsin, is one of the nicest cycle rides on the Mississippi; four lanes, smooth and uncrowded, undulate along the riverbank high enough to afford a constant panorama of the river and its islands. I discovered at this stage of the ride that every gas station, no matter where you go, employs one high-school student who either owns or is about to own a motorcycle and can discuss motorcycles with incredible expertise, usually quoting cycle magazines verbatim. A station attendant in Red Wing told me that my 400F had "an engine that lives just to bury the tach needle." I nodded my agreement, suppressing a shiver of déjà vu and wondering where I'd read those words.

At La Crosse I shifted to the more scenic Wisconsin riverbank and cruised through a dozen small river towns until I reached Wyalusing State Park. The park sits high on the bluffs at the junction of the Wisconsin and Mississippi and offers a splendid view of both rivers. I erected Big Pink near the campsite of a young couple who had a trailer and two curious children. The father seemed determined that the kids stay clear of me and my motorcycle and shouted at them roughly whenever they ventured too close. Feeling rather untouchable (perhaps it was the dead insects pasted to my chin), I sat alone on the bluffs, watching a huge red sun set over Iowa and sipping a little Cabin Still from a brown paper bag I'd brought along.

The day was already calm and breathlessly hot at 7:00 in the morning when I broke camp and rode down to Galena, Illinois, for breakfast. Galena was a prosperous old river town that fell upon hard times and was nearly abandoned, until a later generation recognized the value and charm of the beautiful old homes and shops in the city. Galena is now a tourist attraction, with hundreds of nicely restored buildings and a remarkable collection of brick storefronts along its main street. It is a town that must have the highest ratio of antique shops to population in the entire country. On the edge of town I visited the home of Ulysses S. Grant, which is filled with photographs of the general and his family, Grant always looking a bit rough-hewn and out of place amid the lavish parlor trappings of that era. In my own heat-distorted mind I began to pity the people in the photographs for their lack of shorts and sandals, because it was about 100 degrees in Grant's house. It was good to get back on the Honda.

In Fulton, Illinois, farther down the river, I sat at a lunch counter with two young men who told me that St. Louis was a tough town, and I should steer around it. "You go through St. Louis on that shiny red motorcycle and, sure as hell, someone'll drag you right off that bike and take all your stuff away. I heard about it." The speaker's friend concurred grimly, then ordered a turkey sandwich with gravy. As he ate the sandwich, he leaned over to his buddy and said, "Bird Dog can eat six of these."

"Hail."

"I see 'im."

I walked out onto the street, keeping a sharp eye out for the legendary Bird Dog and wondering if I dared go through St. Louis on my shiny red bike. I tossed caution to the wind and headed south.

I followed the Great River Road (always marked with a green sign that bears a giant steamboat wheel) and cruised through the Moline and Rock Island half of the Quad Cities—factory towns that are incredibly clean and modern looking for a traditional industrial area. The John Deere plant is so gleaming and up-to-date it looks almost Japanese.

Just north of Nauvoo, Illinois, I ran across another touring motorcyclist. At a four-way stop in the middle of nowhere we got off our bikes to have a cigarette and talk. He was Roy Perkins, from Roanoke, Virginia, and he was touring on a Kawasaki 400 triple. "I wouldn't ride anything but a Kawasaki two-stroke," he told me. "I've never had a lick of trouble with 'em. And I wouldn't ride anything bigger than a 400—you don't need any more than that." Roy was traveling even lighter than I was; he had nothing but a backrest with a pack strapped to it and a tent roll across his rear seat. "I'm going to Seattle, down to Mexico, then back home around the Gulf coast and Florida," he said. "The main thing I like to see is Indian mounds. I've seen every Indian mound between here and Virginia, and I plan to see them all along my trip." I thought of Kawasaki's "We know why you ride" advertising slogan, and I wondered if they knew about Roy Perkins and his Indian mounds. Before we parted, he warned me to stay out of Mississippi. I asked why. He kick-started his bike and lifted his face shield for a moment. "Trouble," he said. He flipped his shield down and rode away, waving.

Before sundown I was in Nauvoo State Park, staking down my tent. As soon as my cycle stopped moving, I realized that the only factor preventing me from melting into a smoldering shapeless lump of steaming flesh was the air that moved past me and the Honda all day. By the time my tent was in place I was a sweaty wreck, so I rode into town and had five beers for dinner at an air-conditioned bar, where I watched an entire Pirates vs. Reds baseball game on TV, even though I was not a dedicated fan of either team, being from Brewers country. When the bar closed, I was forced back to my tent for a long night of involuntary weight loss.

In the morning I toured Historic Nauvoo, the last home of the Mormons before they were forced by persecution to move west to Utah, led by Brigham Young. A Mormon restoration corporation is buying up and rebuilding the old brick settlement, and the restoration they have already done is first class. Four acres surround each home and shop in an idyllic setting whose beauty imparts some of the sorrow those settlers must have felt in leaving what they'd built. Before I left town, I bought a bottle of Old Nauvoo Brand Burgundy Wine, a modern legacy of the French Icarians who moved in to plant vineyards when the Mormons left. (The wine was excellent when I got home, even after five days in my tank bag; truly a Burgundy that travels well.)

At Keokuk, I paid 30 cents to cross the Mississippi on a steel-mesh bridge— the kind of surface that sends motorcycle tires into a frenzy of squirming indecision—and was greeted by a sign that said "Welcome to Keokuk, Iowa. Sailors have more fun!" (Okay, sure. But in Keokuk, Iowa?) I turned south on 61 toward Hannibal, Missouri, home of Mark Twain.

In *The Adventures of Tom Sawyerr*, Twain described his hometown as a "poor little shabby village." It's not so little anymore, but the river town that surrounds the block of old houses claiming to be Tom Sawyer's neighborhood has taken on a modern shabbiness to disillusion romantics and young readers. A giant rotating fried- chicken barrel looms just beyond Tom's house, and trucks rumble across the busy highway bridge behind it. A few blocks away, a scrap-metal yard lines the riverbank. There are many small towns, up and down the river, much closer in spirit and form to the village Twain immortalized than Hannibal is today.

I had lunch at Huck Finn's Hideaway, seated beneath woodcarvings of the Big Three (Elvis, Jesus, and John Kennedy), bought a copy of *The Adventures of Tom Sawyer* at Becky Thatcher's Book Store, and rode on toward St. Louis.

Highway 79 from Hannibal to St. Louis is another one of those roads where it's good to have a 400F, setbacks, six speeds, a pair of K-81s, and an engine that lives to bury the tach. It is 50 miles of road that goes up- and downhill through the trees, winding up valleys and bursting into hilltop clearings with observation vistas on the river below. Euphoric and glassy eyed from the ride, I came snarling and downshifting into Wentzville, like Hailwood pulling into the pits at Douglas on the Isle of Man. Wentzville, Missouri, just west of St. Louis, is the home of Chuck Berry; a living legend of rock 'n' roll.

A group of giggling thirteen-year-old girls on Main Street told me where Berry lived. "Just follow that road out of town. It's called Berry Park. You'll see it. He should be home. He was in town with his Cadillac this morning, and I saw him shopping." More giggling. "He's not too popular around here anymore."

"No? Why is that?"

"Well, you know . . . he's kind of old and everything. He's just not . . . too cool."

They all blushed and giggled, and I thanked them for the directions. Not too cool? Granted, I thought, he's not Shaun Cassidy, but still . . .

Berry's house was right where they said it would be, about 5 miles out of town; a fenced-in country estate with a duck pond and some houses and buildings hidden back in the willows. The gate was open, so I walked up the driveway and talked to a young woman who told me that Chuck was playing in St. Louis that night, at the Rainbow Bar. As I walked back down the drive, a bronze Cadillac rolled in with none other than the Brown-Eyed Handsome Man himself at the wheel. He smiled and waved, if a little thinly, doubtless underawed at the novelty of another camera-carrying stranger stalking his grounds.

I found the Rainbow Bar and checked into a nearby motel. Berry was a knockout that night, playing to a cheering crown of about three hundred who'd jammed into the little roadside club. He led off with "Roll Over Beethoven" (tell Cha-kosky da news!), "Johnny B. Goode," and "Sweet Little Sixteen," cranking out guitar riffs that are copied by every rock musician in the world, doing his famous duckwalk and leering happily at the crowd over his earthiest lyrics.

Unfortunately, Berry is not too cool, so at 2:00 in the morning, after three frenzied encores, and despite the objections of the wildly applauding crowd, he quit playing and everyone went home.

In the bleary morning light I rode past the awesome St. Louis Gateway Arch and somehow managed to sneak out of the city without being dragged off my bike by local toughs. I turned south on Highway 3, through the lower tip of Illinois. (Illinois is, subjectively, the longest state in the Union.) I crossed the river at Cairo, where the Ohio joins the Mississippi, and it is here that the river begins to Mean Business. The Ohio actually dumps in twice as much water as the Mississippi, much to the embarrassment of Mississippi fans.

I pushed south toward Memphis, where the police were on strike, the National Guard was in control, and 8:00 p.m. curfew was being enforced, and thousands of people were flocking into town for the first anniversary of Elvis's death; a truly irresistible combination. I camped outside the city, part of an army preparing for a dawn invasion.

I got into town early and searched out Beale Street in downtown Memphis. Once the lively bar and nightclub mecca of Mississippi Delta musicians heading north, the famous Beale Street is now a victim of urban renewal. Only two blocks of the old street remain, and they are rundown, vacant, and boarded up. The rest is parking lots. After a moment of silence for the vanished street, I rode out to Graceland, home and final resting place of Elvis.

One year and one day after his death, a large but respectful crowd rummaged through the shopping center of Elvis memorabilia and then crossed Elvis Presley Boulevard to file up the lawn of the Graceland Mansion to see his grave. Elvis is buried next to his mother in a little alcove near the swimming pool. The grounds and grave were decorated with hundreds of floral tributes, variously shaped like gold records, hearts, hound dogs, and teddy bears. At the gate, a man was trying to sell a Harley XLCH that he claimed was one of Elvis's stable. I shuffled past the bronze tombstone, following a family of four who had driven 2,200 miles straight through from Nova Scotia, just to be there on the anniversary of his death. They were a day late. "It's still worth every mile of the drive," the man told me. "Being here is something we'll never forget as long as we live."

Dizzy and dehydrated from standing in line for two hours, I was glad to get back on the 400F and enjoy the luxury of moving air. I crossed into the flat, hot cotton country that is Mississippi's Yazoo Delta and is—to a blues fan and record collector—Holy Ground.

For reasons that are unclear (something in the water, perhaps), this north-western corner of Mississippi produced nearly every great American bluesman in the twentieth century. Son House, Robert Johnson, Howlin' Wolf, Muddy Waters, John Lee Hooker, and Charlie Patton, to name just a few, all came from a small area around Clarksdale, Mississippi. And, as if that were not enough,

William Faulkner's home at Oxford—the center of this mythical Yoknapataw-pha County—lies just to the east. Never was such a small area of the earth graced with so much genius.

I stopped at a music store in Clarksdale and bought a couple of magic Fender guitar picks, one for me and one for my friend David Rhodes, who already plays guitar quite well and doesn't need a magic pick as badly as I do. The people at the music store said that not much is left of the old music, since all the bluesmen went north in the forties. Clarksdale was not the somnolent little cotton town I'd expected. It is a bustling go-into-town-and-shop farm community, indistinguishable from a thriving county seat in Wisconsin. It has a McDonald's and a small, but significant, suburbia.

I threw the guitar picks in my tank bag, downed three glasses of iced tea at a little air-conditioned restaurant, and rode out of Clarksdale. Highway 61 is not exactly Racer Road as it runs through the Delta. The pavement is straight and flat, and towns appear on the highway as islands of buildings and trees in the sprawling cotton fields. The most visible sign of life between towns is the large number of colorful crop dusters that sweep back and forth over the road. The landscape everywhere is dotted with rusted tin roofs of old sharecroppers' houses, many of which are abandoned, relics now on the big corporate planta-tions. As you ride, the air has a distinctive fuel-oil smell left by the crop dusters.

By evening I found myself in Arkansas on a river-made peninsula that is Chicot State Park. I was rather a mess, having ridden late in the day through a plague of four-winged, dragonfly-looking insects called snake doctors by the local people. These things burst on your knuckles and chin like small pigeons' eggs. Miraculously, the park had hot showers and a laundromat. I showered, left my clothes to test the competence of the washing machine, and examined my faithful Honda. Other than lubing the chain and checking the engine oil, I hadn't touched the bike. The oil level was unchanged since I'd left home, but the chain was sagging a bit, so I tightened it. The rear K-81, never intended as a touring tire, had vaporized about 40 percent of its tread somewhere on the Great River Road, which left me 60 percent to make it to New Orleans and home—or about the right amount.

Before leaving home I'd installed plugs two ranges colder than stock, think-ing of long, fast rides in the hot sun. This was a mistake, since on a trip of this kind I did much more duffing and bogging around towns and parks than I would do on my home turf. But the plugs looked okay, and they still worked. I adjusted my valves and cam chain and revved the engine; the 400 sounded like the same competent, enraged little sewing machine with whom I'd left home.

With clean clothes and an adjusted bike, I cruised down Highway 61 into Rolling Fork, Mississippi, the birthplace of Muddy Waters. "Yes, yes," said one of the old men on the park bench in the town square, "I knew McKinley

Morganfield (a.k.a. Muddy Waters). He was here in a big black Cadillac six years ago when his mother died. His brother Robert and his sister-in-law Frankie live in that yellow house down the street."

I stopped at the house and talked to Frankie Morganfield. I said that Muddy had a lot of fans up in Wisconsin, and she said, "Yes, he told me a lot of you white folks like that music up there." I laughed. "Yes, we sure do." She thanked me for stopping and said she'd give my best to Muddy. I rode away confident that I'd done my share of tiresome meddling for the day.

At the hilltop city of Vicksburg I finally got high enough above the levees to see the river again. I rode out to the military park and cemetery and toured the 16 miles of road that wind through the battleground. When Grant took Vicksburg, the Mississippi was opened to the Union, and the war was over for the South, though the Confederacy struggled on for another two years. The graves at Vicksburg go on and on, as far as you can see; antique artillery pieces are poised at each ridge and hilltop beside bronze plaques of explanation. The battleground is one of those places where the historian could spend a year, and the passing tourist just long enough to realize how little he understands from what he sees.

The same is true of Natchez, an old, old city with a colorful and varied history and a collection of beautiful antebellum homes. It is the terminus of the Natchez Trace, the canyon-like ancient trail, now paved, that cuts cross-country nearly to Nashville. I wandered around Natchez in the evening looking for a motel room and found that everything was filled because the Corps of Engineers was in town (the Corps has built most of the levees that keep lower Mississippi towns from floating into the Gulf each spring). I rode south to Woodville, where, I was told, I could find a motel.

The road to Woodville ran through dark and hilly pine-tree country, with lots of traffic coming the other way. I began to assemble reasons for why I hate riding at night. I decided that they included: (1) drunks, (2) deer, (3) bright headlights that force you to ride blind down a lane that may be littered with hay bales, dead possums, or kegs of nails fallen from trucks, and (4) insects. By the time I got to Woodville, half of the flying insects in Mississippi had made a graveyard of my shirt and face shield. I found a roadside motel with vacancy and cleaned up for my early-morning sweep into New Orleans. My room was hot, so I cranked the air conditioner up to full and went to bed.

In the morning I woke up dreaming I'd died and gone to Alaska. The room was freezing. Feeling very refreshed, I stepped out into the steamy-hot morning at about 6:00 and rode off into the mist and dawn light into West Feliciana Parish, Louisiana. This stretch of Highway 61 passes more Southern mansions than I thought existed in all the South. With huge oaks hung with Spanish moss shading their pillared façades, like something out of *Gone with the Wind*, they pass by with names like the Catalpas, the Oaks, or the Cottage (yes, some cottage, you are supposed to think). The homes along the road became newer and less grand as I entered Baton Rouge, city of smoking oil refineries and Huey Long's tower building. I stayed on 61 and rode along the south shore of Lake Pontchartrain to New Orleans.

I took the Vieux Carré exit, down Orleans Avenue and Toulouse Street into the heart of the French Quarter. Anxious to get off my bike and look around, I found a room at the Cornstalk Hotel on Royal Street, changed my shirt, and walked out on the town. The French Quarter, which surrounds St. Louis Cathedral and Jackson Square, was old, beautiful, and much larger in area than I expected. The Quarter is a labyrinth of narrow streets, old hotels, fine restaurants, topless/bottomless joints, night clubs, cool, dark bars, souvenir shops, oyster bars, bookstores, coffee houses, and expensive antique shops, all thrown together in wonderful unzoned anarchy. Music is everywhere; the great jazz clubs are open to the street. You can stand in the street, listening and watching, or sit down with a $1.50 beer and relax at the bar or a table. The music is good; not some contrived Dixieland Muzak for tourists, but genuinely well-played jazz.

I sat in Maison Bourbon, listening to the Robert Jefferson Jazz Band for a while, lunched nearby on oysters and gumbo, and then wandered down to the river, where I stumbled upon the French Market and its open-air stalls of fruits and vegetables. At the edge of the marketplace was a sight for sore and weary eyes—the French Market Café. I had café au lait, chicory style, of course, and an order of beignets—a sort of square donut—all brought by waiters in ties and black coats. Reminded of my original goal, I looked through the nearby shops for some French roast chicory coffee and immediately found a 1 pound can for $2.85. Suddenly the whole trip was worth it. I took the can back to the hotel, locked my door, and carefully packed the coffee away in my tank bag. All that remained was to get it home.

I counted my money, found that I had $32 left, and suddenly realized that my trip home was going to be, of necessity, a straight shot of dreaded Interstate, with few food and rest stops. I had just enough money for gas and a couple of Big Macs.

On an early Sunday New Orleans morning, with the streets nearly vacant, I rolled out of the Vieux Carré, turned north onto I-55, snicked the 400 into sixth gear, and opened all four throttles. I was all buzzed up and ready to ride, speeding on four cups of black coffee. I rode and filled my tank, rode and filled my tank, stopped for a Big Mac, and rode and filled my tank until it was too dark and cold to ride. Just south of St. Louis, after fourteen hours on the bike, I pulled off the I-road, rolled up in my tent behind an abandoned gas station, and slept. I got back on the bike at 5:30 a.m., filled my tank, drank more coffee, rode my bike, ate a Big Mac, and rode like an express train.

Thirty-four hours after leaving New Orleans, I entered Wisconsin with $5 in my pocket and the 400 still running like a champ. I patted the side of the tank with my sunburned hand and said, "This is a very, very good motorcycle." The odometer showed just over 11,000 miles, or 3,000 more than I'd left with. I was burned out, punch-drunk, and traveling in a senseless state of tunnel vision from the long ride, but as I crossed the border I still managed to grin. My bike was running perfectly, I hadn't been issued a single traffic ticket, my bald rear tire was still holding air, I'd not met even one unpleasant person on the entire trip, despite vague and shadowy warnings to the contrary, and there had been, incredibly, no rain in seven days on the road. But, best of all, I knew that buried deep in my tank bag was a $2.85 pound of Louisiana French Roast chicory coffee, with a Wisconsin street value of nearly $6.

'SNOW PLACE FOR A MOTORCYCLE

Should a Norton Come Out of Hibernation at Winter's First Thaw?

THERE ARE CERTAIN REGIONS clearly delimited by Nature as off-limits to humans. They are places you shouldn't go, even on a bet, and most people are fairly adept at spotting them. A short list of examples might include: the north face of Everest during the monsoons, the Lake of the Woods in blackfly season, the Colorado River in spring flood, and, for the motorcyclist, Wisconsin highways in winter. You can go to those places if you wish, but only with the understanding that you go in harm's way, and that there are perfectly good reasons why nobody will be there when you arrive. Uninhabited zones, like pinnacles of success, tend to be lonely simply because everyone is off somewhere else having a good time.

These notions weighed heavily on my mind as I sped down the road on my 850 Commando, dodging knife-edged drifts on the plowed highway and watching angry snow clouds scud in from the northwest, a solid, fast-moving bank of leaden gray and purple. There were no other motorcycles on the road, and very few cars. It was hardly noon, and yet the streetlights with their photocells sensitive to the growing darkness were switching themselves on in the small towns. In the country, farmyard lights were blinking on. I wasn't sure whether it was the absence of light or of heat that set them glowing. The temperature had dropped about 1 degree per mile, as though synchronized with my odometer. It was growing dark and cold.

I knew, dumb frozen beast that I was, that as soon as my brain thawed out I would blame Wargula for this whole fiasco. It was Jim Wargula, an old college roommate, who had phoned me at 8:00 on a Saturday morning in March to see if I wanted to do some country roadracing. Jim lives 100 miles away, in Oshkosh—the city with the name that gets laughs in Catskill nightclubs.

"Get up, Egan," he said. "It's beautiful outside. I just went out to feed the dogs and discovered that a warm front is upon us. It must be 50 degrees out there. Spring is here! What do you say we blow the cosmoline out of the Nortons?" Jim and I had both bought Norton 850s, his red and mine black, in the last days of the empire when Norton was trying to recoup some capital by sell-ing Commandos for a song. We had reunions several times a year in which we met at some chosen place and then frightened ourselves all day on twisty back roads, dodging bullchips and farm dogs. Most of these rides took place in the summer, that magical time of year when you can see the ground.

Jim waited on the phone while I climbed out of bed and raised a window shade. As soon as I recovered from the sudden searing pain in my eyes, I could see that it was a bright, beautiful morning. The streets were wet with melting snow, and there was the sort of vaporous white haze in the air you see only on winter mornings that are unusually warm.

"Okay," I said. "I'll go for a ride. Where do you want to meet?"

"How about the A&W in Columbus," Jim suggested. "It's halfway between here and there, and it has an indoor restaurant. We can eat lunch and then go for a ride."

I made some coffee and then went downstairs into the dungeon that is our garage and basement to have a look at the Norton. It was in the corner, covered with a white sheet, like the furniture of the rich when they have left for the south of France. I bought the sheet, then couldn't afford the vacation. The bat-tery was out; the gas tank drained, I'm not prepared on short notice to ride in winter anymore. I've had too many close brushes with death-by-shivering. As a student I spent most of one winter commuting to class on a Honda CB160, and that experience taught me a lot of valuable lessons. I learned, for instance, that if you corner a motorcycle with bald tires fast enough on new-fallen snow it is possible to narrowly miss a skidding city bus and knock over three garbage cans filled exclusively with eggshells and grapefruit rinds while sustaining no injury more serious than a sprained thumb and a term paper on Kierkegaard ruined by slush. On a more metaphysical level, I discovered that hot tea is inherently Good, while cold wind represents a sort of Evil.

When I couldn't stand it any more I sold my 160 and bought a sports car—a 1959 Triumph TR3 with no side curtains and a hole the size of a cannonball in the otherwise opaque rear window of the convertible top. The Triumph, of course, was no warmer than the Honda, but since it never ran more than three minutes at a time I never had a chance to get really cold. Also, when you tapped the horn button the steering wheel began to smolder and melt, which added a touch of comfort in cold weather. The wiring harness finally burned up, and I sold the car for a tremendous profit and bought myself another bike: a 305 Super Hawk. By that time it was summer. I was done with winter riding for good.

I took the sheet off the Norton, dumped in a gallon of stale lawn-mower gas, strapped its trickle-charged battery back under the seat, and went upstairs to dress. I put on all the clothes I owned and then went down to the garage to get my waxed-cotton Belstaff jacket. My wife won't let me keep it in the regular coat closet because she says it smells like creosote. I wrapped a scarf around my face and buckled my helmet. The Norton's anemic electric starter went "dit," so I started the bike with just enough kicks to steam up my face shield with hot panting breath.

The streets in town were wet, but out on the highway the pavement was dry and clean, bleached bone white from three months of salting by the county road crews. I stopped at a gas station to fill my tank. "Beautiful day for a ride," the attendant said. "I heard we were supposed to get some snow, but it sure doesn't look like it now."

I agreed, a little uneasily, and remarked that I'd put on too many layers of clothes and actually felt too warm riding through town—unheard of in early March. I pulled out on the highway feeling good about the weather and happy to be back on my bike and going somewhere. The sun shone down on the fields and woods and the birds sang brightly on the telephone wires—or so I imagined, in the whistling isolation of my Star 120.

Then 10 miles down the road, a small shiver passed over my body. Not an actual, visible shudder, but the kind of shiver that is a more psychic than physical. The sun had gone behind a cloud. I turned and looked over my shoulder. Wrong. The sun had gone behind a lot of clouds. It had disappeared behind a textbook vision of the rolling cold front. A mass of dark winter clouds moved across the sky from the northwest like a giant focal-plane shutter. I shrugged; the air was still nice and warm. About 10 minutes later I plunged into one of those zones of sudden cold that are as vivid to a motorcyclist as a brick wall, or a border on a colored map. From red to blue, faster than you can say "brass monkey." I felt as though I'd dived into Lake Superior. In fifteen minutes the day had gone from benign to angry. I tucked my chin a little tighter into my collar and pressed on.

By the time I'd made the 50-mile trip to the A&W in Columbus it was dark and cold. The sky was a uniform turbulent nasty gray, and the lights from the restaurant had a warm orange glow. I walked in stiffly, knocking small icicles off my beard, and ordered a very large coffee. The waitress asked cheerfully, "Is that for here or to go?" I was too cold to be kind. I just looked at her and said, "You must be joking." I took the coffee back to a window table and waited for Wargula.

Motorcyclists in cold weather are always in a quandary over their speed. Should they ride fast and get it over with, enduring the ravages of high-speed wind, or should they ride slowly, prolonging a slightly less terrible agony?

Jim had chosen Slow Death. Coming down the highway his bike looked like one of those lone cavalry horses returning to the fort with a dead rider full of arrows slumped in its saddle, stopping here and there to nibble on sagebrush. I'd never seen Jim ride so slowly, or so stiffly. And I'd never seen a motorcycle turn a corner without leaning, but Jim did it as he pulled into the parking lot. He pulled to a stop and sat on his bike; just sat, not bothering to shut the engine off, as though he expected some kind of emergency ground crew to run out of the restaurant and lift him off his Commando. No help arrived, so he slowly reached for the key and turned it off. A minute later he tilted his head downward and began to look for the kickstand. A stiff robot leg caught the edge of the stand and kicked it out.

He swung his other leg over the bike, stood up, looked around to see where he was, and then walked toward the restaurant door with a ponderous I'm-so-cold-now-there's-no-need-to-hurry dignity.

He walked right past my table without looking at me and went to the counter. "Coffee," he said. The waitress started to ask if that was for here or to go, but something in his voice made her think the better of it. She quickly set out a large white Styrofoam cup with a plastic lid. Jim paid and walked over to my table. He sat down heavily, without speaking, and peeled the lid from his cup with a hand like a claw. He took a drink and looked darkly into the cup. I feared for a moment that he might dump the stuff over his head, or at least pour it down his boot. But he just warmed his hands over the steaming cup and looked at me, raising one eyebrow in a sudden show of levity.

"Been here long?" he asked.

"I can't tell yet."

Jim looked out the window. "Lovely weather. It looks like midnight."

"It's supposed to snow."

Jim nodded. "We better warm up and head for home. I don't want to spend the winter in this place." He looked around. "Even it if is warm."

It took us about two hours to warm up. We'd both quit smoking, but we bought a pack of Lucky Strikes out of the cigarette machine, just for old times, and smoked one after the other. (When you are cold enough, there is something ineffably charming about a glowing cigarette and great clouds of smoke.) Then we had some hamburgers and more coffee. We talked about motorcycles and summer and what it must be like to live in California and then had some more coffee. Snow flurries began to blow against the window. My watch said it was 2:00 in the afternoon, but the darkness of the sky made it seem much later. A light dusting of snow settled into the quilting pattern on our cycle seats and formed a wind-blown vee on the pavement around our tires. It was time to go, so we smoked another half a pack of cigarettes, drank some more coffee, and sloshed out the front door reeling from an overdose of caffeine and nicotine. Jim brushed off the seat, started his cycle with one kick—aided slightly by the electric starter—and closed his face shield. He waited until my bike was running, then held up his hand in a gesture disturbingly similar to a papal benediction. We put the bikes in gear and split off at the highway in opposite directions.

All of the cars had their headlights on and left swirling wakes of dry, hard snow that worked its way down the back of my neck and melted. I discovered in a very short time that I'd worn too many layers of clothes in the restaurant; I was a little on the warm and sweaty side. The wind made short work of the heat I'd brought with me, and soon I began to shake. I shook mildly at first, with a sort of high-pitched tuning-fork resonance, and then more heavily, my uncontrolled shuddering moving down the scale to roughly an open E, played on a bass guitar with a badly wound fourth string. It went from there to the kind of all-out jerking and twitching usually associated with wind-up toy monkeys that hop and play the cymbals at the same time. The rhythm began to feed into my handlebars, sending the bike into those deadly vibrations that warn of an upcoming tankslapper. I slowed down, got a grip on myself, and several miles down the road pulled into a roadside tavern. There I had a plastic cup of evil brown acidic fluid, which the bartender jokingly referred to as "coffee." I asked if I could have the remains of yesterday's *Milwaukee Journal*, which lay on the bar, and then retired to the men's room. I stuffed the want-ad and comic sections, respectively, down the pantlegs that covered my left and right thighs; two more pages went up around my calves and tucked into my boots, and the entire front page was spread across my chest, tucked into my belt, and buttoned into my shirt. I emerged from the men's room and crinkled my way stiffly out of the bar, to the momentary distraction of a row of bored farmers who were watching the halftime show of a Texas football game—broadcast from a mythical land where the grass is green, the sun shines, and the cheerleaders wear neither Belstaff jackets nor, as far as I could tell, newspapers stuffed in their undergarments.

I stepped out into the frozen North, mounted the bike carefully so as not to disturb my armor, and motored down the road. The snow, I noted, had taken a turn for the worse. The flakes grew steadily larger and began to stick to the road instead of blowing across it. My headlight shone into a billowing cloud of whiteness where the snow came at me in perfectly horizontal flight, parallel to the road, rather than falling from the sky. Headlights loomed in my mirror and a semi roared past and disappeared, heading into its own swirling snowstorm, leaving me blinded to the exact location of the highway. I slowed down to about 35 and then realized that my Norton and I would make a fine hood ornament for the next Peterbilt to catch us from the rear. I cranked it back up to 50, fish-tailing slightly on the slippery road. On a long sweeping curve the bike began a slow drift to the outside, dangerously close to the berm of the snow. I pulled in some opposite lock and stuck my foot out in a clumsy, half-speed parody of Dick Mann at the San Jose Mile. This move caused me to break out in perhaps the world's coldest sweat, so I slowed down again.

When the road straightened out I began to grin, as best I could, inside my scarf and helmet. It was the same self-deprecating grin I might use if I discovered that a con artist had tricked me out of my life's savings and stolen my car, taking my wife along as a willing hostage. Tricked again. Had. Lured from my snug house by the shabby promise of a warm day in winter, the flip side of a cold day in hell. I must have been crazy. I'd broken all my own rules; I'd gone to a place where I don't belong.

Going where you don't belong, I decided a long time ago, is the root of all misery and the soul of all adventure. For instance, if you jump out of an airplane and find that your parachute doesn't open, you realize very quickly that your problem is much more basic than a malfunctioning silk canopy; the real problem is that you are 5,000 feet off the ground and falling through space. That is, you are in a place where you don't belong. Or if you are a Formula One driver and you hit some oil in a very high-speed curve, say in the Karussel at Nürburgring, the problem is not so much that you've hit oil; the problem is that you are in a very fragile machine going 120 mph. You are—you guessed it—in a Place Where You Don't Belong. If you hadn't gone there you'd be home now. Everything would be all right. There are hundreds of other places where people don't belong; mountainsides in the Himalayas, foxholes in foreign countries, 13-foot sailboats in the mid-Atlantic, bars full of drunks, spying in the Kremlin, whorehouses, New York, milking rattlesnakes, hang-gliding off El Capitan, shrieking down Bray Hill on an OW-1, dodging bulls in Pamplona, consorting with minors, and so on. All wonderful adventures, but fraught with some degree of peril because you really shouldn't be there. You are more or less asking for it. And if you get it, not much sympathy will be forthcoming. You've gone by your own device to a place without mercy. Sometimes a motorcycle is a place where you don't belong. Like in the winter, when the first good blizzard of the year blows out of the northwest and clogs the road with drifts of blinding snow. Sometimes you find yourself in a place where you don't belong not because you are adventurous, but because you haven't got the sense God gave a chipmunk. Because you are, in the words of my third-grade teacher, a silly goose. And, yes, because you are dumb as a stump.

A four-wheel-drive Bronco sped easily past me. Two children in the back watched me wide-eyed and then waved. I waved back by cautiously lifting a couple of my fingers from the grips. The children suddenly turned away and made animated gestures of conversation with their father, who was driving. I couldn't hear the conversation, but I knew what they were saying. (Daddy, what does "cretin" mean?)

The road was ridiculous. A solid layer of snow now blanketed the pavement, except where the strongest wind swept across it. Drifts were forming at a diagonal to the centerline. My front tire began to turn more slowly than the rear; it was only a matter of time until the front fender jammed with ice and snow and set technology back ten thousand years by turning my wheel into a skid—or a runner. A restaurant billboard told me that I was still 5 miles from town, and I suddenly had to ask myself, "Is it possible to go any farther?"

"No," said a voice that I barely recognized as my own, but was nevertheless glad to hear. "Dump this two-wheeled deathtrap somewhere and thumb it home."

Just then, like a mirage in a frozen Sahara, there appeared a lighted building on the roadside. It was a turquoise steel building in the middle of nowhere (i.e., just west of Sun Prairie, Wisconsin) with big display windows across the front and a giant yellow Yamaha sign shining like a star in the east out of the snowy darkness. "Thank God for tin buildings and giant international corporations," I mumbled to myself, punching my left turn signal switch with a remote, frozen appendage I recognized as my left thumb.

When I walked inside two men and a boy in fluorescent orange deer-hunting hats and open galoshes were trying to trade in a purple snowmobile with a leopard-skin seat, bargaining with a salesman in a camouflaged duck-hunting hat and open galoshes. Each of the four had one foot on the snowmobile in question. The salesman smiled and said, "Hell of a day for bikes! We're supposed to get fifteen inches tonight. I suppose you come in here to buy a set of chains for that thing!"

"Snow tires, prob'ly," one of the men said, and we all had a good laugh. Then I asked if they had winter storage space for motorcycles.

"You bet. Five bucks a month. Pay when you pick it up. Bring it around back."

I pushed the Norton around to the rear of the building while the salesman opened an electric overhead garage door. It was a dark, cold warehouse-style room with maybe one hundred bikes jammed in tank to tank. A winter tomb for the two-wheeled undead; consecrated earth in a Dracula's castle of slumbering bikes who only come out when it's warm. The salesman looked over the sea of mirrors and handlebars and finally found an open space. I shut off the fuel, wiped the bike down with a rag, and eased the Norton into a slot between a Honda 305 Dream with a duct-tape seat and a full-dress Yamaha 200 Electric Start with ape-hangers and a backrest that somehow reminded me of the monogrammed aluminum screen door on my neighbor's house. The Norton looked lost in the vast stygian chaos of bikes, and I felt a tinge of regret when the lights went out and the garage door came down; it was like leaving my dog at the kennels. But blizzards were Nature's way of telling you to park your bike.

I told the salesman I'd be back on the first warm day of spring, then trudged out to the highway to hitch a ride. It was snowing harder, and the flakes were coming down the size of small paper plates. The wind was really blowing now. The headlights of passing cars were nothing but soft globes of whiteness in the swirling snow. The third car to pass suddenly locked up his tires and stopped just down the road. I ran up and got in. A young man was driving. He had hangers in the back window and looked like a college student.

"Terrible time to be out hitchhiking," he said. "How did you ever end up way out here?"

"I rode my motorcycle," I said.

The smile froze on his face and he cast a sidelong glance at my clothes and the helmet in my lap. He laughed, a little uneasily. It was the same reaction you get if you tell people you've just arrived from the planet Mongo. With a more subdued and cautious voice he asked, "Where are you headed?"

"Home," I said, savoring the word and thinking about a steaming hot shower, "where I belong."

DOWN THE ROAD AGAIN

Life Can't Pass You by as Long as There Are Triumphs

THE RAIN CAME DOWN IN SOLID SHEETS, like one of those B-movie monsoons where you suspect they're dumping a watering can in front of the lens. It was the kind of downpour a friend of mine from Texas calls a toadstrangler. Barb and I were waiting it out in an abandoned barn along the road, standing one foot back from the door, perfectly dry. We'd seen the storm coming. Our motorcycle was parked behind us, still making hard plinking sounds as it cooled. The barn smelled like pigeons and burlap dust.

The sky didn't promise any sudden change, so we sat down in a corner of the barn and leaned back against the wall. I took a cigarette from the bent, crumbling pack that stays in my Barbour suit for just such occasions and settled back for a long gaze at the motorcycle. I didn't care if it rained all day; I never got tired of looking at the bike.

It was a 1967 Triumph Bonneville, burgundy in color, on its maiden post-restoration voyage. We were traveling to a country-blues festival in a little Wisconsin town called Arena. Muddy Waters, Luther Allison, and the Ozark Mountain Daredevils were supposed to be there. The radio had been plugging the concert for weeks. Mass quantities of beer and bratwurst were promised. It all sounded good, but for me the trip was more than just a chance to sit on a grassy hillside, snacking and listening to music. It was the fulfillment of a half-forgotten, leftover dream. And, in some twisted sense, a small private revenge on the likes of Melvin Laird, and a couple of ex-presidents to boot.

Just ten years late, a mere decade out of sync with the mainstream of American culture, I was finally going to a music festival on a Triumph motorcycle. It had been, in the immortal words of David Crosby, a long time coming.

It started in the late 1960s, when I was languishing in college. Back in those days I thought that the three finest things in the world were a Nikon camera, a Martin guitar, and a Triumph motorcycle. (I was trying hard to shun materialism but hadn't quite got the hang of it.) I was certain that if you could latch on to those three items your earthly needs would be forever complete. Sure, you might need some clothes, a place to sleep, an occasional meal, and a few Jack Kerouac novels, but those were all minor, secondary considerations.

In this simple material hierarchy the Triumph was important above everything. It allowed you to go to all the right places where you could take pictures with the Nikon and play your Martin guitar, and to properly punctuate those arrivals and exits with a certain romantic flair. It was also important just because it was a Triumph, the best-handling, best-looking all-around motorcycle an enthusiast could buy. The machine was a cultural legend.

Everyone who knew anything seemed to have a Triumph. Dylan appeared on the cover of *Highway 61* wearing a Triumph T-shirt and was reputed in whispers of the rock grapevine to have been riding a Triumph 500 at the time of his reportedly terrible, possibly disfiguring accident near Woodstock (?) that may or may not have nearly killed him and ended his career. Arlo Guthrie sat astride a Triumph on the cover of *Running Down the Road*, and everyone knew that when Arlo said he didn't want a pickle but just wanted to ride his motorsickle, he was talking about his big Twin. Steve McQueen made the national magazines desert-sledding his 650, and even on the screen he chose a thinly disguised Wehrmacht-gray Triumph for his Great Escape (you could hardly expect him to jump a ten-foot fence into Switzerland riding a BMW and sidecar with armor plate).

In the real world of competition and road riding, Triumphs were the universal motorcycles of the 1960s. They were expected to go everywhere and do everything well, just as today's roadburners are not. They won at desert races, flat tracks, enduros, TTs, Bonneville, and Daytona. The great names—Nixon, Elmore, Romero, Castro, and dozens of others—all wore leathers emblazoned with that swooping Triumph emblem.

With minor changes in pipes, handlebars, carbs, and gearing, the 500s and 650s could be set up for any purpose. An ordinary, everyday owner expected to be able to use his bike for touring, cowtrailing, stoplight drags, or suddenly peeling off a country road to tear across some farmer's field of new-mown hay. Triumphs were not generally transported in pickup trucks; riding started from your garage.

If you had a garage. Or a Triumph. Which I did not.

I had a Honda CB160. I didn't have a Nikon or a Martin, either. Just a secondhand twin-lens-reflex camera and a $50 Harmony guitar. I was attending the university and sharing a student-dive apartment with three roommates who did their dishes once a week with a can of Raid. Those were wonderful times. We all lived in a world of gray underwear because we didn't sort colors from whites at the laundromat, and we thought chivalry was hiding old pizza cartons under the sofa when someone's girlfriend came for the weekend. Every night, about 9:00, the police cruised by and shot a tear-gas canister onto the front porch, just as a warning.

Next to the typewriter on my desk was a coffee can with a slot in the top, marked "Triumph Fund." I was working nights unloading trucks at the Coca-Cola bottling plant and setting aside a share of those earnings for a new cycle. Any Triumph would have been acceptable, but I had settled on a Competition Tiger 500, not only because it was the cheapest of the line, but because it looked like the most versatile. It had a single carb and ET ignition, which I imagined would make it easier to tune, and a 500 seemed like a sensible step between my 160 and the ultimate purchase, a Bonneville.

But even a 500 cost over a $1,000, which represented a lot of truckloads of Coke bottles in those pioneer days of inflation, and somehow the Triumph fund never grew large enough for even a respectable down payment. It was always being robbed for tuition or going to see Blow-Up for the fifth time. One of my roommates was also working at the Coke plant and saving for a Triumph, with about the same success. The idea was we would buy a pair of them, at some tremendous volume discount, and then take the Ideal Trip to some rock festival or other celebration against doom. We worked and saved, unloaded bottles and calculated profits, but never seemed to gain much financial ground.

Then one day my roommate got lucky. He showed up in the driveway on a nice blue-and-white T100R; a Daytona. He'd got an absolutely incredible deal on the bike. He bought it from a fraternity boy who had flunked out and was selling off all his luxuries—cowboy boots, Head skis, Four Tops albums, stolen beer steins, etc.—in that timeless ritual of prodigal sons everywhere who return home dishonored and humble. My roommate paid the poor guy just enough for some sackcloth and ashes and a bus ticket east.

The Daytona was put to hard use. In the months that followed it made dozens of flat-out runs between Madison and Chicago. My roommate, after a heated phone call with his sometime-girlfriend, would slam down the receiver, hop on his bike, and dash off to Chicago in the middle of the night. When he got there he'd pound on her apartment door and have a terrible fight in the hallway, then ride back home at high speed, arriving at our apartment in the early hours of the morning, completely worn out and looking like frozen Death. Then he'd crash into bed, still wearing his boots and leather jacket, and sleep for about two days.

Nothing quite so dramatic was possible on my Honda 160. You could get to Chicago and back with no problem, but the 160 was missing an element of passion and fire-breathing style that only a raucous British Twin could deliver. The Triumph was good theater; it was made for the dashing arrival and the bellowing, angry departure. When you left on one people were supposed to watch you shift off into the distance and think, "That guy's out there somewhere on a Triumph now. I hope he's all right . . ." If you rode a 160 they just assumed you were fine, which was no fun at all.

The money never fell together for a Triumph. School ended and a slightly desiccated lady at the draft board branded me US Choice. Most of the next two years were spent perspiring, carrying a radio around on my back, and driving a Jeep down tropical roads clogged with Honda 50s and 90s. We all went on a lot of neat hikes and cookouts. It was fascinating, but we missed things that were happening at home and had to enjoy them vicariously through letters and movies. *Woodstock* and *Alice's Restaurant* came to camp and were projected on the side of a reinforced concrete latrine with a sandbag roof. (Odd concept, the rocket-proof latrine; even odder when you're in one and Hendrix is playing his unearthly version of the "The Star Spangled Banner" on the other side of the wall.)

My ex-roommate kept in touch with letters and told exotic tales of dry socks, air conditioning, and riding his Triumph on country roads—and going to Chicago. He also sent along a color brochure of the new Trophy 650 for 1970, a nice green bike with high double pipes. The brochure was carried around until it finally broke in half from being folded and refolded. Whenever I got the chance I'd sit down to look at the Triumph picture and reflect on the merits of being out of the army. It was during those idle moments that the vision gradually formed; a single enduring image that seemed to embrace everything good about civilian life. It came as a recurring dream. It was a scenario in which I was on a motorcycle trip, going it-didn't-matter-where, dressed in clean civilian clothes of my own choosing and seated at a roadside restaurant, drinking coffee and looking out the window at a Triumph motorcycle. That was it; nothing more than a simple daydream. An American still life waiting to happen.

But it was winter when I got home, so I bought a car with a heater and snow tires and went back to school. By the time there was money for another cycle the Triumph plant was closed with labor and management problems, British bikes had been eclipsed by new Japanese offerings, and I was lured away by a fast, reliable machine with a lot of cylinders and exhaust pipes. There was no more Triumph fund, and the notion of owning one was allowed to simmer on a back burner. I'd bought a Nikon camera by then, but still didn't own a Martin guitar because you have to play well to deserve one. The Harmless Seventies slipped by, various bikes were bought and sold, and Triumphs became something admired from afar and regarded wistfully when seen on the street.

Then last summer I took a weekend motorcycle trip. While passing through a little unmapped bar-and-gas-pump village I spotted an old and very ratty Bonneville leaning on the wall of a defunct garage. I inquired after the bike at some nearby houses, but no one was home. The bar and gas station were closed. I left reluctantly and continued the trip, but all through the next winter visions, of that neglected, weatherbeaten Bonneville caused me to toss in my sleep, eat poorly, and lose weight. There were troubled dreams of an old garage with a giant snowdrift blown up against the wall and nothing sticking out of it but a chromed clutch lever.

In spring I returned to the village. The bike was still there, though it appeared to have been used—the carbs dripped gas and the chaincase was streaked with fresh oil. An old woman was in her yard nearby, watering some flowers clumped around a little windmill. The windmill had a crank and rod arrangement that caused a small wooden lumberjack to drag a saw back and forth over a log. She directed me to the farm of the Bonnneville owner, some 2 miles away, and said the man ran a sawmill. Sawing wood was a big industry in the village.

I found the man ripping through some logs at his mill. He shut down the saw to talk to me. Yes, he was interested in selling the bike. Property taxes were coming up. He wanted a lot of money for the Triumph and was not interested in taking less; the bike was worth it, he said. He was right, of course. You don't find country folks anymore who have old vehicles and don't know their value—if you ever did. On the contrary, there are farmers who think a Studebaker Lark is worth money. But the myth of the $50 Henderson covered with hay bales is right up there with Babe the Blue Ox.

We went back to the village, and I took the Triumph for a test ride. Every-thing was loose, but the bike ran fine. So after a moment of silence for my life's savings, I swallowed hard and wrote out a check. We were only 25 miles from the city, so I decided to live dangerously and ride the Bonneville home. Barb drove our Volkswagen. "Follow me, but keep your distance," I advised. "Watch for falling parts and blink your lights if you run over anything."

The trip home was my first ride on a Bonneville. As I motored along those country roads the bike struck me as a great bundle of conflict and paradox. It vibrated and surged annoyingly through town in lower gears, but you could drop it into fourth and rumble along on the idle circuit with no commotion at all. And at full chat (a foreign term peculiar to the sound and feel of British bikes) it smoothed out into a rushing, headlong resonance no more disturbing than the clicking of rails on a fast passenger train. The brakes were terrible, but every time I dived into a corner at unchecked, suicidal speed I discovered there was no cause for alarm; the Triumph heeled over into an easy arc and came out of the corner without flinching. The hand and foot controls felt crude and antique after the velvet-and-Teflon smoothness of those on my Japanese Four, yet the performance of the bike was anything but antique. The speedometer needle touched a surprisingly easy 105 mph as I moved out to put some dis-tance on a gravel-tossing milk tanker. The Bonneville tracked down the road with an uncanny, almost gyroscopic stability at that speed, encouraging you to go faster than twelve-year-old maladjusted engines full of dirty old oil ought to go. I got a firm grip on my enthusiasm, slowed down, and made it home without blowing the thing up.

Most modern Triumph dealers now handle another line of bikes and sell new models and parts on an order-only basis. But in our small city I found no fewer than four repair shops who welcomed Triumph work and stocked bins of new and used parts. In a few trips I dug up the appropriate tank emblems (missing on mine), primary and drive chains, gaskets, fork seals, gaitors, cables, tune-up parts, and miscellaneous Whitworth nuts and bolts whose standard of measure is the instep of some dead king or the distance between two ale-houses; I can't remember which. The rear tire was replaced with a K-81 Dunlop I had lying around, but it didn't look right. Only the original K-70 had the necessary bulk to fill that roomy fender

well, so I bought a new one. The front got a new 19-inch ribbed Continental because it looked nearly authentic and someone gave it to me.

Original tank kneepads were unavailable and long gone everywhere I checked. ("If you find any, let me know where you got 'em.") No one had a paint code for a 1967 Bonneville or knew where I might find one. A magazine out of my 1967 archives showed a dark burgundy tank, a color described as "Aubergine," with white and gold trim, and I finally found a very close match with (*Gott in Himmel*) a Mercedes Medium Red. The tank looked good in a solid color, so I decided not to spoil it by trying my hand at white accent lines and gold pinstripe to match the old photos.

Stripping the tank and sidecovers for painting rivaled the labors of Schliemann unearthing the layered ruins of Troy. The paint revealed a varied past. Beneath the outer coat of flat-black primer was a thick layer of metalflake blue, and under that white metalflake with the understated elegance of a sequined bowling shirt. Then came a Kalifornia Kandy–apple red overlaid with green pinstripe patterns of trapezoids and triangles with the artist's initials, "J.R.," at the bottom. ("That's Joe Rembrandt," my friend Wargula pronounced without hesitation. "Sam Picasso's cousin.")

And on the bottom coat, painted into the original lacquer at the corner of each sidecover, was a small white peace emblem.

In three weeks of weekend and late-night fanaticism the Triumph was ready to roll. With the mechanicals refurbished and the paint nearly dry, we rolled down the driveway and turned west, in the general direction of the country-blues festival. The trip was to be a 300-mile meandering backcountry ride that would allow us to visit some friends on a farm, hit the festival, and then circle home. The tank was too wet for a tank bag, and a luggage rack was aesthetically out of the question, so we left with our pockets bulging and clanking. Just to be safe, we took enough tools and spares to do a major roadside overhaul; everything but a frame jig and crankshaft lathe.

We made it to the end of the block before the Triumph stopped running. The tach cable had pushed the hot wire off the ignition switch. No problem. I rerouted the wire, plugged it in, and we were on our way.

Just out of town I smelled gasoline and pulled off the road. We were suffering from that dreaded British ailment, Petcock Failure. The brass flare nut was cracked and fuel was hissing onto the hot exhaust. I pulled a tube of silicone sealer and a 7/16 Whitworth from my coat pocket, made an instant O-ring, and everything was fine.

There were no other problems on the rest of the trip. The big twin thundered serenely along twisting valleys, up and down hills, and across bridges without missing a beat. And at one point it absolutely blew the doors off a rallye-equipped Scirocco when the driver foolishly tried to race with us, apparently believing that a pathetic 90 mph would keep us in his dust. "So long, pal," I said, tossing off a Lafayette Escadrille wave as the car became a dancing speck in our mirrors. "This bike had your name on it."

The Triumph was made for fast, winding country roads. At right around 70 mph it came into its own and maintained the pace easily, backing down from only the worst curves. I didn't know if it was any faster than my Multi, but it certainly had more grace under pressure. We reached our friends' farm in two euphoric hours; record time. We had a nice evening on the farm, eating, drinking, playing guitars, patting dogs on the head, and examining horses.

The sky was threatening rain when we left early in the morning and headed south for the music festival. Around 10:00 the air became suddenly cool, and the wind dropped off to a deathly stillness that could be sensed even on a motorcycle. We got to the old barn just before the storm landed.

The old Bonneville was a pleasant object to contemplate on a rainy day—or any other time. It provoked a bad case of XKE Syndrome; impossible to park and walk away from without looking back over your shoulder. It was a simple, clean design with all its elements in harmony. I never looked at it and thought, "Nice bike, except for the gas tank," or "I'd buy one if I could throw the seat and mufflers away." I couldn't find an offensive piece or a jarring transition of line anywhere on the motorcycle. It seemed, like the DC-3 or the Winchester saddle gun, to be the final product and distillation of everything learned about balance and proportion in the era that preceeded it. Its lines were, as Saint-Exupéry once said of a favorite aircraft, not invented but simply discovered.

Owners of more modern bikes often commented that you could "see through" the Triumph, or "see what all the parts are for." The starkness and simplicity fostering that impression translate into a unique road feel. At 363 pounds the Bonneville is light for a 650 and carries its weight low in the frame, so that the roll axis of the bike feels to be between your ankles rather than sloshing and lost somewhere in the gas tank. It gives you the odd, anachronistic sensation you are riding a motorbike—a genuine motorized bicycle; a Schwinn paperboy special with a big hairy engine bolted into the frame—rather than a two-wheeled transportation module. Perhaps the heart of the Triumph's appeal lies in the subconscious feeling of eternal wonderment that you are hurtling down the road without having to pedal.

The 1967 Bonneville's big advantage, of course, is that it was built just before unelected public servants got into vehicle design. So the Triumph has a front fork unburdened by turn signals, beepers, reflectors, timers, dashboards, and idiot lights, which makes the steering light and precise. The taillight, though visible at night, is smaller than a breadbox, and the shift lever is on the right because, by God, that's where the transmission is. The muffler muffles without strangling (silencer, the British term, is an exaggeration), and the engine has no emission controls to help motorcyclists atone for the past sins of Eldorado owners.

But like all machines of character, the Triumph had a few spanners designed into its venerable works. By modern standards, it is not a perfect motorcycle. It suffers from medieval wiring (though at least repairable by anyone with a basic waterpipe concept of electrical flow), an engine with all the well-documented vibratory failings of the vertical twin, and brakes that make reversing the props on the *Queen Mary* or recalling the Three Hundred from the Valley of Death seem quick and positive. The clutch plates like to stick together on cool mornings (below 80 degrees Farhenheit), though they can be freed by bumping the bike or jabbing the kick starter with the clutch out. The carbs are sensitive to lean angle and engine heat, and they wear out from their own jittering. (To compensate for carb problems, however, the factory always listed thousands of needle and jet options to help in your personal search for the rhythmic tickover and the light-chocolate electrode.)

The rear wheel is installed so that suicide seems a rational alternative to changing a roadside flat (improved, like most of these problems, on later models). And then, of course, the carbs, petcocks, and gaskets tend to seep, further reinforcing a popular belief that the British should never have been allowed to handle any fluid less viscous than chilled window putty.

But I knew all these things when I bought the bike. I didn't expect mechanical perfection. If I wanted that, there were plenty of other motorcycles to choose from; machines like Interstate highways—much better than the old roads, but not always as interesting. The Triumph was no four-lane Interstate. It was a twisting country lane with potholes, loose gravel, one-lane bridges, and switchbacks. And old barns.

The rain ended just before noon. The clouds parted, and a shaft of sunlight streamed through the open barn door onto the motorcycle, like some heavenly message from a Charlton Heston epic. The Triumph started, as always, halfway through the first kick, and we were on the road again.

The first band had just begun to play when we arrived at the festival. I parked the Triumph under a tree, between a KZ1300 and a GS1000, and we found a comfortable spot to sit on the hillside not far from the stage. We got something to eat and drink and sat back in the sun.

Festivals haven't changed so much in ten or twelve years, I decided. True, Ken Kesey and the Hog Farm didn't show, Canned Heat was absent, and the Airplane was off somewhere being a Starship. But there was a dog who wore a red bandana and caught Frisbees in midair; a band of jugglers who juggled nonstop all afternoon and evening; a pioneer couple whose blond children ran naked around a VW bus, a smattering of outlaws, a girl who wore a rose in her hat and blew soap bubbles that floated away in the wind, a lone flute player oblivious to the music coming from the stage, a tanned, aging man with a ponytail who did yoga beneath a tree, and a girl in a long dress who danced near the stage by spinning around and around with her arms floating outward until she fell down. We sat next to a man with a wispy satyr beard who smoked a small brass pipe and offered it to everyone who passed, or sat next to him.

With the last rays of the sun slanting through the low cloud of blue smoke and dust that only a crowd of several thousand can raise, Luther Allison offered his last song to the memory of Jimi Hendrix and played a half-hour low-down version of "Little Red Rooster."

We headed home at dusk and rode into darkness. A fog settled on the river valley, and droplets of water formed on my face shield and gloves and blew to the side. The headlights of cars were yellow and vague in the mist, a nice touch at the end of a day in bright sunlight. Halfway home we stopped at a roadside restaurant for a late dinner. We sat at a window booth where I could look out at the Triumph and sip coffee.

We sat in silence for a while, and then Barb asked, "What are you thinking?"

"I was just thinking," I said, "That riding well is the best revenge."

A lady in the next booth overheard me and snickered, then began to cough and choke on her Bacon-Burger Deluxe. When that was over, she turned in her seat for a look at the person who had uttered this wonderful truth. I stared back and she returned to her dinner. She'd get no apologies from me. I was dead serious.

When we got home I picked up my guitar and started to plunk around on it, running through my cheating, half-the-hard-stuff-missing version of "Little Red Rooster." In the end I sat up half the night practicing. I figured maybe if I got good enough I'd finally deserve a Martin guitar. Then I'd have everything I needed.

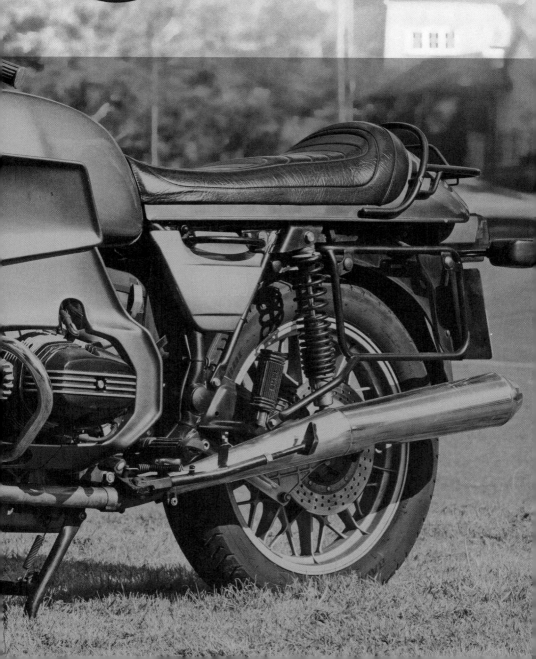

LOST HIGHWAY: IN SEARCH OF OLD 66

"**Y**OU ARE GOING TO BE** mighty disappointed," our friend John told us. "There is no such thing as Route 66. Not anymore. I've been out to California and back twice, and 66 is gone. Nonexistent. Finished. It is an ex-highway. It's called Interstate 40 now. Four big lanes nearly all the way from Chicago to L.A."

"Gone?" I rolled one fearful, suspicious eye in John's direction, doing my best impression of Jack Elam acting incredulous.

"How in thunder can 2,500 miles of the most famous road in America be gone?"

"Okay. Maybe there are still a couple of places in Arizona or New Mexico where I-40 bypasses part of the old road, but the rest is pretty much paved over."

I was stunned. Route 66 gone? Paved over and renamed? It was like planning a raft trip down the Mississippi and being told the river was all dried up. Nothing but a dusty riverbed full of catfish skeletons and old tires. Impossible. I'd wanted to take a motorcycle trip out on Route 66 to California ever since my budding passion for bikes had collided head-on with a TV program named after the highway. Two guys named Tod and Buz started it all.

They appeared one evening two decades ago on the black-and-white snowstorm of my parents' 12-inch TV screen. It was a new program with an unusual premise. It seemed these two single guys had bought a Corvette and set out to work their way across the country. They were searching for something but didn't know what. Every time they cruised into some dusty little town they found jobs driving forklifts at the plant or erecting oil rigs. They inevitably got tangled up with some menacing local types who were dragging their knuckles around and looking for trouble, and usually there was a wistful young (but aging fast) woman who worked at the diner, waiting for someone to take her away from it all. In the end Tod and Buz always left town a little wiser but still searching, alone in their Corvette on Route 66.

Stirling Silliphant wrote most of the fine, hard-hitting scripts, and the music by Nelson Riddle had a jazzy, spirit-of-the-open-road kind of sound. The Corvette, the lost women, the music, the freedom . . . it was a heady combination to a twelve-year-old who was, at any given moment, in hot water with his parents for not raking the lawn or painting the other half of the garage door.

A few years later, when I got so I could read without moving my lips, I discovered John Steinbeck and read *The Grapes of Wrath*. This story traced the misadventures of the Joad family, a clan of Dust Bowl farmers, from their ruined Oklahoma homestead to a supposedly better life in California. They suffered every setback a long journey can dish out to folks without enough money. Route 66 in the 1930s was the setting, and Steinbeck described the two-lane road and its towns, car lots, and roadside camps so well the Joad family and the highway itself became American institutions.

By 1965 I'd become an R & B fan, listening to Chuck Berry and the Rolling Stones belt out their own versions of Bobby Troup's much-recorded song, "Route 66." "Well it winds from Chicago to L.A., more than two thousand miles all the way . . . well get your kicks on Route 66 . . ." That was enough for me. I'd seen the TV program, read the book, and now my record player was driving the message home. It was clear no self-respecting person could call himself an American if he hadn't checked out this fabled highway. Route 66, the pipeline to California, path to the Promised Land, was a fixture in the American consciousness as surely as the Mississippi River, the Natchez Trace, Pennsylvania Avenue, Main Street, and Sunset Strip.

It was the kind of trip, sooner or later, you have to make. Especially if you are a motorcyclist and always looking for a good reason to travel. Or in my case even a fairly mediocre reason of practically no discernable consequence or socially redeeming value.

The opportunity came last summer. Editor Girdler dispatched a Suzuki GS1000 to cover the Winston Pro races at Elkhart Lake in my home state of Wisconsin and asked if I would ride the bike. My wife, Barbara, could go along for the ride. The plan was this: take the most direct northerly Interstate east, making all due speed with a Gypsy Scout radar detector scanning for cops; cover the races and then make a more leisurely return trip on Route 66.

Borrowing from our stock of items to evaluate we outfitted the GS with a Silhouette fairing, a Lockhart luggage rack, a clip-on Tourmaster rack bag, my old eclipse tank bag, and a nice set of low Superbike bars I carry around and bolt on to every bike I ride. The GS1000, with 3,000 miles on the odometer, got an oil change and plugs. We made it to Wisconsin in three days on the Interstate and got one speeding ticket, $50 worth, at a speed trap near Denver. It was a visual speed trap—no radar—where they time your progress between two stationary objects. They said we were making too much progress.

We averaged 85 mph for the trip. The radar detector saved us from at least a dozen other tickets in Iowa alone, which was literally crawling with police, all throwing out enough radar beams to fry an egg or raise your voice one octave. The GS1000 got 40 mpg and used 1 quart of oil and a small can of chain lube.

It was in Madison, Wisconsin, after the Elkhart races that our old friend John Oakey cast his rather large, hulking shadow on our return trip. "Dull," he pronounced. "Nothing but freeway and desert. I don't envy you."

The map indeed showed only a few small portions of road marked US 66. There were a few miles in Oklahoma parallel to I-40 west of Tulsa; a patch of incomplete I-road near Tucumcari, and a stretch that followed the Rio Grande south of Albuquerque. Arizona was most promising, with a big northern loop of old 66 bypassing the freeway from Ash Fork to Kingman.

There had to be more; maybe some small traces of the old road going through the small towns. There must be old motels, gas stations, and restaurants still intact near the four-lane. It couldn't all be torn down, hauled away, and gone. America covers its architectural tracks fast, but not that fast. The time was clearly ripe for another of those field trips in Contemporary Archaeology and the Study of Modern Antiquities, those same quasi-academic disciplines that search out and preserve Gene Vincent albums, 1959 Cadillac Coupes de Ville, unfiltered Camels, and jukeboxes that look like neon cathedrals.

We left Madison on a blistering hot Wednesday morning in June and headed down Highway 51 to pick up I-55 (a.k.a. US 66) at Bloomington, Illinois. We hit the Interstate just in time to join an accordion of cars following a black-and-white sedan from the Illinois State Patrol at 55 mph. Exactly 55 mph. We shifted down a gear and waited. There's something fairly pathetic about ten or twenty adults backed up and crawling along in orderly procession behind a squad car. It reminds me of following my fourth-grade teacher down the street on a class trip to the fire station. The patrol car finally eased itself down an exit ramp, and the tailpipe of every trailing car coughed out a sigh of relief and picked up speed. Barb and I rolled up to 65 mph, or about half speed for the Suzuki.

Route 66 caught us by surprise. We had mistakenly counted on the state map, which was reasonably detailed, to show any remaining sections of the old highway. There were none on the map, and I-55 travels nearly straight and level across Illinois, so we assumed the new road had been laid down over the old. Not so.

Just north of McLean, Illinois, Barb gave me a jab in the ribs and pointed to our right. There, cutting a narrow concrete swathe across meadows, through clumps of trees, and across creeks on small bridges, was an abandoned highway with tufts of grass growing between the slabs of patched pavement. It was clearly the one and only original Route 66 of song, novel, and television. One look and you knew it was the real thing.

We got off at the next exit and found a spot where the old highway crossed a country road. The intersection was unmarked: no stop signs, no manicured apron at the corner, no signs of any kind to say what the highway was; 66 was a Highway with No Name. You had to drop down over a low dirt shoulder from the country road even to get on it. The highway was just there; nameless and heading off inviting and empty through the rural countryside. We shut off the bike, removed our helmets, and sat for a few minutes looking down the road. There was no noise, just the wind through the trees, and it was somehow ghostly; the busiest road in America recently gone silent. You could almost hear the fading echo of a 327 Corvette rumbling off into the distance.

We put on our helmets and headed southwest.

The old road was in remarkably good shape despite weeds, grass, wild oats, and the occasional sapling growing up through the seams. The concrete slabs were solid, showed little weather damage, and were in relatively good alignment. The road was made from thousands of squares of white concrete laid end to end and joined with small strips of black tar. In a few places the broken white and solid yellow lines were still visible, but most of the paint was weathered away.

We started cruising tentatively, watching for chuckholes and broken glass, but soon found the road clean and smooth enough for normal speeds. After twenty minutes we were cruising at 70 or 75 mph, or anything we felt like. The highway was like a science-fiction dream; a scene from one of those postnuclear novels where a few people find themselves alone on an empty earth; a road of your own, a fast motorcycle, and nothing to slow you down.

Almost nothing. True to the Last Inhabitant fantasy, the only risk came from animals. Conditioned to an unused road, they'd grown bold around the pavement, living, hunting, and nesting and generally carrying on as animals will in the long grass beside the highway. The dipping, erratic flight of roadside blackbirds had Barb gripping my sides as they narrowly missed our windscreen. Rabbits, chipmunks, strolling pheasants, and something that looked vaguely like a mud hen were all stirred up by the passing commotion of our big Suzuki. Uncomfortable with my sudden role as bull in Nature's own china shop and general despoiler of woodland tranquility, I backed off on the throttle.

None too soon either. We crested a rise, and I clamped on the brakes. The highway had ended. The road was cut off by a black-and-white striped barrier and then disappeared under the soil of a cornfield. Ahead was a high embankment formed by an exit ramp from the nearby I-road. Short of jumping the barrier and plowing corn for 50 yards with the Suzuki, there was nothing to be done. We turned reluctantly around and backtracked for 5 miles to the last entrance ramp, climbed onto the Interstate, returned 5 miles, and took the very exit ramp that had blocked our path. On the other side of the cloverleaf we were able to dirt track our way onto old 66 again.

The scene was repeated over and over again. Route 66 ran roughly parallel to I-55, and each time I-55 threw off an exit ramp 66 ended. Sometimes you could play dirt bike, go around the barrier and cross the exit ramp to the other side, where 66 resumed; sometimes there was a dirt-road detour off the old highway, especially near small towns, so you could circle around the exit; and sometimes, most of the time, you just had to go back 5 or 10 miles and get on the Interstate. A dirt bike with knobbies and a pair of wire cutters might have helped, but not always. Particularly in one spot, where a washed-out bridge had been left washed out.

At every chance we left the freeway and traveled down the boxed-in sections of old 66, genuinely resenting having to mingle with the vacationing boat-towing masses on the four-lane. Sixty-Six was never very far from the Interstate, but it was close enough to farmhouses and trees that it could be said to go through the country rather than over it. Its curves and hills followed the topography of the land, and the roadcuts were small. The bridges, smaller and more elegant, were built as overhead trestles or as reinforced cement work and craftsmanship lost on public works since the days of the WPA. Depression bridges were best.

We had hoped 66 would take us through a lot of small towns, but found we couldn't count on it. Even back in the old days 66 was a fast road. It went past a lot of towns rather than through them, affording only a passing, sidelong glance down the main streets of small farm communities on the roadside. You could go into the towns but you had to want to. It was a road in a hurry that paralleled the railroad tracks and didn't dump you off in every burg and speed trap from Chicago to L.A. Which is why our highway ended so often at exit ramps instead of taking us into town.

An exception was McLean, Illinois, where 66 brought us right up to the front door of the Dixie Trucker's Home, a truck stop and restaurant recommended in *RoadFood*. *RoadFood* is a guidebook that lists and describes eating spots deemed worthy of the cross-country traveler's patronage. It said the Dixie Trucker's Home had, among other things, good fried chicken. The truck stop was crowded and busy, one of those gleaming-clean places where you could eat off the floor, as my grandmother used to say, but they had plenty of tables and plates and we didn't have to. The chicken was very good.

We followed 66 wherever possible through the afternoon and rode into a warm, soft summer evening in Lincoln. It was just sundown, and baseball diamond lights came on brilliantly as we passed the city park. A drive-in theater along the highway began its show, and we caught a glimpse of the wordless previews to *The Long Riders*; much noiseless shooting, smoke, and commotion going on. We decided to press on a few hours longer to Springfield. After a hot day the merely warm evening felt so good we hated to give it up.

After a 5-mile stretch of old 66 and another sudden dead end, we chose to ride on I-55. The strain of watching for barriers, broken glass, and red animal eyes on the deserted highway took too much concentration at the end of a 500-mile day. We stopped for the night in Springfield, Lincoln's hometown, at one of those budget (read: cheap) motels with a dollar figure in its name, of which inflation has now made a mockery. The sign out front advertised "Good Rest, Sweet Dreams," a seductive promise. The rooms, balconies, and restaurant upholstery were mostly turquoise and orange, colors that somehow came to denote modernness in the late fifties. The painted cement-block construction and the colored-steel balcony panels with traces of rust gave the place the subtle flavor of a postwar barracks for officers in the New Army. We had good rest, but in the morning could recall no dreams.

We stayed on 66 all the way into St. Louis the next day, where the highway lost its identity somewhere in a maze of cloverleaf bridges and we found ourselves in a minor manufacturing district near the old Cahokia Indian Mounds. We got back on I-55 and crossed the Mississippi, past the big arch that is the Gateway to the West. The arch glinted golden in the noon sun. "I'm suddenly hungry for a hamburger," Barb remarked.

We stopped at a truck stop in St. Louis, a glaring, barren place with bright fluorescent lights. I had a perfectly square block of hash browns and a perfectly round hamburger dwarfed inside a perfectly round bun. A perfect meal.

In the beautiful rugged hill country west of St. Louis, Route 66 suddenly reappeared beside the main road, curving in and out of the woods and climbing hills beside the (now) I-44 roadcuts. It looked too inviting to wait for the next exit, so we just pulled off the Interstate and wallowed the big Suzuki down a rain gully and launched ourselves up onto the time-scarred pavement of 66 again.

Near Stanton, Missouri, we swept down through a wooded glen, rounded a hairpin turn at the bottom, and crested the next hill to find an amazing collection of old motels, all abandoned except for the Ozark Courts, where the restaurant had been turned into a home. We stopped to take a look around and a nicely dressed woman and her daughter came out from behind the motel to talk to us. The woman said she and her husband ran the restaurant for ten years before the Interstate came through in 1963. The motel closed, as did the others nearby, and the restaurant went broke. Her husband, she explained, now works at a McDonald's in Stanton.

"The place was really jumping back then, before they built I-44. We were open twenty-four hours a day, and the counter was always full. There was a bad stretch of road near here, though." She pointed east down the road. "That curvy section you just came through, where it goes downhill through the trees, that place caused a lot of accidents. People would cross the yellow line and hit head-on. Seems like there was an accident nearly every other night, especially when it got foggy down there. Must have been twenty, thirty people killed there over the years." She brushed a strand of hair out of her eyes and pointed to the traffic droning by in the distance on I-44. "That new road is a whole lot safer," she said quietly. "It was bound to come."

She wished us good luck and she and her daughter walked around to the back of the empty, windowless Ozark Courts. The restaurant in back had been converted into a very nice house, but from the front it was impossible to tell anyone lived there.

Central Missouri was Jesse James country. Competing signs wanted us to visit one of several true James Gang hideouts in the nearby river caves. By midafternoon the heat in Missouri was astounding, and the idea of hiding in a cave began to have a lot of appeal. We didn't know it at the time, but we were seeing the first weeks of one of the hottest, driest summers ever in the Southwest; a livestock killer. We stopped at the Windmill Restaurant near Stanton, a restaurant that really has a huge windmill (motor driven, in an odd twist of technology), and drank a few gallons of iced tea in the cool darkness of the place. When we left, the heat and sunlight hit us like a pail of white steam.

Wine-country signs for the Rosati Winery began to appear along the highway, so we stopped in the little town of St. James to buy some wine in celebration of our anniversary. A sporting-goods store advertised "Minnows, Worms, Packaged Goods." Not being all that fond of bait, we settled on Packaged Goods and bought a bottle of Rosati Concord.

In western Missouri old 66 had some trouble deciding which side of the Interstate it wanted, so we had to do some switching at overpasses and exits. Much of the road is still used as a sort of frontage road, or an alternative for local farmers who don't want to bother with the limited access of I-44, and the pavement is in good shape. The old concrete slabs have been paved over with a smooth salmon-colored tarmac of some kind. The road was unpatrolled, but we slowed down a few times when we found ourselves under scrutiny by state troopers on the nearby Interstate. The rest of the time it was an exhilarating high-speed roller coaster through the hills.

The Suzuki was hard to hold at low speeds. It cruised so smoothly and effortlessly at 90 mph and above that other speeds felt willfully slow. At around 75 mph the air behind the Silhouette fairing became almost still. We could hold high speeds without fluttering to death, and a pleasant sense of tranquility, almost a speed euphoria, set in. Above 80 we'd draw ourselves into a silent shell in all that motion, the engine and wind noise seeping past our earplugs with the sound of a bullet whine. High speed has a serenity of its own, a relaxed flow not found at lower velocities. And when the radar detector went off, as it did approaching one small town, it was like having a phonograph needle suddenly skate across the grooves of your favorite record. The spell was broken. You slow down to 55 and it feels like covered-wagon speed; you are sure you could hop off the bike and run alongside picking flowers. Climbing back to 90, you are always amazed at the shortness of distance between two towns. You get into high gear and suddenly you are downshifting again. Barb and I talked about it at lunch; the smooth abandoned highway was turning us into speed junkies.

By nightfall we were headed into Joplin, Missouri, and 10 miles from town we passed a small badge-shaped sign that said "66 West". It was the first written admission on the entire trip that there was indeed a highway by that name. In every other town and intersection it was either nameless or stuck with some dull municipal title like Frontage Road or Business 55. Somehow it was unfair to pin those unimaginative new names on the old road. A sense of tradition would have left it Route 66, just as Kennedy Airport should have remained Idlewild (Lord, what a beautiful word that was to have erased from our maps). But here, on the edge of Joplin, was a sign that said "66 West". We got off to take a picture.

We'd planned to celebrate our anniversary in Joplin by staying at a nice old downtown hotel, going out for dinner and maybe a movie later, and opening our bottle of Rosati Concord. On entering town our hopes faded. We could find no movie theater anywhere near the center of town, and the only downtown hotel looked like it had been closed since the Korean War. There were no people on the street and very little traffic. The only activity we found was a revivalist tent meeting in a windswept field at the edge of town. It was another city where the open-all-night life had been drawn away to the junctions of highway and Interstate. To travelers the town was not Joplin, Missouri, but Joplin Next Five Exits, and no one strayed very far from the exits.

We gave up the search and headed out of town to the Interstate, where we found a motel and a nearby restaurant staffed by some high-school girls who seemed to be getting the most out of their grape gum. We had a dinner of enchiladas out of a can sprinkled with a kind of cheese product. The enchiladas were cold, but were served with hot lettuce; proof that lettuce heats faster in a microwave oven.

The number of people in the restaurant business who can't cook to save their lives is staggering. If they were plumbers our houses would all be flooded. If they worked for the government things would be just as they are now.

Back at the motel we celebrated our anniversary with the Rosati Concord from our tankbag. It was good; mellow without being too sweet, and had a nice full flavor of red grape. A little island of quality that almost made up for the lack of movie, grand hotel, and good dinner.

West of Joplin 66 is a real highway with traffic and road signs. It enters Oklahoma past a sign that reads "Entering Indian Country." Where 66 and the Interstate cross you are offered a choice: "Free Road, 66 West," or "Will Rogers Turnpike. Toll Ahead." We figured Will Rogers himself probably would have chosen the Free Road, so we took that. Oklahoma is the Sooner State, named after those enterprising types who jumped the gun in the land rush, and we passed Sooner Cafés, Sooner Hotels, Sooner Used Cars, and Sooner Bars and Grills in the dozens of small towns along the highway. The land flattened out a bit, and a new state technical college in one town advertised, among its other accreditations, a New Storm Cellar. The western sky was full of high cirrus clouds, and we passed through a landscape of small slag mountains from zinc mines. Another road sign read "Buffalo Ranch Ahead. Live Buffalo." That last apparently to discourage traveling flies.

True 66 continued all the way through Tulsa and Oklahoma City, I-44 taking most of the traffic load so 66 could carry the local traffic. Oklahoma City, true to song, looked oh so pretty but was very hot at noon.

We were both sleepy by midafternoon and pulled into a coffee shop in a small town west of El Reno. There was no one on the street and the sidewalk was raised high off main street, Dodge City–style. A strong late-afternoon wind was blowing, and a faded Greyhound sign creaked in the wind above an abandoned waiting room. As we took off our helmets a late-1940s DeSoto pulled up, and a woman and little girl, both in cotton print dresses, got out of the car. The wind swirled up a cloud of dust in their faces, and the little girl covered her nose and mouth with a white handkerchief and they went into the coffee shop. A chill passed over me. I hadn't imagined a scene like this since the last Woody Guthrie album I listened to. This was dry country, and it was suffering through an unusually dry and hot summer. I had a feeling the Dust Bowl and the Great Depression might be over, but the weather here wasn't so sure. The wind in Oklahoma certainly did come sweeping down the plain.

We stopped for the night in Shamrock, Texas, "The Most Irish City in America," checked into the Shamrock Inn, and then rode into town, which actually had a working movie theater. *Foxes* was playing. A man and wife and their little boy climbed out of a pickup and bought tickets just ahead of us. The man collected his ticket and said, "I shore do hope your air conditioner's workin', or else we've just wasted five bucks." The girl in the booth smiled. "It shore is," she said, "and the movie's just fixin' to start." The street was dead when we went into the movie, but we came out to find a virtual parade of pickup trucks going nowhere, cowboys and their dates honking at one another. The main-street bars were busy, and Waylon Jennings's heavy thumping bass runs could be heard from the sidewalks. We had a beer in a friendly, crowded bar, then went back to the motel for a late dinner. At midnight the air was still wiltingly hot. On the wall of our room was a shamrock-studded Irish blessing that began "May the road rise to meet you . . ." As a motorcyclist I wasn't so sure I liked that image. But it ended with a promise of wind at our backs.

When you travel 66 you have different feelings about the changing landscape. In the Midwest your thoughts and observations are largely botanical in nature, full of trees, valleys, and rivers; in west Oklahoma and Texas the theme is agricultural, all cattle ranches and big farms; but in the Southwest, very near the border of New Mexico, the landforms become mystical. The flat-topped buttes and the layered, painted sandstone, the purple tinge of distant ranges and the clean dryness of the place create a sense of peace and stillness that is more than a geography. Georgia O'Keeffe had it in her desert paintings. You turn off the motorcycle and the loudest thing you can hear is your own breathing and heartbeat.

Where Route 66 is not the only highway across New Mexico it splits off from I-40 and runs parallel to it in unused isolation. We stuck to the old highway, an endless succession of concrete slabs divided by tar seams. Broken up, they would make enough patios for all of Long Island or enough foundations for all the tract homes in suburban Los Angeles, or the parking lot for one really large K-Mart. We are a rich country, I thought, that can abandon 2,000 miles of pavement, our own Appian Way, buy an entire new right-of-way nearby, and build another 2,000 miles of four-lane. A lot of measuring, grading, and contesting of property rights must have gone into both roads. ("Sorry, folks, the new road has to go right through the front porch of your homestead.")

For the photographer of bygone Americana, old 66 offers a lot of opportunity in the Southwest. The road is littered with the bones of truck stops, cafés, and motels left high and dry by I-40; it is a virtual gallery of Art Deco signs and architecture and old American sedans left overturned in the dying cockroach position, usually riddled with bullet holes. We saw the remains of our first Burma Shave signs in New Mexico, everything weathered away but the word "Shave" on the last sign.

A brilliant red desert sunset had us about 30 miles east of Gallup on I-40. Barb nudged me and pointed to the railroad track that paralleled the highway about a quarter mile away. We were being passed by El Capitan, the flagship passenger train of the Santa Fe Line, a train I rode to California as a kid.

"How fast do you think it's going?"

"About 80 or 85."

"Let's find out."

I rolled on the throttle and pegged our 85-mph speedometer, but the train contained to pull away. The tracks were straighter and flatter than our road. "We're going to beat that thing to Gallup," I shouted to Barb. "Hold on." There are few opportunities in life, I reasoned, to race the El Capitan down Route 66 with a fast motorcycle into a blazing red desert sunset. At 6,500 rpm, which computed to about 105 mph, we began to gain on the train.

We crested a rise in the road and suddenly noticed a mean-looking guy in mirrored sunglasses surrounded by a police car. He was parked in the median strip. I jumped on the brakes hard enough to leave permanent scars in all three brake rotors. The cop either didn't notice us or thought we always traveled down the road with smoke pouring off our front tire, front suspension bottomed, rear tire chattering, Barb climbing up my back, and our facial features distorted from negative g-forces. He didn't follow, so we shrugged and rolled back up to speed. We beat the train into downtown Gallup by about thirty seconds after 30 miles of unmerciful flogging of the Suzuki, which handled the job easily.

We found our grand hotel in Gallup. It was a place called El Rancho, a big old lodge on Gallup's main street, full of dark timbers, balconies, log furniture, and Indian rugs; a sprawling, gracious place. The waitress at breakfast told us Hollywood movie crews used to stay there on location. They made *They Passed This Way*, *Red Mountain*, *Ambush*, and *Billy the Kid* just outside of town. Gregory Peck, Alan Ladd, Robert Taylor, and many others had stayed there, and as a teenager she had waited on their tables.

We left Gallup in the morning, planning to push all the way to L.A. We wound through the beautiful Painted Desert on I-40, old 66 nowhere in evidence and apparently buried beneath the new pavement. We stopped to gaze down into the famous Winslow meteor crater and enjoyed the signs on the way in: "Free Petrified Wood With Fill-Up. See Painted Village Indian Teepees. See the Live Buffalo. See Winslow Crater, Established 20,000 BC. Prototype of Lunar and Martian Craters." Established? Prototype? Oh well.

Leaving Winslow we saw a sign that read, "Red Man Tobacco. America's Best Chew." That's quite a claim, I thought, and amused myself for the next 40 miles trying to picture the entire staff of *Consumer Reports* and the Consumer Protection Agency turning green around the gills and retching for a solid week as they sampled every known brand of chew to determine if Red Man was really America's Best. "Simpson, that's my spittoon you're using." "Sorry, Miss Jones." "Aaaaarrrgghh . . ."

We climbed the mountains into Flagstaff, where we stopped for lunch. I ordered a milkshake and got one that contained no milk and hadn't been shaken. It was a plastic cup of whipped non-dairy product, and I felt ashamed for eating it instead of making a scene and berating the management. Barb and I vowed to visit a nondairy at the first possible opportunity, to see where the cows were not kept and tour the missing barns and stanchions.

East of Kingman we hit the last really big chunk of Route 66, a loop that circles north of I-40; 80 miles of nearly empty highway that arced through the rugged desert country just south of the Grand Canyon. It passed through ten small towns struggling to survive in the barren landscape, some doing better than others. There was no shortage of gas stations with plywood nailed over their windows.

We descended into the lower-desert heat at Needles, which sounds hot, crossing the California border at Lake Havasu, as the dammed-up remains of the Colorado River are known there. The higher mountain landscape gave way to Joshua trees, cacti, and the occasional palm.

We crossed the California desert in heat that strained credibility. The air rushing past us was like something vented from a restaurant kitchen fan, the one over the oven and deep fryer. I wasn't sure that an air-cooled engine would keep running when the air got hotter than peak combustion temperature, but the Suzuki seemed less bothered than we did. Darkness on the desert brought almost no relief. At 11:30 that night I almost crashed swerving to avoid a black pavement patch I mistook for an animal and decided Barstow would be a good place to find a motel.

In the clear morning desert sunlight we came off the high desert at Cajon Pass and began our long descent into Los Angeles. The steep downhill highway was riddled with cops, apparently looking for fast coasters wasting gas. The landscape suddenly began to look like the Los Angeles of legend; the biblical trees, tall Lombardy poplars, eucalyptus, palm trees bent like sails in a breeze, vines and red flowers overgrowing the bridges, and that particular brand of L.A. sunlight that turns everything into a muted, sun-softened pastel tone; none of the stark, glaring sharpness and spininess of the desert. Irrigation works wonders, combined with sun.

Suddenly we were in San Bernardino, still on old 66. The remnants of a main route into a big city are still there, really old gas stations and motels, mixed with such valuable new services as poodle breeding, tae kwan do instruction, and billiard-table refinishing. We rambled past the beautiful old Spanish buildings of Rancho Cucamonga, the oldest winery in California, and endless developments of encroaching earth-tone housing developments. Stuck here and there in all the newness and commercial glitter were a few early Spanish-style homes and ranch houses, small remnants of taste and elegance looking as out of place on the highway as Catherine of Aragon at a Donut Hut.

Then through Claremont, where huge eucalyptus trees line 66, past the Equestrian Estates of Glendora, where highly paid executives can be cowboys evenings on their 5-acre spreads, around the manicured Santa Anita racetrack, past Azusa City Hall, the Conrock gravel pits, the nice old homes of South Pasadena near the Huntington Library and into what Ross Macdonald called the sun-blinded streets of L.A. Sixty-Six got lost somewhere in those streets, so we took the San Diego Freeway south to the *CW* offices in Newport Beach and our nearby home. After 2,500 miles of heat and drought, it was cool by the coastline, and an early afternoon fog was rolling in.

We parked the bike in the garage, unloaded the pack and tank bag, and leaned them against the living-room wall to be unpacked when we had more energy. We got the mail, mixed up a pitcher of margaritas, and sat out on the back porch to relax.

When you've just finished a big trip it seems only right to have some conclusions. I thought about the trip, looking back at it through that long, slightly hazy tunnel that surrounds a highway journey, especially a disjointed Lost Highway journey. After some rumination and half a pitcher of drinks I decided the trip had left me with two impressions.

First, as long as there are so many of us we are lucky to have four-lane highways. It's easy to romanticize over the old two-lane, but today it would be like any other overcrowded highway, and the romance would soon cool. Those sections of 66 where the old two-lane was still the only highway were a dusty, hazardous alley full of truck blast, train crossings, potholes, detours infested with orange flags and loose gravel, slow campers, trundling mobile homes, and dangerous frustration. There was too much traffic for the old road. We had it best, being able to choose between the empty freedom of the abandoned highway or the smooth efficiency of the Interstate. People who didn't like the old road didn't have to use it, but at least it was there; or parts of it were there. As Chuck Berry said, "Anything you want we got it right here in the USA."

Which led to another thought on the trip, and that was the tremendous variation in towns, restaurants, hotels, and people along the highway. There were prosperous farm towns, pretty little places out of an Andy Hardy movie lot, with white picket fences, tidy main streets, and bandstands in the town park. And then there were towns slightly gone to seed, where eroded expectations had allowed everything built in the last twenty years to be done the cheap, easy way; towns founded by pioneers with great expectations and inherited by people who didn't seem to care. There were good restaurants, terrible restaurants, nice hotels, poor hotels, good coffee, bad coffee, real milkshakes made with ice cream in stainless-steel containers and plastic cups of whipped nondairy product.

The contrasts were most vivid at the end of a trip. If you got out of your house, out of your town, and traveled down the road you noticed the sharp changes in quality. When you were out traveling the good things raised your expectations a little, so when you got home you remembered them and wanted to concentrate some of the good ideas in the place you chose to settle down and live.

At the end of the trip I thought maybe that's what Tod and Buz were searching for. Why they left their homes and towns and traveled Route 66 in a Corvette, other than the sheer fun of traveling. Maybe they were just taking the long way home and bringing something back when they got there. They were finding out how a real milkshake should taste, so when they finally settled down they would never, ever accept a plastic cup full of semisoft nondairy ice-milk food product as a substitute, and if someone tried to give them one they'd have enough sense to raise a little hell. They knew that travel is a gift you bring home.

OLD STONE, GREEN TREES & SPEED

WHY WOULD YOU want to go to the Isle of Man?" the voice on the other end of the phone asked me. "It's a cruel, dangerous place to race, and most of the top international riders avoid it. Why don't you go to Assen instead and see some real racing?"

"I want to go because it's the last real road race," I explained. "There are other races on public roads, but they're really just street races where the track is easy to learn. The Isle of Man Tourist Trophy runs on 37 miles of real road. I've seen the pictures. It goes through villages, over bridges, past farms, up and down a mountainside, and so on. It seems to me there's nothing else like it."

"All the same, I'd go to Assen if I were you. Forget the island. No one should race there."

The man on the phone was entitled to his opinion. As a team manager who had been to the island many times, he'd lost a few acquaintances there, and his best friend had been seriously injured in an accident, never to race again. He'd earned his right to dislike the place, while I (the world's oldest novice at nearly everything) had never been there.

He was not alone in his feelings. Many top roadracing stars have badmouthed or boycotted the race for years, so much so that the TT was finally relegated to minor-league status. People like Sheene, Roberts, Mamola, and Luccinelli didn't race there now. The best riders at the Isle of Man these days raced because they loved it or because they considered the starting money worth the effort, or both. And then true roadracing has always demanded peculiar skills and a different type of concentration than short-circuit racing, so many riders have probably continued to come to the island simply because they are very good at it.

Added to that is the sheer romance of the place. For most of the twentieth century the TT has been the world's supreme motorcycle race. To win at the Isle of Man was to become legend, and every great rider of the past has been required to master the fast, difficult circuit to cement his reputation as a road-racer. Names like Duke, Read, Agostini, Hailwood, and dozens of others are inextricably tied to the TT, and the very bumps, corners, bridges, and hills of the circuit itself are as famous as the riders. Ballaugh Bridge, Windy Corner, Creg-ny-Baa, and Sarah's Cottage are as well known to TT fans as the name Mike Hailwood. A mental map of the track, with all its strange-sounding Manx place names, is a permanent fixture in the minds of most racing enthusiasts in the British Isles and elsewhere.

The race has been held since 1907, when England refused to allow such craziness on its own public roads, and the largely autonomous Manx (they have their own parliament, called the Tynwald) offered their lovely island to the Auto Cycle Union for the Big Race. So the TT has been around a few years longer than the Indy 500. Not a bad tradition.

"Thanks anyway," I told my friend on the phone, "but I think I'll go to the TT rather than Assen. I've been reading about Ballacraine and Cronk-y-Voddy since I was twelve years old. There's a picture on my wall of Agostini and his MV airborne at Sulby Bridge. At home I have a TT record album with the sound of Mike Hailwood screaming down Bray Hill on the Honda Six. It's a place I've wanted to go ever since I gave up shooting frogs with a BB gun, and now, after all these years and at the advanced age of thirty-four, I am finally going, by God, to the Isle of Man."

There are a lot of ways to get to the Isle of Man, but I naturally took the Easy Motojournalist Route, which involved flying to London, borrowing a GS650G from the nice folks at Heron Suzuki GB Limited, riding halfway across England to Liverpool, and taking the Packet Steamship Company ferry to the Isle of Man. My wife, Barbara, came with me.

We left notoriously sunny L.A. in a gloomy rain and arrived in famously gloomy London on a hot, cloudless day. A friendly gentleman named Ray Battersby signed over the Suzuki and drew us a detailed labyrinthine map to guide us out of Greater London. And make no mistake, London is Great. We threw our only luggage, a tank bag and some soft saddlebags, on the Suzuki and headed northwest.

Ray's last words as we pulled out of the parking lot were "Drive on the left!" As it turned out, I had no trouble remembering to drive on the left, but all week I kept looking the wrong way as I stepped off curbs. There are many different types of horns on English cars, and most of the cars have superb brakes.

After looking at Ray's map I suggested to Barb we pay a cab to drive to Liverpool and then follow him with the bike. The map worked fine, however, and after an hour we were free of London and its endless high-speed roundabouts. We avoided the big motorways and headed toward Liverpool on the more interesting two-lane winding secondary roads.

England isn't a very dull country to cross on a motorcycle. The land is so condensed in the overlapping layers of its own history that the name on every road sign seems to be famous for something, be it a battle, king, school, bombing raid, sporting event, novel, factory, or rock group. Our route took us past Hampton Court, Windsor, Blenheim Castle, Henly, Rugby, Oxford, Stratford-on-Avon, and Birmingham, and into Liverpool. England is an old country with an animated past, and humans with something on their minds have been tramping around on its soil for a long time.

We rode into a cool, gray Liverpool late in the afternoon, following signs to the Liverpool Car Ferry with a motorcycle throng that grew larger as we got closer to the docks. Either we were on the right road or every motorcyclist in England had been seized with some kind of lemming madness. Policemen on the wharves directed us into an immense holding shed with a glass-paneled roof, where guards at the entrance checked the fuel level in our tank and gave us a "Tank Inspected" decal. You no longer have to empty your tank for the Isle of Man ferry, but the fuel has to be low enough that nothing sloshes out in a rough sea. The boat company doesn't want a cargo bay full of gas fumes and expensive motorcycles, especially in a country where virtually everyone smokes.

We handed over the tickets we'd ordered in advance (about $38 round trip for two people and a bike) and rode down a steep ramp into the cargo hold. Loading men lined the bikes up on their centerstands, slid them into tight rows, and then strapped each row down with rope about the thickness of a fire hose. They pack about five hundred bikes into each shipload, which is a lot of chrome, mirrors, fairings, and handlebars crammed into a small place.

Up on the passenger deck the ferryboat had the look of a troopship for some kind of motorcycle army. The deck was packed with a crazy mixture of Barbour suits, boots, helmets, racing leathers, touring leathers, and fringed leathers, the predominant color being black with a sprinkling of Kenny Roberts Yellow and Barry Sheene Red. There were hard- and soft-looking women, bespectacled school teachers carrying pudding-bowl helmets, wild rocker types in fringed leather who looked like Ted Nugent with more tattoos, mature Germans with BMW patches on full road leathers, and vintage men with chests full of meet pins glittering on their thorn-proofs. If there was a uniform on the boat, it was black roadracing boots worn over Levis topped off by a Belstaff or leather roadracing jacket and a full-face helmet with a racing-theme paint job.

While some elements in American motorcycling take a lot of trouble to select riding gear that makes them look like skiers or snowmobilers, European and English bikers are less apologetic in their choices. They wear first-rate, expensive paraphernalia that leaves no doubt they are Serious Motorcyclists; they like going fast or appearing to go fast and dress the part when they are riding.

Their bikes reflect the same attitude. It costs money to go to the island and stay there for a week, and most people are using a week or more of precious vacation time to be there, so once again you get a committed rather than casual brand of motorcyclist. Big sportbikes and classic restorations predominate, while the full-dress touring bike is all but absent.

The harbor lights of Douglas, the largest city on the Isle of Man, appeared out of the mist just after dark. As we eased into the dock a voice on the PA instructed riders, in three or four languages, to report to their bikes. We went down into the cargo area and picked our way through the mass of bikes to the Suzuki. The same burly guys who tied the bikes down were removing the ropes.

If Federico Fellini ever gets a little farther out and wants to film a truly bizarre spectacle taken from real life, he should bring his camera crew and sound men into the cargo bay of the Isle of Man ferry on a night when approximately five hundred motorcycles are being cranked over or kick-started all at once, packed together in a steel room about the size of a small gymnasium and lighted by a dim row of 40-watt light bulbs.

The microphones would pick up an ear-splitting confusion of shrieking RDs, high-revving unmuffled Fours, and the general chest-pounding thunder of Ducati 900s, Norton 850s and 750s, Harleys, Triumphs, BSAs, BMWs, and piston-slapping British 500 Singles, all of it bouncing off the walls in an incredible rising and falling wail. The camera crews would get footage of several hundred leather-clad people flipping down face shields and punching starter buttons, with others in the mob of bikes heaving up and down on kick-starters like erratic pistons in some kind of insane smoke machine, headlights flaring on to make a blanket of brilliance and flashing chrome at the bottom layer of the smoke cloud. They could catch the bikes launching themselves row by row up the ramp into the dark night, people spinning their tires on the oil-slick steel ramp or catching traction and disappearing in half-controlled wheelies.

What no film could capture is the mixed smell of Castrol R, several dozen brands of two-stroke oil, and all the other choking, thick exhaust fumes or the instant, furnace-like heat given off by hundreds of motorcycles lighting their engines in a confined space. Also, they'd have to film it through the distorted starburst pattern of a really scratched yellow face shield, just to get the last effect of profound unreality. You wouldn't want to witness this scene if you'd been smoking anything funny or you might just go mad and never recover.

Always quick to notice the obvious, I turned back to Barb and shouted, "This is really something!"

I don't think she could hear me, but I think she knew it was really something.

Our turn came, and we slithered up the ramp with a wave of other bikes. We landed on the docks, and the white gloves of a row of nearly invisible policemen directed us onto Manx main street, the Douglas Promenade. We were on the Isle of Man.

Douglas is an old seaside resort town with tall, narrow Victorian hotels lining the curve of the bay. The hotels are built wall to wall, but you can tell one establishment from the other because they are painted different colors. Side streets with more hotels and rooming houses climb the steep hillside of the bay to the park and cemetery that border the start/finish line of the TT course. The city is one of those places where you could hide the modern cars, take down the TV antennae, and imagine that World War I is still about five years away. There are only two or three modern structures in town, and naturally these are made of concrete and are ugly as hell. The rest of the city is charming.

We checked into a hotel we had picked at random from a travel brochure. It turned out to be a great choice because the staff was a wonderful bunch of people and the pub and restaurant downstairs were both good. The only problems were an occasionally moody water heater and an elevator with a bad memory, so we spent a few evenings scaling great numbers of stairs to reach a cold bath. (Not everyone can claim to have taken a bath "because it's there.") We discovered throughout our trip that the reliable heating of water is something of a mystery on the other side of the Atlantic, though the English and Manx are way ahead of the French, who handle hot water the way we do expensive cologne.

Stepping out onto the street, we discovered the great TT Week pastime, and that is strolling up and down the promenade at night looking at the thousands of motorcycles parked on the street. In one pass you can see an example or two of nearly any motorcycle ever made in every stage of restoration from ratty to concours. For instance, the people staying at our hotel owned—among others—an Ariel Leader, two Heskeths, a Hailwood Replica Ducati, a John Player Norton (not a replica; the ex–Peter Williams bike), a Honda CB900, a 305 Super Hawk, and a BSA Gold Star, those being a small contribution to a row that goes on for 2 miles.

The other great discovery was the people on the street and in the pubs. They formed an impression the first night that lasted all week. The crowd is generally polite, knowledgeable, and enthusiastic. Even with all the drinking and pub-crawling at night, there never seems to be any ugliness; none of the usual fistfights, throwing up curbside, or shouting clever things at passing women. Even the roughest-looking characters never seem to get publicly drunk or nasty. People stand around in groups of friends, pints of Guinness in hand, looking at bikes and talking about racing. I've never seen so many people drink so much and have such a good time without anyone getting out of control. They could obviously use some Mean and Stupid lessons from race fans in other parts of the world.

It probably goes back to the cost and commitment of getting to the island. In order to get there you have to (a) love motorcycles and (b) be smart enough to read a steamship schedule, both severe obstacles to a large part of the human race. The Isle of Man crowd is a fun collection of people.

In the morning we walked downstairs to the hotel dining room, which proved much easier than walking upstairs from the pub at night, and had a full Manx breakfast, i.e. two eggs, two strips of bacon, two sausages of strange consistency, toast with orange marmalade, juice, half a fried tomato (yes), and a pot of coffee or tea. In England this is known as a full English breakfast, and in Ireland it's a full Irish breakfast.

The Formula One race (for bikes like US Superbikes and/or AMA Formula 1) wasn't scheduled until 3:00 p.m., meaning the circuit was open to traffic all morning. We climbed on the Suzuki and rode up to the start/finish line to take our first lap in the brilliant morning sunshine.

Briefly, the circuit is a 37.7-mile rectangle that looks as though it's been shipped parcel post through the US Mail (crushed and dented in spots), running up one side of the island and back down the other. Most of the narrow pavement runs through villages, farms, and wooded glens in gently rolling countryside, but at the north end of the island it climbs the side of Mount Snaefell and then descends in great sweeping stretches all the way to the start/finish line in Douglas.

There are only about a dozen slow corners on the course, so the rest of the circuit can be taken about as fast as memory and icy nerve allow. If you can remember what's around the next blind corner or over the brow of the next blind hill (and most people can't) you can ride large sections of the course flat out. If your memory isn't so good there are a lot of walls, churches, houses, and other fine examples of picturesque stonemasonry waiting to turn you into an ex-motorcyclist.

A first lap around the island is a revelation. Anywhere else it would be a scenic drive through the countryside of a lovely island. But knowing it's a racetrack changes your perspective on the road and its corners. The narrowness of the road and the close proximity of walls and other roadside obstacles would make 50 or 60 mph seem plenty fast under normal touring circumstances. Corners, cars, and pedestrians are upon you almost before you see them.

At about 70 mph the hedges and walls and overhanging trees begin to blur around the edges of your vision, and the road becomes a sort of green and stone and sky-blue tunnel. On a street bike anything over 80 mph begins to feel insanely fast, like a wild roller-coaster ride, and the forks and shocks begin to hammer and kick the bike around; it bottoms in dips and loses contact with the road over rises, making it hard to pitch the bike into blind corners that unfold in front of you, revealing their peculiarities only after you've hit them.

On our first lap my faithful passenger agreed that 80 mph felt quite fast and hinted something a little slower might be more fun (I still have the bruises on my ribs). Racers, of course, go about twice as fast as we did. Really fast guys average about 115 mph around the island, just under twenty minutes per lap. Our best lap was about two hours, with a stop for lunch in Ramsey.

Vance Breese and Mike Ross are two American riders who came to the island for the first time this year, bringing a pair of 1,300cc Harley-Davidson roadracers with them. Their race bikes were late in arriving on practice week, so they borrowed a couple of big street bikes from some sympathetic Manx enthusiasts. After the first practice lap they pulled into the pit lane in Douglas, took off their helmets, and both said, "I hope our bikes don't arrive in time for the race." After a few more laps, however, they began to develop some cautious enthusiasm and decided it might not be so bad after all.

"I was unprepared for the speed of the place," Breese said. "On the map the course looks like it's all corners, but most of those corners can be taken flat out—if you know where you're going."

"You can take one corner on the right line," Ross added, "but it'll ruin the line for the next two, so you'll have to back off to make it, and that can cost valuable seconds. You have to know where you're going all the time and be thinking ahead."

The TT course has to be ridden, at any speed, to be appreciated. Coming back into Douglas after that first trip around the circuit, it didn't feel as though we'd merely done a lap of a race course; it seemed we'd been gone on a week's vacation and were home at last. One lap is good for more changes of scenery and geography than most people see on a long summer holiday. Thirty-seven miles on the TT circuit is a long trip, and each time you come back into Douglas you feel a little older for the experience. The competitors no doubt feel a lot older.

That first lap also instills a combination of awe and respect for any rider who can set a competitive lap time on the circuit, because a fast lap time is irrefutable proof that the rider has both superb concentration and great courage. A short circuit just doesn't tell you as much about the people who lap it quickly.

We watched the Formula 1 race from the grandstand on the start/finish line. Compared with the mass-start mayhem of a GP event, the start of the TT is a relatively relaxed affair. The bikes are numbered according to starting order and are released in pairs every ten seconds. They then race for six laps against the clock, rather than directly against one another. After the bikes are gone, an attentive quiet spreads over the crowd and everyone listens to the progress reports over the PA system, settling back for the twenty-minute wait for the leaders to come blazing through town again.

It didn't take long for Mick Grant to establish himself as the leader in the F-1 race. Three-quarters of the way through the first lap he was reported twelve seconds ahead on the clock, and as his Yoshimura Suzuki came howling through Douglas it was announced he'd set a new lap record of 114.93 mph at 19 minutes 48 seconds—from a standing start. Joey Dunlop and Ron Haslam were second and third, both on Hondas. Before all the riders streaked into pit row for fuel, Grant had built up a huge thirty-second lead. But on the last lap he parked his bike at the Hairpin with ignition trouble, and Haslam took over the race as Dunlop slowed with handling problems. Haslam took the race, with Dunlop second and New Zealander Dave Hiscock third.

Circle-track fans might have a hard time adjusting to a race where the leaders come by every twenty minutes or so, then disappear over the hill for another twenty. Hearing race reports from distant parts of the track, you sometimes feel a little like a civilian listening to war news from the Falklands. But every twenty minutes the war comes through town for a few brief seconds, and when you see the speed of the bikes on the narrow road it gives you pause to realize all those riders have been out there riding like that the entire time you've been sipping your warm pint of Okell's Bitters and relaxing in the shade. The speed of the bikes (relative to the stationary nature of trees, pubs, and your own perch on the wall) is enough to raise the hair on the back of your neck.

In the pub that night everyone was talking about the race, and Mandy the barmaid was explaining to me that a 50/50 mix of Guinness and bitter ale is called a brown split by some and a dark-over-bitter by others. I tried several versions of both and couldn't make up my mind which was better. Everybody was buying endless rounds for everyone else. I discovered you can never sit in a Manx pub without at least two pints awaiting your attention.

Amid all the racing talk in the pub, two names surfaced over and over again, floating through the acrid smoke and endless variety of upper- and working-class British accents. The names were Mike Hailwood and Pat Hennen; Hailwood because he was the absolute smooth master of the circuit and Hennen, the American, because he rode his heart out with an abandon that is still fixed in the memory of everyone who witnessed it.

"I saw Hennen pass a guy in midair at Ballaugh Bridge and then take the next corner with everything dragging and twitching . . . I mean he was scratching, mate. I never saw anything like it. He just bloody well attacked the course . . ." and so on. Hennen was seriously injured on the TT circuit and retired from racing several years ago, but no one who was there seems to have forgotten the smallest detail of his aggressive riding style.

Some pub conversations are easier than others. While it has been said that the Americans and British are two people separated by a common language, it is actually the British themselves who are separated by a common language. There is more stark contrast between the accents of two Englishmen from neighboring shires than there is between a Cajun alligator hunter from Louisiana and a New York stockbroker. Class and education throw up further barriers in language. While some Britishers speak with the clarity of Prince Charles or John Cleese, others can approach you with such a broad regional dialect that conversation is all but impossible. Just before closing time I had the following chat with a man who seemed to be from England:

"Ha pen the nay thrraa queekum?" he asked me.

"Pardon?"

"Ha pen the nay thrraa queekum?"

"Uh . . . oh yeah. Sure."

"Aye?"

"Aye."

"Yer a foofa deekin, then?"

"Yeah. You're probably right. I'm a foofa deekin."

"Ah. 'Tis a shame . . ."

I bought the guy a beer before I sank any lower in his estimation. Then I crawled off to bed. I had no idea whether we were discussing piston rings or his wife, so I decided to clear out before I admitted something terrible.

I walked into the hotel elevator and punched the fifth-floor button, but the elevator didn't want to go anywhere, so I decided to walk up to my room. I stopped for a smoke break on the third-floor landing, and the elevator went by with no one in it. By the time I got to my room the cold bath felt good.

The next day was Mad Sunday, when the track is open to the public and the police and their radar guns look the other way. Barb and I joined the stream of speeding bikes for a quick lap. Most of the riders were relatively sane, under the circumstances. The only hairy part was the downhill off the mountain. Every time we came up behind some slow vintage bike, like a smoking Scott Flying Squirrel, I'd check the mirrors and find we were being passed by a Honda 900F going 90 being passed by a Guzzi Le Mans going 100 being overtaken by a Bimota Kawasaki going flat out. This telescoping speed range can make things exciting on Mad Sunday. We passed some kind of accident and later learned a German rider had hit a car and lost his leg.

Much is made of these accidents when the TT is under fire, but when you see the number of people on the island and the amount of driving and riding they do, mishaps are amazingly rare. Americans and their cars seem to do themselves in at a much higher rate on any given holiday weekend in summer, and it would make about as much sense to cancel the Fourth of July as the Tourist Trophy because of the accident rate. This year there were, happily, no racing fatalities. And hundreds of competitors raced thousands of miles.

Races were scheduled every other day for the rest of the week. On the off days everyone rides around to the numerous vintage and owners-club rallies held in various villages around the island, or people simply go sightseeing. The Isle of Man is such a pleasant vacation spot it's worth a week of anyone's time, even without the races.

The whole island is like a landscape created for a Tolkien novel or a Cat Stevens song. To say the island is quaint does it an injustice; like saying Nastasia Kinski is good looking. There's more to it than that. The combination of seacoast, fishing villages, farms, forested glens, cottages, and villages all fit together to provide a kind of bone-deep charm. There is nothing contrived or artificial about the Isle of Man. Brooks tumble, cattle and sheep graze, roses, wisteria, and lilacs grow around cottage gates and churchyards, and every time the sun comes out the island glows about fifty colors of green. Throw in a motorcycle race and you've got an island that's first on my list of Places I'm Going to Move When I Get Filthy Rich or Retire.

Norman Brown won the 500cc Senior race (for pure GP bikes) on Monday, riding a Suzuki that was quite a bit faster than ours. A dark-horse entrant and pub owner from Ireland, Brown rode a brilliant race, beating South African Jon Ekerold by only 8.6 seconds. New Zealander (people come from all over) Dennis Ireland finished third. Mick Grant had led the race for three laps before colliding with a slower rider and crashing without injury. A happy sidelight to the race was that veteran Charlie Williams, after being sidelined with a kinked fuel line during the race, went back out and set a new lap record of 19 minutes 40.2 seconds at 115.8 mph. Another fast veteran, Tony Rutter, won the 350 Senior convincingly. Rutter turned in another fine ride on Wednesday, winning the Formula II race on a Ducati 600 Pantah. Dave Roper, one of a small contingent of Yanks racing the island, took 12th in the Formula III race on his borrowed 350 Aermacchi, making some of the nicest thumping noises of the week and looking very smooth and fast.

The last race of the week was the Classic—virtually unrestricted bikes—on Friday. After a gloriously sunny week (unheard of) the island woke up to rain on Friday morning. But it cleared off by noon, and by race time the track was dry except for a few treacherous wet patches under the trees. Charlie Williams led most of the race but retired on the 4th lap. Dennis Ireland took the win, with Jon Ekerold second, and Tony Rutter third. The fast guys did well no matter what they rode.

Two of the most interesting entries, at least from an American point of view, were those 1,300 Harleys of Breese and Ross. They'd had a tough week with very little practice and the bikes arriving late. A blown motor on Breese's bike and various mechanical problems had precluded even a full lap of practice on the bikes they were to race. Breese started the race with a hot street motor to replace his blown race engine. Ross retired on the first lap with engine problems, and Breese soldiered through with a missing ignition to finish 38th.

"This is really an endurance race," Breese said later. "Two hundred and twenty-six miles is a long way to go on this road. Next time we'll be ready for it."

Breese and Ross had each completed only six laps of practice when the green flag dropped on their race, yet we watched both bikes come thundering through the glen at Barregarrow quicker than they had any right to, bottoming out on the sharp dip and flying off through the corridor of walls and trees. With all they'd been through, just being out there was an accomplishment, and finishing was a minor triumph. And they sounded good.

We took the boat back to England on Saturday morning and stayed on deck long enough to see the green island disappear in the ocean haze.

I think my friend on the telephone was wrong. It isn't that no one should race on the Isle of Man. It's just that no one should *have* to race. There is no doubt the circuit is difficult and demanding, so perhaps a rider should race the TT only because he enjoys it and loves the challenge of a true road course, but not because his contract demands it. The Isle of Man is far too nice a place for people to race against their will.

I was partly wrong too, of course. The Isle of Man isn't important just because it's the last real road race on earth. It's important simply because there's nothing else like it anywhere, and if it disappears there will never be anything like it again.

Try to find another green island in a misty ocean with 37.7 miles of breathtakingly beautiful road and good draught ale where the friendly inhabitants welcome a contest of speed with open arms and the word *lawsuit* is still regarded with proper disdain. And nowhere else on earth will we find another motorcycle race where the charming ladies of the Women's Church Guild serve tea and scones on blue-and-white fine bone china to the race fans sitting on the churchyard wall.

THE TWO-WHEELED UNDERGROUND CANADIAN RAILROAD

Sometimes the Longest Trip Begins with a Really Long Trip

THE SUMMER JOBS WERE OVER, and Donnelly and I were rich. Three months on a railroad section crew, shoveling gravel halfway from Milwaukee to the Twin Cities, had earned us each a tidy $1,400. In 1967 that was a lot of money. It would pay for our room, board, and tuition at college, with change leftover for a few student luxuries like cigarettes, pizza, and gas for our motorcycles. I had a slightly beat Honda CB160 and Donnelly had a Honda 305 Dream, a little less beat. We both wanted Triumphs but had settled for these used Hondas because they were amazingly cheap, having been bought late in the second semester from other desperate students.

It appeared we were all set for a junior year at the University of Wisconsin. I was an English major and Pat Donnelly was in political science. What we hoped to do with these majors I have no idea. We weren't thinking very far ahead. The war in Vietnam was going on, so between that and various other social perils it wasn't fashionable or especially worthwhile to make plans much beyond the age of twenty-one. There was plenty of precedent for disappearing just a bit earlier than that.

The idea at the time was to join the army if you flunked out of college or happened to think the war was a good idea, or to stay in college if you weren't entirely convinced it was a wonderful thing. Donnelly and I were not entirely convinced. A few years earlier we'd gotten out of high school with a fairly solid collection of patriotic notions. My freshman year in college I'd gone so far as to sign up for the ROTC because I wanted to become a navy fighter pilot. But two years spent reading newspapers and watching the war on TV at the student union had eroded my enthusiasm for the conflict. By 1967 my conventional military fervor had turned to a sort of heartsick malaise. Donnelly, my roommate and best friend from youth, felt the same way.

So when I say it appeared we were all set to go back to school in the fall, I mean we were tossing around some other ideas. One of those was moving to Canada. That was a big step, or course, a trip of no return that slammed the door on families, friends, girlfriends, hometowns, and calling ourselves Americans. Neither of us had ever been to Canada, nor anywhere else outside the US for that matter. We wanted to see this Canada before we attempted to move there; to see what life looked like from across the border, to smell the Canadian air, drink Canadian coffee, and meet some Canadians. Did Mounties still wear red outfits? We were told they looked like FBI agents now. We needed a scouting trip to check it out.

That trip was planned for early September, between the end of railroad labor and the start of the fall semester. In retrospect, our preparations for the trip seem almost quaint. We changed our oil, adjusted valves, lubed our chains, and each took $60 out of the bank. To the rear seat of my CB160 I strapped an army-surplus duffel bag containing a flashlight, a sleeping bag, and Big Pink, a faded red pup tent from my childhood, a tent originally designed to make a pair of dwarfish nine-year-olds mildly claustrophobic. Its lack of water repellency was legend among all who'd been doused within its tiny pink walls.

Rain gear?

Forget it. Motorcyclists didn't wear rain gear in those days (unless they had an ounce of common sense or were older than eighteen). We saw motorcycle rain suits as an extravagance for people who worried about all the wrong things. No, Donnelly and I had our blue jeans, work boots, Bell helmets, leather jackets, and gloves, and that was enough.

The first part of the trip went pretty well. We left early on a gray morning and had breakfast in a truckstop on Highway 51, heading southeast from Rockford. Our first stop for the night was to be Arlington Heights, a suburb of Chicago. Another roommate of ours, Hugh Wessler, lived there. It took us half the day to blunder into greater Chicago and the other half to find Arlington Heights amid the suburban sprawl. We finally found Hugh's house and, with typical courteous forethought, called from a gas station about two blocks away to let the Wesslers know we were in town. Yes, I admitted, we sure could use a place to stay for the night, now that you ask. Hugh's mother wanted to know if we were hungry. I told her not to go to any trouble in a tone of voice that implied if she had a side of beef or maybe half a dozen pizzas around we'd probably eat them.

When we got to Hugh's house he was in the basement, listening to his Heathkit stereo and making an electric guitar in his woodworking shop. Hugh was an engineering major who could make anything, including, it turned out, a living when he got out of college. We had a marvelous dinner concocted by Hugh's mom on short (no) notice and let ourselves out the back door the next morning, leaving a thank-you note propped between the salt and pepper shakers on the kitchen table. We wanted to be in Canada by nightfall.

If you've never been there, Calumet City and Hammond are lovely at 6:00 in the morning viewed from the elevated Chicago Skyway, especially with a light rain falling. The air is scented with the aroma of Bessemer furnaces, industrial arc welding, and coke production, and rain glistens on the axles and driveshafts of overturned cars with their wheels gone. Open gas flames billow from tall chimneys, and everything, including your motorcycle, face shield, and very teeth, acquires a fine patina of cinders and ash. We skirted the south end of the lake through Gary and headed northeast into Michigan on Highway 60.

Traffic was heavy on 60, but at last the factories and scrap yards gave way to green pastures and wooded farmland. Our bikes were running well. Oddly enough, my CB160 was quicker through the gears than Donnelly's single-carb 305 Dream. True to its touring image and ethereal name, however, the Dream cruised at a more relaxed pace on the highway and had a few more mph right at the top end. Both bikes topped out in the neighborhood of 90 mph and cruised at 70 or more without apparent strain.

The only real problem with my 160 was a dead battery, meaning I had to bump-start the bike every morning in a sort of Hailwood-at-the-TT imitation. Once the engine was warm, the kick-starter worked all right. With no battery to regulate things, however, the brightness of my headlight varied on revs, so I tended to flicker and dim at stop signs.

Michigan was my initiation to a basic maxim of cross-country travel. Stated simply: maps are small, while the earth, on the other hand, is quite large. It looked like a short jaunt to Detroit in Rand McNally, but it took us all day to get there. Our original plan on this trip was to ride across eastern Canada all the way to the fishing villages of the Gaspé Peninsula on the Atlantic coast. Halfway through Michigan we began to see Montréal as a more realistic goal.

After a late hot-dog dinner at some godforsaken shopping center in Jackson, we rolled into Detroit at exactly midnight. I don't remember much of Detroit from this trip. We were pretty tired. The enduring image is miles of broad avenues with streetlights throwing a cadence of glare and shadow across my scratched yellow face shield; parked cars, honking and weaving cars, sirens, and the slickness of rain on manhole covers. We looked neither to the right nor to the left, but straight ahead, and passed through Detroit at midnight.

I remember the Canadian border very well, however. I wasn't too tired to remember that.

We pulled up to the US Customs station on the Detroit River, and a uniformed official signaled us to stop. He looked us over for a minute and then leaned into the office and said something. Two more uniformed men came out. They asked us to get off our motorcycles and push them over to the side of the office, under the lights. We were instructed to remove all our luggage from the bikes and bring it in the office. There everything was gone through. I should say we were instructed to go through everything by the officers, who did not deign to touch our motorcyclish belongings. It was, "Take off those leather jackets. Okay, now open the duffel bag. Unroll that pink thing. What is that, a tent? A pink tent? Unroll it. What are those?"

"Tent stakes."

"What's that other thing in there?"

"A flashlight."

"Let's see it. Take the batteries out. That's it. Put them on the table."

And so on.

Then we were searched and told to empty our pockets on the desk. Drivers licenses were checked, social security cards, draft cards of course, and we were told to count our money. We were questioned as to travel plans, hometowns, and possible criminal records. One officer took our ID material into his office and began dialing phone numbers. He talked, nodded, dialed, lit and snubbed out numerous cigarettes, all the while watching us through the glass partition with unblinking reptilian eyes that said he'd seen guys like us before. It was 1967, a war was on, we were of college age, this was the Canadian border, it was midnight, and of course we were on motorcycles. All wrong.

When we had been found unarrestable, they quickly lost interest and told us to pack our scattered belongings and go. After only an hour's delay we were on the road again. For about twenty seconds.

The Canadian customs officials were more efficient. They took about twenty minutes to go through our luggage, grill us as to our plans, and have us count our money. Only one phone call was made, and then we were free to pack and go.

We crossed into Canada at 1:30 in the morning. The drizzle had stopped, and a warm autumn wind was clearing the sky, revealing a nearly full moon. We were so tired Donnelly claimed to be hallucinating various restaurant foods as we stopped for a light in downtown Windsor. I suggested we take Highway 401 out of the city, hit the first likely exit ramp, and find a place to eat and camp.

About 20 miles from Windsor we peeled off into a little town called Tilbury. For 2:00 in the morning, the main street of Tilbury was jumping. Crowded cars cruised the strip, groups of people mingled and walked on the sidewalks, and there was actually an open café. We parked in front of the café, found ourselves a booth inside, and ordered breakfast. "Lot of people out tonight," I said to the waitress.

"Hops-picking season," she said. "Teenagers and migrant workers from all over, and they all come into town on Friday night."

Our bacon and eggs had just arrived when I looked out the café window and realized that three guys in leather jackets of the multiple-zipper persuasion were messing around with our bikes. They looked drunk. One was trying to unhook the bungee cords from my pack, and another was kicking the spokes on Donnelly's 305. The third was watching. We put down our forks and laid our napkins on the table with weary resignation. "Well, let's get this over with," I said.

As we left the restaurant, the waitress and a cigar-smoking cook and several patrons came to the front window to watch. "Be careful," the cook said. "When those boys get drunk they're really crazy."

The three guys wore motorcycle jackets and heavy-duty engineer boots, but they didn't seem to have any motorcycles nearby. I walked up to the one who was meddling with my luggage and shoved him away from the bike. "What are you doing," I said. He threw something back at me in garbled French and shoved me back and then I shoved him and so on . . . the usual boring prefight choreography.

Meanwhile, Donnelly was dealing with the other two. The one who'd been kicking his spokes was a short, stocky guy with a blue stocking cap and curly red hair that stuck straight out from the sides of his head. The other one, who stood back a bit, was slightly larger with a sort of weasel-like demeanor. Donnelly had pushed them away from his bike and was trying to talk to them in our excellent University of Wisconsin Conversational French, sophomore level. He wasn't getting very far. Another shoving match was developing. So much for the UN approach, I thought.

Then I saw the knife.

Right. A knife. The short guy with the shocking-red hair had produced a very long, very open switchblade and was playing it unsteadily around Donnelly's throat, moving him back against the restaurant window. The waitress, cook, and five customers stood watching on the other side of the window glass. The cook was sipping coffee and munching on a donut. Just behind him was a phone on the wall, but no one was using it.

The knife changed everything. My absurd shoving match slowed to a halt, and even the guy I was shoving stopped to watch, and his breathing tightened up. This wasn't fun anymore.

Donnelly looked down at the knife and then back into the face of the red-haired man. Donnelly was a naturally obliging, easygoing person, but he had a rather explosive flash point, and I had personally seen him lay waste to much larger individuals who gave him unsolicited trouble. And at that moment I could see the anger rising in his face.

I think the man with the knife sensed this, even through his glazed, drunken eyes. The way things were shaping up, he'd either have to do something terrible with that knife or get himself all ripped apart by Donnelly. He backed up a few steps and blinked. Glancing uneasily at his pals, he suddenly made a motion with his head and said, "*Allons*." They all backed away from us, then turned and staggered off down the street.

When they were a half a block away we heard the switchblade snap shut. They crossed the street, piled into a yellow-and-white 1959 Chevy, and drove away.

We both let out a long, low whistle and went back into the café. Back to our ice-cold bacon and eggs with the grease congealed on them. The customers returned to their seats, and the cook said, "You don't want to mess around with those boys. They get crazy when they're drunk."

I said, "Yeah, well, thanks for all your help."

He apparently sensed my insincerity because we didn't get any more coffee.

Returning to our bikes, we saw a cop car cruise by, so we flagged him down. We explained the entire incident, complete with the knife descriptions and the color of the 1959 Chevy. Everything but 8 by 10 glossies, as Arlo would say. He listened to our story without emotion and without writing anything down, all the while looking at our boots, jackets, and motorcycles. Then he asked to see our drivers licenses. He wanted to know what, exactly, we were doing in Canada and where we were going. He took out a pad and wrote down our license-plate numbers, then went to the patrol car and made a radio transmission. A few minutes later came a radio squawk reply we couldn't understand. The cop gave us back our licenses, said we were free to go, and drove away.

I looked at Donnelly and shrugged. "Looks like we're innocent . . ."

"Yeah. Third time tonight."

As we rode out of town, a 1959 Chevy peeled out of a side street and dropped in behind us. It took us about three blocks to lose them forever. We turned down an alley, across a parking lot, and through a schoolyard as fast as we could ride. Our friends in the Chevy were last heard running into some garbage cans with their car. They were in no condition to drive.

We took the first back road we found out of town and rode about 5 miles before pulling off on a tractor path into an open pasture. We parked the bikes under a lone oak tree and by the light of the moon and the Dream began to unroll our tent. I was getting the tent stakes out when Donnelly grabbed my arm and said, "Do you hear voices?"

I did.

And laughter and the breaking of glass.

We turned out the bike headlight and climbed a nearby rise in the field. As our eyes adjusted to the moonlight, about twenty-five to thirty cars materialized, parked in the open field. Someone was pumping a beer keg, and we could see cigarettes glowing or being lit. "Great," Donnelly said. "A goddamn beer party. Let's get out of here."

We rolled up our tent, rode another 5 miles, found another pasture, and pulled off. This time there were no voices. We put up the tent and climbed into our sleeping bags. As we drifted off to sleep it became apparent that some sort of drag race was being run on the nearby road. Eventually we heard what sounded like a serious car crash off in the distance. Lots of traffic sped by, and later there were sirens. We didn't care about any of this. We were too tired.

"Welcome to Canada," Donnelly said, and we more or less laughed ourselves to sleep.

Bathed in pink tentlight, we awoke at about 11:30 the next morning, gasping for air. We ripped our way out of the hothouse tent to discover a beautiful autumn morning. We rode under clear, sunny skies toward Highway 3 and the shores of Lake Erie. The warm fall air smelled like the fields of stubble and cornstalks along the road, taking on a cool freshness when we got to the lake. The north shorelines of Erie and Ontario were lovely, and whenever possible we stayed on the two-lane shore road.

Riding again until long after dark, we had dinner in a place called Gananoque at the north end of Lake Ontario, then found a campground in a piney wood south of town. We stumbled our of our tent in the morning to discover ourselves camped about 50 feet from a tall shoreline cliff that overlooked the famous Thousand Islands, where Ontario narrows into the St. Lawrence River. Donnelly had thought to bring a small pan and a jar of instant coffee, so we made a campfire on the rocky cliffs and sat under the pine trees for a long time, drinking coffee and watching the sun rise over the US side of the channel, burning the mist off the green islands. I smoked my last Marlboro, crushed the pack, and made a mental note to buy a pack of Players at the next gas station.

Following the St. Lawrence River, we crossed into Québec Province and made it to Montréal late in the afternoon. After being turned down at three hotels with "VACANCY" signs burning, we learned to leave our helmets and jackets on the bikes while inquiring. In the end, the effort was wasted. We found a room in a downtown hotel so cheap that mere possession of helmets and jackets made us something of a success story within its dark hallways. Most of the patrons were elderly men who talked to themselves and seemed to own nothing but a jealously guarded brown paper bag. The rest were slightly younger women who kept funny hours.

For the next two days we walked all over the hills of Montréal, sitting in parks, poking around in bookstores, and looking over the campus of McGill University. We climbed Mount Royal and looked out over the grounds of Expo 1967. The second evening we stopped in a topless bar, which at that time was a brand-new concept of great novelty. As we sipped on beers, a rather bored-looking woman climbed up on the bar and did some perfunctory topless dancing to Spencer Davis's "Gimme Some Lovin'". Then she sat down at the bar and said "Give me a beer, Ernie." Donnelly and I looked down the bar for a moment and smiled politely. She studied us for a moment and didn't smile back. I don't think she liked my work boots. It was suddenly too quiet in the bar. What do you say to a topless dancer? That was nice dancing? We paid our tab and left. I felt Spencer Davis had somehow been compromised.

It was a long walk back to the hotel. The weather was changing, and a cold, raw wind was blowing down the streets of Montréal. It was a Monday night, and the streets were almost empty, people all gone to their homes or offices, doing routine things. The city around me suddenly felt remarkably cold and indifferent to our presence, and it was my first inkling that foreign cities are not by nature hospitable to people without connections or money. I felt like Bob Dylan on the cover of *Freewheelin'*, except I didn't have my girlfriend clinging to my arm. She was back in Wisconsin.

As we entered the hotel the manager stopped us and wanted to be paid now because he knew we were leaving in the morning. We paid him and tried to get some sleep in our taco-shaped beds.

In the morning we loaded up our bikes in the alley behind the hotel and I pushed mine across the street to a gas station, not wanting to do my mandatory bump-start until necessary. The gas station had signs in English and French, but the English words had been painted over with red paint. The attendant ignored us when we asked about filling up our bikes and buying a quart of oil. Our poor French didn't win him over. Another customer who'd been refused service said, "Don't bother. Go to an English station." The Québec separatist movement was at something of a fever pitch right then, and we'd also been refused service in a French Canadian bar the previous night. To Donnelly and me, who thought of ourselves as civil-rights advocates, this behavior seemed unbearably provincial and small-time. It was another version of something we despised in the States.

We finally found some gas, got my reluctant bike started, and left Montréal on Highway 17, which follows the Ottawa River across the northeastern border of Ontario. Financially, Montréal had taken us beyond our point of no return. We each had about $25 and had to make tracks on the way home.

Somewhere near Ottawa a hard rain began to fall; a chill autumn Canadian rain that angled down in drops like cold steel pellets. The rugged, wooden countryside along the river was beautiful, but much of its charm was lost on us, what with our relentless shivering and borderline hypothermia. We set up our wet tent in a dripping pine forest on the wet banks of the Ottawa River early in the afternoon because we were too cold to ride any further. We climbed into our wet sleeping bags with our wet clothes on and I think I spent the night wondering if it was physically possible to chatter your teeth into pure calcium dust. I slept briefly, dreaming of jackhammers and sidewalks.

Through some miracle of meteorology it managed to rain harder the next day while getting still colder, yet not quite snowing. We rode, with an uncharacteristic lack of cheer, for many long hours down the long, straight pine-forest roads of Ontario. I got a flat tire around midafternoon, so we hid my bike and our luggage in the woods and rode Donnelly's bike 20 miles into the next town for the patch kit and tire pump I wasn't carrying. I repaired the tire, managing to put several permanent sprocket stains on my blue jeans, and we were off again. At 4:30 in the afternoon we were too cold to ride anymore, so we pulled off at a sign that said "WRIGHT'S CABINS", near Pembroke. Sitting just back in the trees, this place had one large log cabin/office surrounded by a horseshoe of similar but smaller log cabins. We didn't have much money, but after two days of rain we had to get indoors for one night and warm up. We were both beginning to shiver and sweat at all the wrong times, when not busy coughing.

Always wary of being refused service because of our motorcycles, I was over-joyed to walk into the office and find that the place doubled as a Yamaha deal-ership, of all things. An elderly woman sat knitting by a kerosene stove. She explained that her son ran the Yamaha end of the business and she managed the cabins. Would we like a cabin for the night or motorcycle parts? A cabin? She'd get the stove and hot water turned on for us, then, and a clothesline to hang up our wet clothes. She explained almost apologetically that the cabin would cost $6.00 for both of us. Was that OK?

It was OK.

We stayed in a tidy little log cabin with two feather beds and a bathtub on feet. In the morning the rain was hammering down on the green shingled roof, and neither of us wanted to get out of bed. We discussed staying in the cabin until the rain stopped or until we died, whichever came first. Lack of money and a driving need for breakfast finally got the better of us, however, and we pushed onward into the morning rain.

At a coffee shop near Sturgeon Falls we ran into another traveling motorcy-clist. His name was Ron. He was a free man, having just gotten out of the US Air Force, and he was circumnavigating all of North America with his brand-new Harley XLH. His Harley had the biggest pile of luggage I'd ever seen lashed onto the back of any motorcycle. It looked like an overloaded pack burro. Prom-inent in this mobile heap of goods were a full-sized Coleman two-burner stove, an ice chest, and the biggest tent I'd ever seen outside a circus.

Ron sipped his coffee and looked in amazement at our damp jackets. "Don't you guys have any rain gear?" he asked.

"No." He shook his head.

"Strange . . ."

He invited us to travel with him and said he had a tent big enough for all of us. The weather at last began to clear, and the three of us cruised along the north shore of Lake Nipissing, across the barren yellow moonscape of Sudbury's sulfur-mining district and down to the North Channel of Lake Huron. It took us a while to get used to traveling with Ron. He cruised down the road with his feet up on highway pegs, looking around at the scenery, never exceeding 60 mph. It had never occurred to Donnelly and me that anyone would ever voluntarily go slower than 85 mph, as long as there were no cops around. We rode everywhere flat out. And here was this guy, motoring along 5 mph under the speed limit, appearing to enjoy himself. It took some getting used to.

It was strange too, listening to the ka-tuff ka-tuff of the low-revving Harley next to our wound-out small-bore Hondas. With his tall windshield, huge padded seat, highway pegs, and thumping engine, this guy was traveling in a different world from us. There was no sense of urgency in his riding. We were always in a hurry, even when I couldn't think of why. He was traveling, of course, and we were on our way home.

We found a perfect campground (Ron had a campground guide) on the shore of Lake Huron, and we put up Ron's tent. I had seen tents like this only in Sears catalogs—the photo where the whole family is playing cards around a table inside the tent. We laid out our sleeping bags, Ron erected his folding army cot (I'm not kidding about this), and then he insisted that we all park our bikes in the tent "in case it rained again." He had cardboard to catch oil drips. He got out the Coleman stove and ice chest and cooked us up a great dinner of Spam and fried potatoes, with bottles of Mosehead Ale. Later we had coffee and made a big campfire. For the first time in days Donnelly and I felt roughly like human beings instead of mud-daubed barbarians of the northern rain forest. "This guy," Donnelly mumbled to me, "really knows how to travel."

"Next time," I said.

We sat across the campfire from Ron and I watched him, wondering what it would be like to be out of the military and free to travel; free to cross borders, work, not work, marry, stay single, go to school, quit school, bum around, or save money for a brand-new motorcycle. Ron's face flickered in and out of the shadows, and I watched his expression for some sign of the calm and serenity that must certainly come with that kind of freedom. In that light it was hard to tell. I grinned to myself and thought, "Ron is on the other side of the fire and we can't see him clearly."

We parted company with Ron at Sault Ste. Marie the next day. He was heading around the north shore of Lake Superior and we were crossing into upper-peninsula Michigan.

We had no trouble getting back into the US and were virtually waved through customs. "Right," I thought to myself. "Volunteers."

The rain had gone away, but a cold, piercing wind was blowing off Lake Superior and the later-afternoon clouds had the pink-and-gunmetal look of winter. I was suddenly very tired of being cold. Once we crossed the border, our homing instincts set in, and we rode absolutely flatout across northern Michigan without regard for police and traffic tickets. Nightfall found us still a long way from home, so we took Highway 41 down to Oshkosh, Wisconsin. Another college friend, Jim Wargula, lived there, and his parents were particularly understanding and good-hearted people. We rang their doorbell at 8:00 in the evening.

They had just finished dinner, so Mr. Wargula ran out and got us a huge bucket of Kentucky Fried Chicken. While he was doing that, Mrs. Wargula made fresh hot coffee, ran bathwater, got out towels, and put sheets on the guest-room beds, all the while chatting cheerfully and asking us about our trip. Jim put the bikes away in the garage for us.

Mr. Wargula returned with the chicken, and we all sat around the kitchen table. While we ate, he noticed that our leather jackets were all cracked and stiff from repeated rainstorms, so he went to the basement and returned with a can of neat's-foot oil.

While we drank coffee, he insisted on cleaning up our jackets and making them supple again. Jim helped him, while Mrs. Wargula brought out a home-made cheesecake. She told us to take off our old damp boots and brought us some clean, dry wool socks. Mr. Wargula put our boots next to the radiator—but not too close—to dry. He said he'd put some neat's-foot oil on those when they dried a little better. Mr. Wargula knew all about proper care of boots because he'd been a soldier in Europe during World War II, and he was presently a colonel in the US Army Reserves. Mrs. Wargula poured more coffee all around and offered to run our road clothes through the washer and dryer later.

We sat at the table gradually warming up, and Donnelly and I exchanged a glance. Through bloodshot eyes from fourteen hours of riding that day and four days in the rain, it was the flat, neutral glance of two people who were thinking exactly the same thing, no expression required. Looking at these friends, I wondered how I had ever thought it possible to cut myself off from them. They were good friends, but would they be able to come to Canada to see us? Wave, perhaps, from across Niagara Falls? It was hard to imagine.

When we got home the next day the welcome mat rolled out all over again. Our parents were tremendously relieved to see us back, and I was quite content to be there. I called my girlfriend, Barb, and we talked for a long time. She said she was glad I was home.

After the trip Donnelly and I never mentioned moving to Canada again. The subject never came up. It took a special courage and conviction to leave everything behind, and I don't think either of us ever really had it. My parents eventually sold the Honda 160 for me when I was in Vietnam. I look at the Canadian trip now and no conventional description of the journey fits exactly; I can't see it as merely an adventure or a fall vacation or a first motorcycle trip. In retrospect, I think it was just practice for subsequent journeys and other home-comings. A dry run.

THE EMERALD TOUR

Ireland on Five Gallons a Day

I **RELAND.** The name provoked all kinds of response in England. You'd sit in a bar in Birmingham and the man who'd just bought you a pint would say, "Well, where are you two adventurers riding next?" You'd answer "Ireland," and a strange hush would fall over the pub. A few people would shake their heads, the bartender would raise one eyebrow, and your drinking friend would equivocate, "Well . . . that might be a nice trip. I guess. But I don't mind telling you I wouldn't go there myself."

"Ever been there?"

"Nope." The answer always came with stunning quickness, like the standard medical questionnaire response: "Any mental illness in the family?" "Nope." "Ever been to Ireland?" "Nope."

A friend in Liverpool reacted the same way. So we asked, "Aren't you curious about a big island right next to your own?"

"Nope. Never been there. You see . . . "—a how-shall-I-phrase-this pause— "it might be very well for you Americans, but if I walked into an Irish pub or hotel with my English accent, I can't say how I'd be treated. I'd be on edge all the while."

Others told us, Americans or not, to stay away. A crazy, dangerous place of no consequence. Trouble. Don't go to Ireland. Tour England.

"We've already toured England. Twice."

"Tour it again, mate."

I learned a long time ago to take this kind of advice with a large grain of salt. I'd been warned by Frenchmen to avoid Italy like the plague, by northerners not to ride through the Deep South, by mature adults to stay off motorcycles, by country folk not to walk around New York City, by all kinds of people not to fly airplanes, and by clergymen to stay away from girls in high school. I eventually learned that these advisors had two things in common: first, they had almost no experience with the thing they mistrusted; and second, they were always dead wrong.

There was, no doubt, trouble to be found if you went looking for it in certain select industrial neighborhoods of Belfast in Northern Ireland, but our plan was to tour the south of Ireland, reputedly peaceful since it became a republic in 1922. We had a motorcycle, a few hundred dollars, and exactly one week of remaining summer vacation.

We left from Liverpool on a Saturday evening, following a line of cars up a steel ramp into the gaping maw of the *Connought*, our ship to Dublin. Cars were packed bumper to bumper in orderly lines, but a loading foreman directed our bike to one side and pointed to a thick coil of rope on the deck. "Take that," he said, "and lash your motorbike to the rail against the hull, in case the sea gets rough." Our motorbike on this trip was a shaft-drive Suzuki GS650G, kindly lent to us by our English friend Ray Battersby, who works for Suzuki UK and lives near London. We tied the bike down, padding the tank with gloves and scarves so it wouldn't scrape on the hull, and climbed onto the main deck.

There was no danger of rough seas. The ocean was mirror-like as we sailed out of Liverpool and into the Irish Sea, with moonlight shining through the scattered clouds. Traveling on the cheap, as usual, we hadn't paid the extra money for a stateroom, so we spent the night alternately sipping coffee at the snack bar, trying to nap in the reclining chairs on the enclosed foredeck, and looking at maps of Ireland. We pronounced the names of counties aloud, just because they sounded good: Wicklow, Wexford, Waterford and Cork; Kerry, Limerick, Tipperary, Clare and Galway. And then there were the Boggeragh Mountains, the Slieve Bloom Mountains, Blarney, Dingle Bay, and the River Shannon. The whole island looked like a Tolkien invention, full of impossible, imaginary names and places.

Barb spotted Ireland first, just before dawn. She pointed out what I believed to be just another low bank of clouds, but it emerged as a lower, greener cloud lying in the early-morning mist. Our ship steamed into Dublin Harbor and, after much roaring and reversing of the props, bumped solidly against the dock, as if to prove the island was solid and not just a hazy green vision in the Irish Sea. The ramp dropped, and after a quick customs check we accelerated out into Dublin's streets, which were just waking up for Sunday church.

Greater Dublin, we discovered, sprawls over a large area, but its downtown is condensed into a pleasantly small area around the River Liffey. The city has an old, stately feel about it, with very few tall buildings and a lot of Georgian architecture. The houses of Dublin are famous for their neatly painted doors and window casings, contrasting with the gray stone and brass trim.

We rode around the largely empty streets for about half an hour, exploring and waiting for the restaurants to open. "I wonder," I said to Barb at a stoplight on O'Connell Street, "if there's anywhere around her you can get two semifried eggs, two undercooked sausages, two slices of boiled tomato, and a cup of truly terrible coffee."

"This is Ireland," Barb reminded me, "not England."

"I forgot. I wonder if they have the same breakfasts in Ireland?"

We camped at the door of a café whose sign promised the place would open soon and met a young American couple named Steve and Kathy, who were also waiting at the door. We all went in and had the Breakfast Special: two semifried eggs, two undercooked sausages, two slices of boiled tomato, and a cup of truly terrible coffee.

Steve and Kathy gave us the phone number of a good bed-and-breakfast place where they'd stayed and suggested we call after breakfast. "Ask for Mrs. O'Donovan," Steve said.

Mr. O'Donovan answered the phone. "Ah, then," he said, "so it's a room you need. You'll be wanting to talk to my dear wife, then. She's just now returned from mass with our two young boys."

I held the phone and smiled to myself. In America, the man would have said, "Just a minute," and left it at that. In Ireland, people painted you small pictures with words, always in a soft, quicksilver cadence that was easy on the ears.

We found the address on a quiet residential street a few miles away, and Mrs. O'Donovan turned out to be a tall, sparkling woman with a beautifully kept house. She was not at all put off by our Belstaff suits, boots, and motorcycle gear, but seemed genuinely intrigued that a married couple would be traveling in this fashion. "Cold and damp, I should think," she said, bringing us hot tea.

I'd heard motorcycle touring in the British Isles described before, but never quite so succinctly.

After cleaning up and unpacking our luggage, Barb and I rode the much-lightened Suzuki back into the city center, where we ran smack into the annual Children's Day Parade pouring through the middle of Dublin. There were marching bands, soccer clubs, dance troupes, drill teams, etc., all children, marching to the scattered applause and flash photography of their parents. The older kids were confident and showy; the younger ones still wide eyed and wary, wondering what kind of civilization they'd been born into that marched them down the street dressed like little pumpkins and leprechauns and drum majorettes.

We stopped in a pub for a glass of Guinness, and a man at the bar looked out the window and said it wasn't a very good parade. "They do it much better in Texas," he declared, "for the football games. Irish never learn to handle the baton properly as Texas children do. Look at them, dropping the things all over the street." I thought they looked just like the kids from my own grade school, but I'm not from Texas, either.

Barb and I later wandered over to McDaid's pub. McDaid is reputed to be the erstwhile hangout of writer and poet Brendan Behan, who supposedly drank there as a young dog. There was a picture of him on the wall and a collection of students, professors, scarved hangers-on, and other rowdy drinking-and-smoking classes at the bar. We discovered that first night that you have to be careful in Irish pubs because genuine draft Guinness is so easy to drink. Guinness Stout, if you're not already a convert, is a very heavy beer—like brew that has the taste of dark roasted malt with overtones of molasses and licorice and has a color that is closer to black than brown. A friend of mine who hates the stuff says it tastes like burnt wool athletic socks from someone's gym locker, but I've grown quite fond of it. Guinness is the official pub drink of Ireland and is also widely drunk in England, commonly mixed half and half with lighter beers and ales. Great stuff, as they say, but it certainly doesn't help you climb stairs.

In the morning, Barb and I packed our luggage, which consisted of a tank bag and two soft saddlebags, and said goodbye to the O'Donovans. On our way out of Dublin we stopped to see the famous *Book of Kells*, housed in the Long Room of the Trinity Library. The book is a richly illustrated manuscript of the four Gospels, believed to have been written around the year 800 AD in a monastery scriptorium. A woman ahead of me in line peered through the glass at the elaborate Insular Celtic script, intertwined with snakes and tendrils and flowers, and said in a New York accent, "I wundah what it says?"

Her husband snapped back, "How should I know?"

I suppressed an urge to read it for them and make it up as I went along: "Gloria entered the room, flushed from her tennis lesson . . ."

We went south first, along the east coast of Ireland, through Bray, Gaystones, Newcastle, and Wicklow. It took some time to get out of greater Dublin, but once we were free, the two-lane road down the coast was wild and beautiful, sweeping down into one harbor after another and back over the cliffs. The weather was cool and overcast with the sun breaking through thin spots in the clouds occasionally, instantly changing the color of the ocean and the green fields. We stopped for lunch at a little town called Gorey. Lunch, the big meal of the day, consisted of roast pork, potatoes, peas, cabbage, tea, and strawberries with cream. There's nothing terribly subtle about the restaurant food in Ireland, but it's good, and you get a lot of it.

Near Wexford we filled up our gas tank for the first time. Gasoline in Ireland costs about 1.55 Irish pounds (or Punts, as they are properly called) per imperial gallon. Only a few years ago, when the Irish pound was worth around $2.20, this was expensive fuel, but now that the pound is approaching parity with the dollar, Irish gasoline is becoming something of a bargain for Americans, if not for the Irish themselves.

There are no motorways or expressways to speak of in Ireland, so there is a fair amount of commercial traffic on the main roads along the coast and between larger cities. Leave the main roads, however, and the traffic drops off to a desultory mixture of sheep, tractors, the occasional car, cattle, donkey carts, and pedestrians, all traveling at roughly the same speed and spaced well apart. Irish drivers tend to be relaxed and easy-going, with none of the murderous serious-ness you find on the Continent. There is a sense of good-natured flexibility and complete patience. Making time on Irish roads is not in the cards, however, and dragging your knee in corners isn't recommended unless you wish to become one with the back of a hay wagon or are especially fond of sheep.

We stopped for the night at Waterford and found a bed-and-breakfast place overlooking a small square, had dinner nearby, went to a local theater for a well-acted production of *Stagestruck* at the Royal Theater, and then wandered around town, exploring at random.

We came across an Egan's Pub and, naturally, dropped in for a pint. The Egans of my own family were supposed to have migrated to the US from Waterford during the great potato famine. I have to admit that I've always been a little bit skeptical of the Roots Movement, since most of the people I know who are overly concerned with the accomplishments of their forebears seem not to be up to much of anything themselves. Still, it's fascinating to wander the streets of a foreign town and imagine your great-grandparents walking down to the docks and sailing off to a new life in America. My own relatives ended up in Minnesota, apparently because Ireland wasn't cold enough for them, or had too few mosquitoes.

Waterford, like many of the cities we rode through, is laced with ancient walls, fragments of towers, bits of old monasteries, and other ruins. Old stone structures that would be national landmarks in the US are so common in Ireland that no one pays them much mind, and they are often integrated into lesser but more modern buildings. The ruins of a thirteenth-century guard tower become the north wall of a tin-roofed auto-repair shop, part of a medieval city wall is used as one side of a pink stucco beauty parlor, and so on. It's an odd mixture of the old and the new, the elegant and the garish.

On the way back to our room in the evening we stopped to talk to an old woman who was leaning out the front window of her small house. "It's good to see a young man and wife walking together," she said. "Now that the pubs serve food and allow women inside, there's no reason a'tall for a man to come home to his family any more . . ."

If she thinks it's bad now, I thought, wait'll they discover *Space Invaders*.

In the morning we rode out to the Waterford Crystal factory at the edge of the city and watched the glassblowers and cutters at work. I'd never seen such a cheerful, good-natured bunch of workers in any factory, but then, the last fac-tory I worked at was a gunpowder plant, where anxiety was our most important product. Barb and I bought a crystal salt-and-pepper-shaker set, after voting them most likely to succeed in a tank bag. Wine glasses and chandeliers were out of the question.

We rode south through Dungarvan and Cork along the coast and then inland to Killarney. Killarney had a large tourist trade because it's the jumping-off point for a beautiful loop of roads around the mountainous Kerry Peninsula. The route is called the Ring of Kerry. We found a nice old hotel in Killarney, and after dinner went looking for some authentic Irish folk music. "This is a big tourist town," I told Barb. "They've got to have a good club somewhere."

We found a pub with a big sign that said "Live Music Tonight" and sat down inside with a drink. A band showed up—four guys in cowboy shirts and bandanas—proceeded to set up their equipment and then launched into a half hour of Waylon Jennings and Willie Nelson tunes. "Not exactly the Boys of the Lough or the Sands Family, are they?" I said to Barb over the thumping Fender bass and the whining steel guitar. When we left, they were singing "Don't Let Your Babies Grow Up to be Cowboys" in perfect Texas twang.

In the morning we rode south along the forested shore of Lake Leane, in the first real sunlight of the trip. When we came to open meadow and mountain country near the coast, we stopped on a hilltop to look over the landscape. If Paris, as Henry Miller said, is composed of a hundred different shades of gray, then Ireland has at least as many shades of green; grass green, moss green, tree green, meadow green, etc. When the sun comes out from behind a cloud, the effect is stunning, like the switch from black-and-white film to color in *The Wizard of Oz*. There's a shifting, moody quality to the light, and the sky seems to move over the island at a faster-than-normal pace.

Partway down the Kerry Peninsula we decided to get away from the tour buses and turned inland on a narrow road that wound through a mountain range with the strange name of the Maggillycuddy's Reeks. This almost empty road took us through a rugged landscape of rocky valleys, sheep farms, peat bogs, abandoned houses, cemeteries filled with Celtic crosses, old stone churches, walls, and the ruins of walls. We came to several forks in the road and made our choices at random. The scenery and the road were so perfect for motorcycling, we really didn't care where we were going.

Until late in the afternoon. We suddenly decided it was time to start wending our way back to civilization or we'd be sleeping on the moors; just us, the Suzuki and its empty gas tank, and whatever it is that howls on the moors at night.

Luckily, you're never far from friendly advice, even in the remotest parts of Ireland. In the countryside everywhere there is a class of individual we came to call the Solitary Walking Man. You see them miles from anywhere, walking along the roads in neat caps, ties, and jackets, walking with canes, walking with hands behind their backs, or strolling along smoking pipes. A sociologist would probably tell us this phenomenon is economic—the cost of fuel, the cost of cars, etc. Personally, I'd like to think that most of the people walk from one place to another because the country is so lovely that a ride is simply a missed opportunity.

We were pointed toward the coast by an old gentleman in tweeds who was walking with his sheepdog. By nightfall we'd found a nice bed-and-breakfast place in the little town of Tarbert, at the mouth of the River Shannon. When we signed the guest register, the landlady looked at what I had written and said, "Ah, you're American. I thought you were English. You have English registration on your motorbike." I looked back at the bike and wondered how many other people had made that same mistake. Probably quite a few, but no one, on the highways or elsewhere, had shown us anything but courtesy and hospitality. In some places I could think of, just being a motorcyclist would have lowered the level of warmth and charm. This lady had cheerfully showed us a room, thinking we were English motorcyclists.

There is a saying in Ireland that if you don't like the weather, just wait a minute. Generally that's true, but sometimes the weather takes more than a minute to change. Sometimes it can take several hours. And if it's gusting a cold, driving rain off the North Sea and you're on a motorcycle, it can take days. We rode toward Galway on a couple of those days.

Barb and I were both wearing Belstaff jackets of the black, waxed-cotton variety, with matching Belstaff pants. They worked great in those famous one-minute Irish showers, but in a steady, lashing rainstorm they began to wick moisture through the inner lining, and by the time we reached Limerick we were so wet we didn't care anymore. In an effort to close the barn door after the horse got drenched, we stopped at a Limerick sporting-goods store and bought the closest thing we could find to Dry Rider suits—a couple of rubberized canvas duck-hunting outfits, olive drab in color.

Slightly warmer, we rode through some of the prettiest scenery on the trip— thatched cottages, the towering cliffs of Moher, endless castle ruins, etc.—all glimpsed through face shields streaming with water and fogged from within. It just wasn't a motorcycle day. We sloshed our way into Galway late in the afternoon and took a room at the first structure with a "Hotel" sign on the wall.

Our hotel turned out to be, essentially, an old men's rooming house with a few extra rooms, the kind where the wallpaper, carpets, and paint were all finalists in some long-forgotten eyesore contest. We draped our wet jackets and riding gear around the room to dry and went down the hall for a hot bath. The hot water was cold, so the hotel clerk said to wait an hour and it would be warmer, which we did, but it wasn't.

The heating of water seems to be something of a black art in most parts of the world I've visited, except for Switzerland, Germany, Japan, and the US The English and the Irish manage to get it sort of hot at certain hours of the day if you give them plenty of notice, while the French succeed in heating water only in coffee makers. Spaniards (as nearly as we could tell during the month we spent touring the Iberian hinterlands) are not aware of any process by which potential bath water can be heated. I've often thought that some benevolent American plumbing magnate should send a missionary to Europe with a cut-away water heater and a pointer, just to pass the technology along and get the ball rolling.

Ireland is a country of not much heat but plenty of warm blankets, so our pneumonia was relatively mild the next morning and had not spread to both lungs. We poked around Galway, then had lunch at a pub, sharing a table with two old retired farmers. One had no teeth or hair, and the other had one eye, a badly scarred lip, and a bandaged hand with yellow iodine stains around his fingers and wrist. We bought each other a couple of drinks and then settled down to a potato, cabbage, and bacon meal.

"So you're American," the one-eyed man said, dropping some food on his lap and deftly returning it to his plate with the side of a butter knife. "Did you know that John Wayne once came to Galway and had his famous fistfight with Victor McLaglen right here, and that John Ford came in this very pub when he was filming a famous American movie called *The Quiet Man?*" I confessed we hadn't known. "Aye," he said, "I saw them all, and I've been to America myself to visit my brother in Baltimore." He dropped some food and searched for it with his good eye, but the food had fallen out of range. "The Americans ask for a lot," he continued, "but they give you a lot when you go there."

"Ah well," said the bald one agreeably, "They work hard and save their money and deserve a good time."

When we'd left the pub, I said to Barb, "There are times when this country makes me feel like Jim Hawkins in *Treasure Island*. At least one of those guys should have had a parrot on his shoulder."

It was almost time for us to go back to working hard and saving for a good time, so we had to turn away from the coast and the stark beauty of Galway to head back toward Dublin. Central Ireland, south of Lough Ree and through Westmeath, is gently rolling country with relatively straight roads, so we made good time.

Regardless of the roads, however, speeding across the countryside is difficult, and I told Barb that the Tourist Bureau should issue horse blinders to travelers who have to follow a schedule, especially if they own cameras. That's the tragedy of traveling in Ireland with a camera: You could stop anywhere in the country and shoot up a roll of film while turning on your heel in a 360-degree arc. You are surrounded everywhere with achingly beautiful scenery, ancient buildings, interesting people, and whatnot. You just have to shrug it off and breeze by castles, ruins, churches, and charming villages without a second look. There just isn't time to investigate everything.

One thing we did stop to investigate, however, was a pub in the little town of Moate, which had a sign that said "P. Egan" over the door. We went in, and the owner, a quiet, friendly man in his forties, introduced himself as Peter Egan. "That's my name, too," I said. We bought each other drinks, and he gave me a handful of Guinness labels with our mutual name printed at the bottom. "These are leftover from the days when we used to bottle our own stout for customers," he said. I gave him a couple of *Cycle World* business cards with the same name on them, and then we said goodbye.

We rode hard for the rest of the afternoon, looking neither to the left nor to the right, averting our eyes from the scenery. We had a boat to catch in the morning and could not be distracted. The Suzuki had run so flawlessly and needed so little maintenance (i.e., none) in our one week of touring that I'd stopped expecting anything else. It occurred to me on that last stretch of road that a 650 was almost exactly the right size for two-up tour in a country the size of Ireland, and possibly at the upper limit of necessity. The narrow, winding roads, the mixture of rural traffic and animal life, not to mention the frequent need to stop, park, and explore, made maneuverability far more useful than huge reserves of acceleration and horsepower. Speeding through Ireland made about as much sense as rushing through a good dinner or a close friendship.

We made it to Dublin late in the afternoon and checked into a bed-and-breakfast place on the north side of the city. We cleaned up, put on our last change of clean clothes, and rode out to a peninsula named Howth Head. We found a famous old place called the Abbey Tavern, had a wonderful salmon dinner, and stayed to hear the abbey singers do Irish ballads and folk songs. After a couple of Irish coffees, we rode back to the bed-and-breakfast late in the evening. In the morning we had a breakfast of two semicooked eggs, two undercooked sausages, two slices of boiled tomato, and a cup of truly terrible coffee.

"From dust we came . . ." I said to Barb.

"I'm beginning to like these breakfasts," she said.

"So am I. Time to go home."

Our departure from the island was like a movie played backward. We tied our bike down in the ship's hold again and went up on the deck to watch Ireland move east on the horizon. Perhaps 10 miles out, the land became that same low, green shape on the water, and in another 5 miles the clouds and mist had swallowed it up. I stood on the deck for a long time, watching seagulls and the wake of the boat, and thinking what a pitifully short time one week was to spend in a place like Ireland.

A motorcycle is almost always one of the best ways to see a country as it should be seen and to get under the surface. And yet, in leaving Ireland, I almost felt as though we'd seen it from the train. It was too complex, an island of too much depth and too many layers. It was a place that demanded a summer of our time, at least, and maybe a slower motorcycle. Or one that broke down a lot.

As our boat approached the coast of England late in the afternoon, I thought about all the well-meaning people who had advised us not to go to Ireland, and I wondered if they were related, in some spiritual sense, to the same people who warned us never to ride a motorcycle.

GUITARS AND MOTORBIKES

"HOW MANY GUITARS DO YOU HAVE NOW?"** I asked my old friend David Rhodes this summer when I dropped by for a visit. David is a writer who lives on a farm in Wisconsin and collects vintage electric guitars.

"About four dozen," he said.

David and I get along pretty well, probably because I'm one of the few people he knows who doesn't bat an eye at the idea of owning four dozen electric guitars. I not only approve but applaud. Besides being a kind of fascinating historical archive done in hardwood, varnish, and mother-of-pearl, David's collection has the added value of making my own paltry hoard of six guitars look like the work of a sane man. In other words, my wife thought I was out of my mind until she met David. Now I appear almost normal. Shoplifting pales next to the Great Train Robbery.

It's hard to explain to an outsider why a man would want more than one electric guitar. (In high school, it was hard to explain to my parents why a man would want even *one.*) Unless you are steeped in the history and aesthetics of rock 'n' roll, blues, jazz, or country music, you aren't likely to care that Chuck Berry sounds best on an ES-355 Gibson, or that Fender Stratocasters with maple necks sound and feel different from those with rosewood necks. (Clapton uses a maple-neck version; 'nuff said.) Old guitars are both cultural icons and expressions of mood, so if you feel like playing a Les Paul Gibson and all you've got is a Gretsch Country Gentleman, you're just flat out of luck. Stuck with Greek, when you're hungry for Mexican.

Motorcycles, of course, are the same way. At least for some of us.

It is possible to get by with just one motorcycle, I'm told, and lead a fairly normal life. Single-bike ownership, after all, is the very thing for which dual-purpose motorcycles were created: to go anywhere and do everything reasonably well. Get yourself a good XL or KLR 600 and you can ride to the Arctic Circle, see the dusty side of Baja, commute to work, or carve up a canyon, all on one bike. You're set for life, right?

Wrong. Dual purpose is about six purposes too few, if life is to have the proper balance and variety. For instance, what if you've got an XL600 in the garage and suddenly take a fancy to the idea of polishing and admiring the kind of inch-deep chrome pipes and mufflers found only on old Nortons and

Triumphs? Ever try to find one piece of good chrome on a modern dual-purpose bike? Or what if you do own an old Triumph and want to ride to the Arctic Circle but are not fond of hitchhiking in the cold and living with timber wolves? What if you've got a nice, long-legged BMW for touring but suddenly get homesick for the insane race-bike whoop of a high-revving Japanese four?

Funny you should ask. Those are the very questions I've been asking myself lately.

The reason, as you might have guessed by now, is that I've had the same two bikes for nearly five years—a KZ1000 Mk II and an old XL350. Good bikes. Great bikes, even. Trouble-free, competent, honest machines on which I can go almost anywhere, across continents or deep into the desert. The discerning eye will note, however, that there are no British singles or vertical twins in this little collection of two; no American or Italian V-twins; no lightweight canyon screamers with the souls of GP bikes; no tall-geared German boxers to lope over the open highway with seven-league boots. In other words, I've got some serious gaps here, holes through which you could drive an aesthetic, philosophical, and functional truck.

The cause of the problem is that for the past five years, my wife, Barbara, and I have been Saving for a House. Yep. The original gold-plated guilt trip. The one you see reflected in the bloodshot eyes of houseguests who've slept on the hide-a-bed in the living room once too often (the one with the steel bar across the rib cage, just beneath the Wonder Bread–thin mattress), their mute, accusing stares asking, "How can a guy spend all his money on motorcycles and live in such a tiny excuse for a house? Why doesn't his wife divorce him? And, while we're at it, who's in the bathroom?"

Well, we sold some bikes, saved our money, and, just this year, bought the house. Three bedrooms, two bathrooms, family room, nice yard with rosebushes and trees, two-car garage. The world is now safe for houseguests and relatives; the dreaded hide-a-bed is gone. I've paid my debt to society, and the guilt trip is over.

Buying the house was Plan A. Now it's time to activate Plan B.

Plan B is a complex, long-imagined strategy in which I make up for lost time and past error by gradually tracking down clean versions of at least three of the bikes I never should have sold and a few others I've never owned but always admired. First on the list is a late-1960s high-pipe 650 Triumph TR6C Trophy Special. After that I'll stay flexible, ear to the ground, eyes peeled, for targets of opportunity, like the '74 black-and-gold Norton 850 Commando, and the Honda CB400F, and the . . . well, I won't run on. One thing at a time. I'll find them all, eventually, if there's any money left after house payments.

The only other thing that could possibly slow me down is if I run across a certain Les Paul Gibson, the famous Black Beauty model with three humbucking pickups. The kind Keith Richards used to play . . .

GARAGE IKEBANA

ALL I CAN SAY IS I'm glad there's no such thing as a surprise psychiatric inspection. You know, an unannounced raid on your home, a Freudian version of what the fire inspector does when he suddenly drops in on your place of business and writes you up for having oily rags smoldering in uncovered cans. If psychiatrists did spot checks, I'd have been taken away for sure.

It was a Thursday night, and there I was, out in the garage all by myself (wife gone visiting), drinking hot sake, positioning a chair in each corner of the garage like points on a compass, and moving three vehicles around into various experimental poses and juxtapositions—just like a Japanese *ikebana* artist arranging fern stalks and lotus blossoms in the most pleasing and Zenful way.

And—speaking of Lotus—one of the three machines was a car by that name, a 1964 Lotus Super Seven. The Super Seven is a lightweight English roadster that has been called "a motorcycle on four wheels," which, of course, it isn't. A motorcycle has two wheels, and that's that. Never mind that we now have touring bikes that outweigh cars.

But I digress. Let's backtrack a bit. Here's the deal:

About three weeks ago, I traveled to my home state of Wisconsin to pick up the Lotus and trailer it back to California behind a Chevy van. My old friend and employer Chris Beebe agreed to take a short leave from his foreign-car repair shop in Madison and help with the driving. After we'd loaded our luggage and spare Lotus parts, I said to Chris, "Wow, there's a lot of empty space in the back of this van. What else have you got around here that I need?"

"Well, I have two red 1975 400F Hondas," Chris said, grinning, "and I'm using only one." I'd been hinting strongly for about ten years that he might like to sell me his spare 400F, so we wheeled it into the back of the van and hauled the bike to California along with the car.

No sooner had we arrived home and offloaded these treasures than I picked up the local newspaper, perused the motorcycle classifieds as usual, and found my breathing suddenly arrested. Under the heading "TRIUMPH", which very seldom appears any more, was an ad that read: "67 TR6C 650cc, stock, classic, immaculate, 13,000 mi., $1,295 obo."

Now, I don't know about you, but I had been looking for a clean, complete, unbent, unraced, unchopped, unchromed, unruined, stock, late-1960s high-pipe single-carb Triumph 650 TR6C (or Trophy, as they called it some years) forever. Since 1967, actually. Only a few of these bikes have turned up for sale over the years, and always at the worst possible time, like while I'm standing in line to buy lifeboat tickets on a sinking steamer, or during some similar crisis.

This time wasn't much better. I was almost broke, and there's something wretchedly excessive about stuffing three new/used project vehicles into your garage within any twenty-four-hour period, even for me. But still, a Triumph TR6C . . . the Holy Grail itself.

I called the owner, got directions to his house, found the Triumph to be as clean and original as advertised (the engine was a little clattery, but these things can be fixed), gave him a $100 deposit, and went to the bank. The following evening I paid for the bike and rode it home on the Pacific Coast Highway, the dual side mufflers booming through the night, waves crashing on the moonlit empty beaches, Lucas headlight flaring and dimming with the rise and fall of revs. It was wonderful.

When I got home and parked the Triumph in the garage, there was no one around to share my elation, but I felt that some sort of celebration was in order. Usually, I open a bottle of Guinness Stout on these occasions, but there was nothing in the refrigerator except a few cans of Coors Light, which seemed too weak a brew for such a heady moment. So I heated up a bottle of sake, which has a certain ceremonial aura about it (never mind that Edward Turner was probably spinning in his grave), and returned to the garage.

It was then, unobserved by anyone except our two cats, that I began the experimental placement of the three machines for most harmonious viewing. Garage *ikebana*, the new art form. After many false chess moves and shuffles, I finally discovered the magic combination. Many personal interpretations are possible, but in the end I concluded that the Lotus looked best from the front left quarter because of its superb nose and fenderline, the Honda 400F from the right front quarter where the sensuous curves of its 4-into-1 headers can be seen, and the Triumph from the left rear, where its pipes and the waspish narrowness of the tank were most visible. With all these angles and elements properly arranged, I sat back for a long time and studied the three machines.

Suddenly I focused in on the Triumph, its pipes, the air cleaner, the lovely tank, the perfect chromed bullet headlamp, the just-right curve of the sloping seatback, the artful finning of the cylinder head, and realized that I was seeing perfection within perfection, *dharma* within *dharma*, a garage load of stuff that was fun to look at, where the true pleasure of it began with the smallest things.

All three machines were designed in different places by different people, yet each designer knew that beauty starts with a thoughtful sympathy for the pieces that make up the whole. "We're talking *oneness* here," I explained to the cats, "the kind that radiates outward and gravitates inward." They blinked calmly.

I poured another cup of hot sake, held up a toast to the people at Lotus, Honda, and Triumph who cared enough for detail to give us their best, and whispered, prayerlike, "Hot damn."

ALAS, ALBION

I **WOKE UP IN THE NIGHT** feeling uneasy, half dreaming something in the house was wrong. It was an odor. The human nose has a way of sending wake-up calls to the brain, probably dating back to the caveman's fear and loathing of wolf breath, and mine had phoned a message that something was not quite right.

I sat up in bed and sniffed the air, confused for a moment. Then I relaxed. It was only the Triumph.

Ah, the British.

The aroma that filled our house had its source in the garage but had somehow found its way to the bedroom through a 5-by-7-inch cat door, across an entire dining room, and down a long hallway to the exact opposite corner of the house. Still, there was no mistaking it for anything other than the distinctive fragrance of leaded gasoline leaking past the float-bowl gasket of an Amal Monobloc carburetor, and from there dripping its way onto the engine cases beneath, like slow Chinese water torture. Even in the dark, I could picture the entire process.

It wasn't merely the smell of raw gasoline. It was a special English smell you get when a perfectly controlled rate of eternal seepage allows gasoline to half evaporate before it drips, leaving a thick red deposit of lead and heavy mineral spirits on the underside of a carb body, along with a smell so pungent you suspect that fossil fuel might be reverting to its original state of primordial soup in a warm tropical sea. There are other elements in the aroma, of course, like mildly decayed, cotton-insulated wiring, old foam beneath the vinyl seat cover, and motor oil heated and chilled a hundred times on the outside of the engine; however, the main ingredient, I think, is still gasoline, or whatever remains when the volatile ghost of gasoline has left the scene.

Like a farmer who feels compelled to get up and see why the dogs are barking, I heaved myself out of bed to go check the Triumph, just to make sure I hadn't left a petcock open, flooding the garage floor with fuel. I got dressed and shuffled out to the garage to have a look.

No major leaks or oil spills, just the usual seeps. A warm spring wind was blowing against the garage door, no doubt wafting the smell into our house with more force than usual. I ran my finger along the underside of the Amal, and there was the usual residue, oozing thickly red. Despite my best efforts.

The float-bowl side cover had been leaking badly when I bought the Triumph, so my first action on the bike's behalf had been an attempted repair. The carburetor had been designed to leak, of course; nobody but a child, inexperienced in the ways of the world, would seriously believe that a flat metal plate, a paper gasket, and three screws would hold back a reservoir full of a sneaky, low-viscosity fluid like gasoline for long, especially if the carburetor were rigidly attached to a hot, vibratory 650cc vertical-twin motorcycle engine.

"Use two gaskets," my friend Bill Getty at British Parts Old and New had told me. "That usually cures the problem."

So, I'd put on two gaskets, after carefully checking the plate for flatness and filing down the small, raised volcanoes around the screw holes where the metal had pulled through. It still leaked. Next, I would try various glues and gasket cements from my large drawer of same. Sooner or later, I'd find a solution.

What was needed, of course, was a rubber O-ring. Not only a rubber O-ring, but a float bowl designed like a cup rather than a bass drum, allowing the bowl to have its sealing surface above the fuel line. Like the one on my '82 Honda XL500, which sat nearby. (Triumph later switched to a concentric Amal with *real* float bowls that didn't leak as much, except when you deliberately made them overflow by using the starting ticklers.)

What was it, I wondered, that so mystified and eluded British engineers when it came to the design of gaskets, seals, and mated surfaces? They never did get the idea, right up until the end, that fluids belong on the inside of an engine, while fresh air and sunshine belong on the outside, and that there is seldom any real advantage in having these disparate elements swap sides, except in the case of combustion gasses.

All of the British bikes and cars I'd owned had leaked one or more fluids from some orifice. I'd never owned a British airplane, but Spitfire pilots tell us in their memoirs that the smell of hot, leaking glycol from that big, water-cooled Merlin is one of their most pungent memories of flight.

Old road tests I'd seen in English publications had actually suggested that oil leakage was a desirable trait in motorcycles and cars because it preserved their lower extremities from rust.

Leakage is so universal in these machines, it has now become part of the lore and romance of owning British, and half the fun of restoring an old Triumph, Norton, or BSA lies in reducing fluid loss to a minimum through careful assembly, subtle filework, double gaskets, aftermarket sealants, and right thinking.

Still, as I sat in the garage and looked at the Triumph, I couldn't help wondering where the British motorcycle industry would be today if they had discovered O-rings, precision surfacing, and horizontally split engine cases. Some people simply won't forgive a motorcycle that wakes them up in the night. Others of us are willing to overlook a little nighttime seepage—provided the bike doesn't put us to sleep during the daytime.

FIRST IMPRESSIONS

IN THE OPENING SCENE of the movie we find ourselves looking down on a motorcycle parked in front of a garage or shed, on a paved driveway. The motorcycle has a chrome-plated tank, in the old English fashion, and is bristling with rods and levers and interesting hardware. The apparent owner, a young blond fellow, is methodically, almost lovingly, tending to the motorcycle. He wipes off real or imaginary smudges with a rag and carefully adds oil to the side tank from an antique-looking oil container. We aren't told the time of day, but from the sunlight it looks like early morning, and there is a relaxed aspect to the man's movement that makes us think it might be a Sunday. When the motorcycle is ready, he sets several of the levers, just so, and lowers a set of round government-surplus-looking goggles over his eyes. A boot makes a sharp stab at the kick-starter, and the engine, a big V-twin, fires to life. The camera shows us a brief glimpse of the engine. It has the initials JAP on its polished cases.

Now the bike is moving through a village, around a road-repair crew and then onto an open country lane. The rider shifts up through the gears, going faster and faster, with that big V-twin making glorious music. There's a shot of the rider, grinning to himself as patches of sunlight flicker rapidly across his face. The trees on both sides of the road are beginning to blur into a golden-green haze, and the rider's head bobs erratically with the motorcycle's stiff suspension. The bike and rider are really moving now, and the narrow pavement is flowing by at an impressive rate. Suddenly there are children on bicycles in the road, the rider brakes and swerves, and we see a shot of the motorcycle, riderless, hurtling over a ditch, then lying on its side in a hedgerow. Wrecked.

The movie, of course, is *Lawrence of Arabia*, and the blond fellow was a young, newly discovered Peter O'Toole, playing Lawrence himself. The motorcycle was a Brough Superior with an engine supplied by JA Prestwich. The movie was made in 1962, and I first saw it when I was a highly impressionable fourteen years of age. Twenty-seven years ago.

When it was announced several months ago that *Lawrence of Arabia* was returning to the big screen, reedited, expanded, and better than ever, I started a daily vigil, watching the newspapers to see when the movie would open. I, for one, planned to be there on the first night, seated front and center with a large supply of popcorn and Junior Mints.

cademartori '18

Besides being a magnificent piece of cinema in its own right, Sir David Lean's *Lawrence* was one of two powerful influences that caused me, way back in 1962, to suddenly turn my back on years of folk wisdom and parental advice and take up the sport of motorcycling. The entire movie was memorable, but it was those opening few minutes of footage that stayed with me when I walked out of the theater, slightly dazed.

What, of all things on earth, I thought while riding my bicycle home from the movie, could possibly be more perfect than to have a motorcycle, and to wheel it out of a garage early on a sunny morning, wipe it off with a rag, check the oil, ride quietly through town to warm it up, then go hurtling down an empty country road, listening to the engine and feeling the wind in your face?

The answer, of course, was that nothing could be more perfect. Nothing. On that day, a general curiosity about motorcycles was solidified into a genuine passion. I was hooked.

Just to make sure the hook was in good and deep, fate stepped in with a second tug of the monofilament about one week later. I found myself hitchhiking, without much success, to a junkyard in the nearby town of New Lisbon, Wisconsin. (I used to spend a lot of my spare time wandering around junkyards, sitting in old cars, smoking cigarettes, avoiding mud wasps, etc.) I'd been standing by the highway for some time when two full-dress Harleys came thundering by. To my amazement, the front rider signaled a stop and pulled over. I ran up to the bike, and an older man in a white T-shirt and a yacht-captain's hat grinned and said, "Hop on."

I climbed on the back of a huge sprung saddle with fringe and conchos and we roared on down the road. I remember looking over the guy's shoulder at the speedometer and noting that we were going 80 mph The whole ride was a crazy overload of sounds and sensations: too much to take in. What struck me about it, though, was the absolute sense of freedom. I looked around myself at the Harley and thought, "With one of these you could go anywhere." On that big motorcycle, the open road seemed to beckon endlessly as it never had when I rode in a car.

I never made it to the junkyard that day. The two Harleys stopped at the New Lisbon Harley-Davidson shop to see about some parts or service, and I spent the rest of the afternoon hovering around the edges of the hardcore bike crowd who hung out there, listening to their talk and trying to learn something about motorcycles. It was the beginning of a habit that persists to this day. While other people are out shopping at the mall, I'm usually hanging around a motorcycle shop.

A few years ago my friend John Oakey asked how I got interested in bikes and I told him this story about going to the movie and then hitching my first ride on the Harley. He laughed and said, "Jeez. I saw *Lawrence of Arabia* that same year and vowed that I would *never* ride a motorcycle. The guy got *killed*, for God's sake!"

I just shrugged. "A fluke," I said. "Bad timing."

There's no accounting for what grabs people's attention and what doesn't. But Sir David Lean and the friendly guy on the Harley certainly captured mine. If there is such a thing as compound interest on a good idea, I owe them both more than I could possibly repay.

THE MUSEUM OF PREHISTORIC HELMETS

I **HAVE THIS DREAM** occasionally that my wife, Barbara, and I will turn up missing and the police will come to our house to look for clues. After picking the lock or prying the door open with a crowbar, the chief detective and his assistant will wander around our house for a few minutes, hands thrust deep into their trench-coat pockets, saying nothing. Then, finally, one of them will speak.

"What do you make of it, Bob?"

"I dunno. You tell me."

"Strangest thing I've ever seen. Helmets everywhere."

"Pretty sick."

We've all got our weaknesses, and one of mine is that I've probably got a few more motorcycle helmets around the house than I actually need for my own protection. There are four or five lined up on top of the bookcase, like so many beer steins in a Heidelberg fencing club, and at least one or two more lurking in every closet in the house.

Some of these helmets are perfectly modern things that I use daily, while others represent either a refusal to dispose of the past or a suspicion that I might someday need one for some kind of Halloween costume. (For the same reason, I've kept my army uniform and a paisley shirt that looks like something from a *Monkees* rerun.) At any rate, there are too many helmets.

After trying to clean out my den room and closet this weekend, I decided I should do one of two things: either (a) give most of my helmets away to needy children in the neighborhood,or (b) get a grant from the Smithsonian to open a helmet wing of the science and technology museum, or at least have them erect a small display called "Twenty-Four Years of Progress in Head Protection, 1965–1989."

I like the museum idea better than the notion of giving them away. A nice little display at the Smithsonian would get most of the helmets out of my den, but I could still visit them. They could be organized in the order acquired, as follows:

EXHIBIT A: We'd have an empty pedestal here, a memorial to the Missing Helmet. My first helmet was a Bell TX500, white in color, bought in 1965.

I paid $38 for it, shunning the $19 metalflake discount-store variety, because I was sure it was the last helmet I would ever need to buy. It was stolen off a parcel rack in the men's restroom of the chemistry building at the University of Wisconsin in Madison while I stood nearby, helpless, in the vicinity of a tall porcelain fixture. The guy who stole it looked like a cross between Corporal Klinger (without the cocktail dress) and Dustin Hoffman as Ratso Rizzo. If you see a guy who looks like this, wearing a TX500, call me collect.

EXHIBIT B: Bell TX500, replacement for the above helmet, only I still have this one. It's a beautifully made helmet with soft earpads of genuine leather and a 1968 Snell sticker inside. I painted it dark blue once, Dan Gurney fashion, but then my roommate borrowed it to ride his Triumph to Chicago and threw it through a plaster-and-lath wall after a fight with a girlfriend, scratching the paint, so I changed it back to white. I thought this helmet was cool at the time, but it looks dated and tight fitting now, with the effect that the wearer's head appears to have been shrunken by pygmies. I continued to wear it occasionally until just a few years ago, when then-*CW* executive editor John Ulrich told me I looked like a nerd. I checked in the mirror and saw he was correct. Now the helmet sits on a shelf.

EXHIBIT C: One Everoak brand helmet, white in color, with the reassuring legend "Manufactured to British Standard" stitched into its red silk lining. This is without a doubt the oldest helmet I own, though I have no idea what year it was manufactured because it was thrown in free with a used Honda CB160 I once bought. It has a genuine cork inner shell, and the outer shell is made of some semiflexible substance that looks like canvas impregnated with glue. I used to call this helmet "the Dive-Bomber" because its pudding-bowl shape required that the accident victim arc through the air with a certain amount of precision and land directly on top of his head. Otherwise it was useless. My roommate Barry wore the trusty Everoak Dive-Bomber to a campus antiwar demonstration to protect his head from nightstick-wielding riot police. As I recall, the police caught right on to this little trick and poked him in the stomach. Not that the helmet would have done any good.

EXHIBIT D: A 1975 Bell Star. We're getting into the modern era here. This was the first popular full-face helmet. I hated these things when they first came out because I thought they made you look like a propane tank with eyes, but I later grew to like them. Especially after I crashed my Box Stock KZ550 at Riverside. Without that chin piece, I'd still be eating oatmeal through a straw. This helmet has a big streak of Turn Seven blacktop embedded in its shell. It did its job, leaving me without so much as a headache, so I retired it and bought a newer version of same.

EXHIBIT E: A Bell RT, open faced, blue in color. This was my dirt helmet, until a spinning back tire tossed up a piece of Mojave Desert, which I cleverly caught in my mouth like a dog going after a Milk-Bone. Now, for desert riding, I wear . . .

EXHIBIT F: A Bell Moto III, with chin protector.

I suppose I'd better cut the museum donations off there, or I'll end up with only three or four helmets for everyday use. Which would be almost as bad as having only three or four motorcycle jackets.

Which brings up another terrific idea for a museum display . . .

IN THE LAND OF THE LONG WHITE CLOUD

Touring New Zealand by Triumph 1200 and F650 Beemer

"**H**ERE'S THE KEY TO YOUR ROOM, SIR,**"** the cheerful woman at the reception desk said. "Would you like some nice fresh milk?" She held out a cold, dripping carton of milk.

Okay. Non-sequitur time. My mind was addled for a moment. Maybe because I'd been on an airplane for seventeen hours.

"Uh, thank you," I said, taking the carton. Perhaps it was the custom here to slam down a carton of milk every time you checked into a hotel room. Good health practice. Yet no one else in the lobby seemed to be drinking the stuff.

"It's for your afternoon tea," she said, smiling. "There's a tea kettle in your room."

"Ah."

Needless to say, we weren't in Kansas anymore. We weren't even in Wisconsin or California. We were, in fact, about 1,400 miles southeast of Oz, on the Colorado-sized twin-island nation of New Zealand, which I am here to tell you is a long way from anywhere, but none the worse for it.

More specifically, we were on a Beach's Motorcycle Adventure tour called the "Maori Meander," Editor Edwards and I. We'd boarded an airliner in L.A. just before midnight of an October's eve and awakened to a clear golden dawn over the endless blue South Pacific. An hour later the airplane banked, and we could see New Zealand, or at least the long streaks of gray and white cloud that obscured New Zealand, off to starboard.

"Land of the Long White Cloud" was what the first Polynesian settlers, the Maoris (pronounced MAU-reez), had called these two big islands when they arrived in their open boats one thousand years ago. The mountaintops rising out of the sea make their own weather, forcing the moist Pacific air to rise and deliver.

Through holes in the broken ceiling we could see emerald-green sheep pasture and thick forest, then the mostly single-story houses and businesses of

Auckland as the plane descended over Manukau Harbour (says the map) and landed. Lovely modern airport, but built on a human scale, just the right size. It's like landing on the set of *Casablanca*.

At the airport we hook up with Rob Beach himself, whose parents started this touring company (2763 West River Parkway, Grand Island, NY 14072-2087; 716/773-4960) in Europe, years ago. Rob, a former WERA roadracer, now lives in Niagara, New York, but leads New Zealand tours every chance he gets. He loves the country and has made a lot of Kiwi friends. We also met the other seven members of our tour group—two married couples (the Werners from New Jersey and the Kulls from Florida) and several random single guys—and our other guide, a New Zealander from Christchurch named Bob Wilkins.

On the van ride from the airport it starts to rain. Hard. Someone asks Rob Beach what the weather forecast is like for the rest of the week.

"Hot and dusty," Rob says quickly, establishing a phrase that will be our standing joke for the rest of the tour.

It doesn't rain all the time in New Zealand, but it is seldom dusty. The climate, like the landscape, seems to combine elements of Washington State, Scotland, southern England, and the Canadian Rockies. Also, October is early spring in New Zealand, about like March or April in the Midwest. We will end up using our rain gear about every other day.

To say I've been looking forward to this trip would be an egregious understatement. First, there's the appeal of seeing a new country, which I know only from stunning travel posters and by reputation, for its legion of great racers, mountain climbers, bungee jumpers, yachtsmen, fighter pilots, ANZAC military heroes, and other rugged outdoor risk-takers. It's a country where laughing at danger seems to be a national pastime.

And there is the added inducement that David Edwards and I are to ride a pair of new and (for us) untried bikes: a British Racing Green Triumph Trophy 1200 and a BMW F650 "Funduro." A big roadburner and a lightweight, agile single. Perfect yin-yang combo.

The afternoon rain clears, and we drive over to a large Harley/Honda/Triumph dealership called, ambiguously, Shaft Motors to pick up the Trophy 1200. There we meet New Zealand's Triumph importer, a bearded, affable fellow named Geoff Robinson, and I get to see my first new-generation Triumph in the flesh. It's stunning. Luminous dark green with Union Jack emblems. Handsome also are the Laverda-orange Speed Triple and the black Daytona. Hot damn; the Brits are back in business.

Geoff Robinson tells us the bikes have been virtually trouble free and have been selling well to Harley owners who want more performance. The bikes, he says, have great appeal to traditionalists, as well as sportbike buffs. It turns out we will be borrowing two Triumphs, at least for the time being. One of Rob's

BMW K75s has failed to make it to the hotel (trucking problems), so Shaft Motors is lending us the orange Speed Triple for a day or two. David and I do not protest.

As we leave the hotel the next morning, Beach reminds us about riding on the left side of the road. "All day long, I want you to say to yourself, 'Ride left, look right; ride left, look right,' so we don't have any accidents."

I smile to myself a private know-it-all smile, having had lots of experience riding in England. Then I almost pull out in front of a truck. "Ride left, look right; ride left, look right," I tell myself for the rest of the day. The mantra of the still-living.

On the first day of the trip I'm on the Trophy 1200 as we head southeast out of Auckland, along the coast, and then back inland to Rotorua, which sounds to me like a kitchen appliance but is actually a very nice resort area. The Trophy is a big, fast, comfortable sport-tourer, with hard Givi bags attached for plenty of luggage room.

The motor makes no particularly interesting sounds, but it has the kind of torque you could use to move your house to a new location. It feels and sounds somewhat like my old ZX-11 but pulls a little harder and more usefully at the bottom end and is not quite so silky and explosively fast near redline. No handling vices, a big-hearted motor, and ergonomics that are just right for all day sport-touring.

Where the 1200 Trophy exudes a kind of solid, head-of-the-family virtue, the Speed Triple is the wild, good-looking son who smokes cigarettes, runs around with girls, and stays out too late. It is a lithe, low, and fast café racer that feels dense and compact, as if cast from a single billet. It also has one of the most charismatic engines to enrich our sport since Ducati got back on its feet. Responsive and punchy, it has a growly, torn-canvas exhaust note that cures depression, boredom, and ailments of the nervous system.

The riding position looks extreme before you get on the bike, but it isn't. It's at least as roomy and moderate a layout as my 900SS, and the seat is better. I manage to hog this bike for the entire afternoon and would gladly ride it on the whole trip if it didn't have to go back to the dealer. This is a motorcycle with enough personality to warrant its own Richard Thompson song.

That first night on the road we stop on a lake near Rotorua—an area of geysers, bubbling mud ponds, and steam fissures spewing forth sulfurous gasses—and go to a Maori territorial meeting house called a Marae. At the edge of the property we are greeted by a fierce-looking Maori warrior who does a traditional threatening speardance of warning and/or greeting, depending upon our intentions, which are good. So he lets us into the Marae for a visit and a dinner cooked on hot rocks in a large underground pit.

The Maori are a lively, self-assured people who did not exactly roll over and play dead when Captain Cook first landed Englishmen on these islands two hundred years ago. In fact, a few early landing parties were greeted, measured up, cooked, and eaten.

These days, the Maori are famous for their musical talent (Kiri Te Kanawa, the great opera soprano, is Maori) and they sing for us some of the most beautiful, rhythmic, multipart harmonies I've heard. Our group is handed a guitar and expected to sing a song. After a brief huddle, we burst forth with "Michael Rowed the Boat Ashore." It turns out Ralph Werner of our group is an excellent guitar player and Mary Ann Kull has a professional-class voice. The rest of us muddle through, and everyone is happy. Thank God for Scout Camp musical training.

In the morning we rise early and don wetsuits for a whitewater raft trip down a nearby river gorge. Our raft guide is a lovely woman of outdoor radiant health (does no one look sickly in this country?) who says her name is "Ista."

"Beautiful name," I remark. "Unusual."

"Not unusual here," she says. "Ista is a name from the Old Testament."

Edwards and I look at each other for a minute, blankly. "Ah," David says, "Esther."

"Right," she says, "Ista."

After years of canoeing in Canada, I have learned to be wary of water that moves fast enough to rip your arms off. Nevertheless, we go through some heavy rapids, then over a 20-foot fall with me in the front of the raft and nose straight into the roiling water below like a Stuka with a broken elevator cable. I am flung out of the raft (holding onto a rope) and then flung back in, with a little help from Ista. Thrilling stuff, even if I have sprained my thumb and will spend the rest of the trip putting on my right glove with my teeth. Such is the price of glory.

Riding south toward Taupo, the road takes us through high timber country with areas of towering green volcanic cones and wonderful winding roads. The roads in New Zealand are nearly all paved with a coarse grained blacktop that seems to provide excellent grip, wet or dry, and they are smooth and unblemished by frost heaves, expansion strips, or potholes. A dream surface through a fantastic landscape that lends itself to endless curves. This is a great country for sportbikes—or any bike that is quick and light. As I discover.

Midway through the morning, I trade my 1200 Trophy for David's BMW F650. It takes me about ten minutes to decide that this, like the Speed Triple, is a fine motorbike. Having written a whole column on this bike, I won't belabor the subject, but on tight, winding roads I can actually keep up with the flying Mr. Edwards, and I find myself laughing at muddy-road construction sites and awkward parking spots. The F650 looks ugly as a warthog to me, but it is pure pleasure to ride, and it has a great engine. As the week goes on, its handling and maneuverability cause me to reconsider my whole concept of motorcycle design, back toward the lean and spare.

Just north of Lake Taupo, we come across Huka Falls, where there is a geothermal power station, a prawn farm, a waterfall, and some jetboat rides. So David and I naturally take a wild jetboat ride to see the waterfall and the power station, then eat prawns in garlic butter at a riverside restaurant. We are in the country of doing stuff, so we must do it. God forbid we should go half an hour in New Zealand without a new thrill. I manage not to sprain my thumb but now have garlic breath.

After Lake Taupo, it's back to the east coast, along Hawke Bay to Napier. Vineyard country. New Zealand now produces a tremendous number of top-flight wines, both red and white. Like the US, New Zealand has had a sort of revolution in food and wine over the past two decades, going from a meat-and-potatoes fifties culture to a land of fine restaurants and great wines.

The Kiwis may be a long way from anywhere, but they travel a lot (every young person is expected to have an OE, or Overseas Experience), and they bring good ideas home with them. The result is a remarkably cosmopolitan, open-minded, and with-it population. Everything is up to date in Wanganui.

There is an oft-repeated (by Americans) myth that New Zealand is just like the US, only twenty-five years behind the times. But it seems to me we are ahead of them only in population growth, nihilistic violence, mean-spirited talk radio, and the production of really stupid television shows. With any luck, they'll never catch up.

A sunny, late, cool afternoon finds us in the old mining town of Waipawa. David and I tour an old museum of local history and then meet our group in a nearby parking lot, where we are to meet our hosts for one of New Zealand's traditional "farm stays." It's a program that allows tourists to meet real people and stay on farms or sheep ranches. Our group is split in two, and David and I ride to the sheep ranch of Barbara and John Bibby, a 4,000-acre slice of heaven on steep green hills overlooking the ocean, in terrain that reminds me of the California coast around Big Sur, but greener.

The Bibbys are charming, lively, well-traveled people whose children are grown and out of the house. John takes us on a late-afternoon Land Rover climb through the spectacular steep hills, and then we have a roast-lamb dinner that can't be beat and after-dinner drinks by the fireplace.

The Bibbys, for some reason, find themselves answering questions about local property values and the economics of sheep ranching. It has not escaped anyone's attention that this is a wonderful place to live. Imaginations soar into the night.

More supremely beautiful roads take us south toward Wellington, where we will board a ferry to go to the South Island. On the way south, we stop for lunch at a biker bar with a row of Harleys out front. Here we encounter the only New Zealanders of the trip who do not respond when we say hello. They've seen one too many American movies with bad actors playing dim bikers and know exactly how they are supposed to behave. Life imitates artlessness.

Elsewhere on the road, we pass roving bands of vintage British bikes, Japanese sportbikes, and a fair number of dual-purpose bikes rigged out for hard travel. New Zealand is a highly motorsports-conscious country and seems to have far more than its fair per-capita share of motorcycles, sports cars, racetracks, and transportation museums. English heritage and good roads make it almost inevitable.

Wellington, at the south tip of the North Island, turns out to be a lively port town with a Seattle flavor—and wind. The day we arrive, you can lean on the wind, unsupported; Marcel Marceau imitators are everywhere. This city is supposed to have forty days a year when the wind blows at more than 60 mph. All of New Zealand, in fact, has been quite windy on this tour. The sky moves overhead quickly, and, like England, it often feels more like a ship at sea than a large island.

We lash our bikes down in the hold of the car ferry, Isle of Man–style, and watch the North Island disappear as the South Island heaves greenly and mountainously into view. Everyone has told us if we like the North Island, we will love the South Island. It's less populous, studded with the snowcapped Southern Alps, and generally wilder; kind of a large national park with the occasional city.

First impressions bear this out. Leaving Wellington and arriving at Picton is sort of like leaving Upper Michigan for Alaska. As we wend southward, deeper into the island, the ever-changing landscape becomes an unreal mixture of seashore, subtropical rain forest, cloud formations, volcanic peaks, pines, palm trees, and giant fern-like fans of vegetation that seem leftover from the Age of Dinosaurs, all held together with those same smooth, twisty, grippy roads. You don't know whether to ride or gape, so we do some of both.

We stay at Nelson and Westport, then head on to Fox Glacier, which is a product of the towering Mount Cook. I dirt-track the Trophy down 5 miles of wallowing, wet, muddy road in a rainstorm to see the glacier, while Edwards rides the F650. Someday I will get even. The glacier is big. It is raining and cold.

We ride into clearing windy weather down to Queenstown, a pretty mountainside resort town on Lake Wakatipu, packed with expensive shops and hordes of Japanese tourists buying woolens and sheepskin coats. Unable to resist, I have my first hamburger of the trip at a café called Wisconsin Burger. I ask the waiter why it's called "Wisconsin Burger." He says, "I guess it just has a nice ring to it."

One of our group, Steve Reustle, returns to the hotel at night having just made a bungee jump from a high bridge on the nearby Shotover River. David and I look at each other. Our eyes narrow with resolve.

On the ride out of Queenstown, we stop at the famous old Kawarau Suspension Bridge (built 1881) on the Shotover Gorge, where the world's first bungee jump was made. The bridge is 143 feet above the river. We join a big busload of Japanese tourists who are watching some of their own tourmates bungee jump off the bridge. It is freezing cold, dark, and windy, and David and I are wearing motorcycle boots, leather pants, and nine layers of underwear and sweaters. Not dressed for it, we tell ourselves.

"Besides," David says, "it has never been my lifelong desire to commit suicide in front of a busload of Japanese tourists." We decide not to jump and ride on.

Twenty-five miles later I pull over, flip up my shield, and say to David, "I've been thinking about that jump."

"Me too."

"Let's go back and do it. We'll never be here again."

"Right."

So, we ride back, pay our money, get weighed (for bungee length), walk out on the bridge, and get in line, David first. They wrap a towel and a nylon strap around the ankles of his motorcycle boots and latch the bungee to the strap. David tells them, "I'm kind of worried, because my boots are about two sizes too big for me. They're pretty loose."

The kid who hooks up the rope says, "If it feels like you're going to slip out and fall into the river, just curl up your toes."

David does not laugh as hard at this joke as you'd think.

The man just ahead of David jumps off the bridge and disappears from our sight. The kid looks over the edge and cries, "Oh, NO!"

"What happened?"

"Ripped both his legs off!"

David smiles wanly. Then it's his turn.

He bravely jumps without hesitation and disappears into oblivion. Then I see he's been lowered into the tethered raft on the river below and returned to the riverbank. He is actually waving and smiling.

My turn. I hop to the edge of the bridge platform, my feet tied together, and look down.

If there was ever anything that goes against five million years of human evolution, it is the concept of diving headfirst off a 143-foot bridge over cold rushing water with your feet tied together. There is a special place in your brain set aside for the express purpose of telling you not to do this thing.

Nevertheless, I jump. The moment of jump is an odd existential experience, but the stretch and triple recoil of the bungee is pure and simple whoopdee-doo fun, like being tossed in a blanket, and is surprisingly unstressful on the joints, muscles, and spine. When you are lowered into the raft (like a side of beef) you feel relaxed, refreshed, and loose. Another triumph of endorphins over reality.

David and I have a celebratory Been-There-Done-That Coke from a vending machine, put on our riding jackets, and hit the road, feeling years younger.

Farther down the road we stop for coffee and hook up with our sometime riding partner Wayne Henneck, and then we come across Steve Reustle and Guy Crossley, two riding buddies who signed up for this trip together. It's one of the nice aspects of this tour that you can ride in a big group, in a small group, with a partner, or even alone (though this isn't recommended). You have a map and a bike, and the only requirement is to show up that evening at the next hotel.

On a couple of days we ride with Rob Beach, who is one of those fast, smooth, skilled riders who can go at any pace you care to set. But most days we just meander, going fast or slow as roads, mood, and scenery dictate.

As on the Alpine trips I've taken, every night is essentially party night at the hotels, which are well chosen for their local charm and color as well as mattress and shower-stall quality. We eat well, drink lots of good New Zealand beer, wander through towns, and sit around fireplaces telling true stories. And making friends. It is an unavoidable part of group motorcycle tours (this is my fourth) that you make friends for life. This is a natural byproduct of hanging around with examples of the world's only known species of consistently superior human, the avid motorcyclist.

Cost of a two-week trip like ours, for solo riders, is $2,700, and an extra $1,975 for a passenger, including motorcycle with unlimited mileage, dinner, breakfast, and hotel. Airfare, lunches, and gas are on you, as are drinks and roadside snacks. Single riders can also add $200 to that if they are not willing to share a room. For those who have time, Rob Beach prefers to lead a three-week tour ($3,775 solo and $2,850 for a passenger; $275 extra for private single room) because you can see so much more of the country, and there's a lot to see. Maybe when I retire.

On our last day we ride from Lake Tekapo to Christchurch, a lovely city on a bay, backed up by steep mountain ridges and looking northwest onto a coastal plain of Kentish-looking farms and fields. We have some time to kill before flying out, so David, Bob Wilkins, and I make a visit to the superb New Zealand Air Force Museum.

Naturally there is a guy there giving aerobatic rides in a nice old yellow Tiger Moth biplane (one of my all-time favorite airplanes), so I am forced by fate to sign up, put on a sheepskin jacket, and go for a ride. Besides, it's almost lunchtime, and I haven't risked my life since breakfast.

Christchurch looks lovely upside down from 3,000 feet on a crisp sunny October day. It's an odd view, what with the green, rugged horizon hanging above the blueness of deep space, but a fitting last vision of the Land Down Under.

CHARGE TO CHIHUAHUA!

Touring Northern Mexico in the Footsteps— and Tire Tracks—of the Revolution

FRIEDRICH NIETZCHE once said, "Without Italy, Germans would go crazy." There is some evidence that Germans occasionally go crazy anyway, with or without Italy, but one can understand his meaning.

Those of us who live in uptight, highly organized northern climes seem to require a place in the mind that is more relaxed and Latin in temperament, where the trains do not always run on time. A warmer, more spiritual place where good food and drink temporarily induce a kind of memory loss and make time stand still. Not to mention the elevator in the hotel. Mexico, for a lot of *norteamericanos*, is that place.

It has been for me, for a couple of decades now. When we lived in Southern California, I fell in love with Baja and the modest, courtly good manners of its people. I became a student of the place, reading books and maps and exploring the whole peninsula by motorcycle and Jeep. But in all those years, I never made it to mainland Mexico.

So I was naturally gratified and beside myself (see Dualism) when my old riding buddy Gil Nickel called from California to say that this year's ride of the Napa Valley Touring Society (NVTS) would take us on a late-October "Charge to Chihuahua," led by Skip Mascorro of Pancho Villa Moto-Tours.

The NVTS—which, curiously, looks like "NUTS," spelled in Roman letters—is an interesting mix of people. Several members are in the wine business in Napa Valley, but the rest are from all over the US and Canada. Essentially, it's just a bunch of Gil's riding pals, the only consistent theme being an irreverent sense of humor and a fierce, abiding veneration for the cocktail hour. And the several golden hours that follow, to include dinner.

Previous NVTS trips, organized by different members, had taken us through the Ozarks and the Canadian Rockies. This year's Mexico trek was orchestrated by Stan Rosow, a semiretired lawyer from Chicago who is using his spare time to explore the four corners of the earth on a motorcycle.

After Gil invited me on this latest adventure, I walked over to my Rand McNally wall map of North America to ponder my options. The trip was to start in El Paso. All very well, but that's four days' ride from my home in Wisconsin, and four back. Added to eight days in Mexico, that was a long time away from work, deadlines, and family. Too long, maybe.

Gil to the rescue. He offered me his prized yellow BMW K1 (just repainted) and said he and his wife, Beth, could ride their other bike, a red BMW R1100RS. Stan was hauling a truckload of bikes from Napa to El Paso, and there was room for one more. Perfect. I could fly to El Paso and ride from there.

So on a Friday in late October, I said goodbye to my long-suffering wife, Barbara, whose job prevented her from going along this time, and left Madison in a blinding snowstorm. The plane landed in a warm, dusty, sunbaked El Paso, where our Ryder truck full of sardine-packed motorcycles had just arrived at the airport Hilton.

After the usual warm greetings and fraudulent compliments about not looking any older, fatter, or more senile, our reunited band of sixteen riders and passengers began the nerve-wracking task of backing ten bikes—eight BMWs, one Harley, one Yamaha FZR1000—down a tall ramp. Much advice, many outstretched hands (picture, if you will, the biblical distribution of the loaves and fishes), but no fatalities, hernias, or ruined backs. Good start.

At the hotel I met Skip Mascorro, the friendly, affable fellow who owns Pancho Villa Moto-Tours (685 Persimmon Hill, Bulverde, TX 78163; 800/233-0564), and his co-guide, Kenneth Upchurch. Interesting guys, both, with a solid background in Mexican culture.

Seems Ken Upchurch's great-grandfather, an American sugar magnate, not only founded and laid out the Mexican city of Los Mochis on the Gulf of California but also helped pioneer the trans-Sierra railroad line that joined the Pacific Coast to Chihuahua. As a result of these long family ties to Mexico, Ken speaks Spanish so fluently I can barely understand it.

Skip is also a Mexican-history buff. He's from San Antonio, but his great-grandfather was Mexican, so Skip gradually developed an interest in his Hispanic roots, traveling in Mexico and teaching himself the ways and language. It's no accident that he's named his company after Pancho Villa.

Villa, of course, was the famous Mexican revolutionary who led American General "Black Jack" Pershing (and a young lieutenant named George Patton) on a merry chase all over northern Mexico. President Wilson and the US Army were after Villa because he supposedly crossed the border and attacked Camp Furlong, near the town of Columbus, New Mexico, in 1916.

Some historians now believe, however, that Villa didn't know about the attack and was not there. They suspect that German emissary Franz von Papen (who much later helped bring Hitler to power) may have been behind it, in an attempt to draw Wilson's attention away from the war in Europe.

Whatever the truth, Villa is one of the great romantic and colorful heroes of Mexico, and—significantly—was once photographed with one foot up on the floorboard of an old F-head Indian V-twin, grinning devilishly at the camera. It's this picture that Skip uses as the emblem of his company.

That first night, we decided to do a little border raid of our own, so we crossed into Juárez for dinner, taking a hotel bus to a wild, noisy place called Chihuahua Charlie's Bar and Grill.

On the way over, traffic came to a standstill. Our bus driver explained that someone had phoned in a threat to blow up the bridge at the border. "Why would someone want to blow up the bridge?" I said.

"They don't," he said, "but it forces the police to close the bridge and check for bombs. Then, the traffic backs up and they don't have time to check for drugs. Too many cars and trucks."

We finally made it to Charlie's and discovered, much to our delight, that they had a nearly inexhaustible supply of margaritas, Mexican food, and guitar music, much of it served up by lovely señoritas and great big guys in concho pants and crisscrossed ammo bandoliers. We passed around a huge Mexican hat and got our pictures taken by a canny photographer who somehow detected we were tourists.

After that rehearsal, our first day of riding took us 260 miles down the US side of the Rio Grande in Texas. We went east to Cornudas, then south to Van Horn and Marfa, where the 1956 movie *Giant* was filmed, cutting southwest toward the border on Highway 67.

All of this was on a wide-open two-lane road with almost no traffic, a mixture of purple mountains, high prairie, limitless cattle ranches, swooping arroyos, and descents into broad valleys full of sweeping turns and climbs—fast, open road through a classic Western landscape, under a huge, clear West Texas sky.

Gil's K1 did not subtract from the pleasure of this first day. Six years ago, I attended BMW's introduction of the K1 in San Antonio, rode the bike for two days, and must admit that I was only partly impressed. It seemed too long and heavy for a sportbike yet lacked the luggage or comfort to make it a good sport-tourer. The reach to the handlebars, even with my long arms, gave me a literal pain in the neck.

Gil's K1, however, had set-back blocks to bring the handlebars rearward a couple of inches, which revolutionized its comfort level. Still no luggage, but a tank bag and a rear seat pack carried enough for a solo rider (Skip's Chevy Suburban carried a little extra luggage for each of us.) Also, Gil had installed a 4-into-1 header and recalibrated the EFI, so the bike had a wonderful deep growl and perfect, crisp throttle response. It felt solid, fast (150 mph), dead stable, and precise. By the end of the day I understood why Gil had never been able to bring himself to trade the K1 in on his new RS; it has a kind of bone-deep composure and a high level of mechanical polish that makes it wear well, hour after hour.

That night, our destination was a restored adobe cattle ranch and private fort called Cibolo Creek Ranch, located 4 miles off Highway 67 on a dirt road. While other bikes squirmed and wobbled, the heavy, long-wheelbased K1 sliced through the dust and loose gravel like a Coast Guard cutter. A pleasant and unexpected surprise.

Cibolo Creek Ranch was built during the 1850s by pioneer/cattle baron Milton Favor and was just recently restored by the Texas Historical Commission. The workmanship is exquisite, and the care they took to get it right is remarkable. It has fortress walls, moats, stables, a big screened porch, a shaded colonnade along the guest rooms, library, music room, and an elegant Spanish-style dining room.

It also has a big outdoor firepit, where we stood around a mesquite blaze at night, warming ourselves and sipping from the agave and mescal family of fine drinks. Skip and I got into a long, complex (or so it seemed to us) discussion in which we explored moral relativism, the internal conflicts of Hegelian ethics, and which current dual-purpose bike would be best to buy.

Being one of the four "single" guys on the trip, I was assigned a roommate, and he turned out to be none other than the upbeat, irrepressible Randy Lewis, retired IndyCar driver and now president of Lewis Vineyards in Napa. A genuine fast guy: despite never having a really first-rate ride, Lewis had managed to grid himself on the fourth row of the Indy 500 three years running, alongside the likes of Mario Andretti and Al Unser Jr.

The same speed and talent showed itself in his motorcycle riding, and I spent a good part of the trip trying to keep Randy's disappearing FZR1000 in my distant sights, while not actually killing myself. A recent convert to motorcycling, he rode faster than anyone on the trip and never put a wheel wrong. So much for genetics vs. experience.

The next day was free for local exploration and riding, so I took a solo trip down the Rio Grande toward Big Bend National Park. The river road, Highway 170, between Presidio and Terlingua, turned out to be a landmark piece of motorcycle pavement—tightly twisting, rising, and falling through the narrow river gorge of painted rock that's half badlands and half fantasy. The K1 loved it, growling and wailing, cutting up distance like a well-oiled chainsaw.

I stopped at the mining ghost town of Terlingua, home of the famous annual chili cookoff. The town itself is nothing but a bunch of fallen-down adobe walls, yellow dust, and a couple of stores. In the general store I bought myself a "Viva Terlingua" bumper sticker to put on my guitar case back home, in honor of Jerry Jeff Walker. The chili cookoff was less than a week away, and already the nearby arroyos and parks were filled with campfires giving off a heady mixture of wood smoke and simmering Texas red.

It was too late in the day to explore Big Bend Park, so I cut north through Alpine and then headed back through Marfa. I'd hoped to see the old ranch house from *Giant*, where James Dean, Rock Hudson, Elizabeth Taylor, Mercedes McCambridge, *et al.* had once worked their magic, but a gas-station attendant told me it had been wind damaged and then torn down. That grand two-story mansion, he told me, was "nothing but a bunch of boards nailed on telephones poles."

The next day we crossed the border at Ojinaga after a short delay in which Mexican immigration officials frowned at the mass of paperwork Skip had prepared for each bike, then stamped, notarized, embossed, signed, collated, stapled, and blessed each document as if it were the Treaty of Ghent. Young soldiers with automatic weapons looked on.

Funny how there's always an inverse relationship between the number of official documents and the effectiveness of government. You'd think bureaucrats might notice this embarrassing connection.

Free at last, we rode into Mexico.

Chihuahua!

To Mexicans, the big northern province of Chihuahua is their own Texas, the mythical West of their national imagination. It's a land of mountains, cattle ranches, fertile valleys greened by precious water, and wide-open spaces. Villa's home turf, where nearly every town was fought over, taken, and retaken about a dozen times during the revolution. Bloody ground.

Seems peaceful now, and the ride into the city of Chihuahua was our third day of astoundingly beautiful road, this time cutting through the Rio Conchos valley, over high, windswept mountains, and down into a wide basin. Two lanes, good pavement, lots of turns, no traffic. And no cops.

Chihuahua is a clean, busy town with a nice cathedral square, lots of banks, modern hotels, and restaurants. We stayed at the Palacio del Sol, right in the center of town, and had a good dinner at a small restaurant called Rincon Mexicana nearby.

From Chihuahua we headed west through farming and ranch country and began our curving, upward climb into the Sierra Madre toward the old logging village of Creel and Mexico's famous Copper Canyon National Park. Best riding yet, in a series of great riding days.

For some reason, the name Copper Canyon (Barrancas de Cobre) had suggested to me a rather desolate, dry, and dusty mining region. Not so. It's high, rugged country, but green and covered with pine forests, encompassing the largest and deepest canyon system in North America. Deeper than the Grand Canyon, it is over four times as vast. The name Copper comes not from mining but from the color of the exposed rock. Spectacular country, almost unknown to most Americans.

The Mexicans call this area the Sierra Tarahumara because the almost inaccessible valleys and peaks are home to some fifty thousand Tarahumara Indians. A shy, private people renowned for their stamina and swift running ability, they never "surrendered" or entered into any political discourse with the government of Mexico. When pressed or threatened, they just disappeared farther into the hills, thereby missing out on several revolutions, two world wars, the disco craze, both O. J. Simpson trials, and the civilizing benefits of network television.

To survive, they hunt and grow small hillside gardens and also make beautiful baskets and other handicrafts, which they sell at tourist sites along the tortuous Chihuahua al Pacifico railroad line.

We stayed at a nice motel in Creel, parked our bikes for a day, and then took an overnight trip by bus to the high Cliffside Hotel Mirador. We were supposed to take the train, but a landslide had closed it down for a few days. All along the line, marooned tourists had to accustom themselves to being stuck in one of the most beautiful places on earth, with only Mexican food and margaritas to survive on. Grim stories emerged of people forced to drink their own wine. Which we certainly did.

Our group included no fewer than four California vintners: Gil and Beth Nickel of Far Niente, John Trefethern of Trefethen Vinyards, Ren and Marilyn Harris of Paradigm, and Randy Lewis of Lewis Vineyards. Each of them brought a few cases of wine along and packed it in our Suburban chase car— the luggage and winemobile. If Skip had crashed, he would have drowned in cabernet sauvignon.

Fortunately, he didn't, so some of our evenings are lost to history, with no reliable witnesses. I do know that Gil told at least one joke that required him to stand on the table and clutch his ankles, but telling it here would only cause problems.

So we arrived by bus, and the Hotel Mirador turned out to be, like Cibola Creek Ranch, one of the most beautiful lodges I've seen. Timber, adobe, and tile put together in a superb piece of Southwestern architecture, built into the cliffs on the rim of the canyon.

The average American conception of rural Mexico (well, mine, at least) might scarcely credit such a place existing on the Great Divide of the Mexican

Sierra. But this was true of all our hotels; they were as good as—or vastly better than—most places I would stay on a bike trip in the U. S., cheapskate that I am.

My own cost on this trip, incidentally (single, with my own bike), was $1,289 for eight days of travel, covering hotels and two meals a day. Lunches, gasoline, drinks, and air travel to El Paso were on me. As the trip progressed, it seemed like a bargain.

After Copper Canyon, the trip back to El Paso felt like a downhill run toward home, but it was good riding all the way. Well, except for the border crossing. After a night at another good hotel in Casas Grandes, we crossed back into the US at Palomas, which has a main street of hippo-sized ski moguls fashioned in mud. A hydrant had burst, and the whole downtown was a giant mudhole.

As we slithered and bobbed up to a stoplight, I raised my face shield and said to Gil, "This town is a disgrace! Don't they have a mayor they can run out of office?"

But we were back at the border, and border towns have ever been transient places where normal rules do not always apply, where cultures rub up against each other, generating frictional smoke and showing off their worst traits. Mexico can't control its birth rate, which always outstrips its resources, and the US can't control its appetite for cheap goods—as if there could ever be such a thing—and the border towns are a product of those two facts. Improvidence meets avarice. There's a sense that no one is in charge.

This time we were waved across the border without even being stopped. We had lunch in the town of Columbus, where Pancho Villa either had or had not made his historic, ill-advised raid on the US The fast ride back to El Paso on the border road would have been unremarkable except that Ken blew a rear tire on his GS BMW and managed to ride out the worst high-speed tankslapper I've ever seen. He calmly replaced his tube on the roadside with simple tools, and we were on our way.

Back in El Paso, we loaded our bikes at an airport cargo dock, while across the runway Air Force One sat on the ramp. President Clinton was in town, making one of his last speeches of the 1996 presidential campaign. The bellhop at our hotel told me most of the Hilton had been filled with Secret Service agents for the whole week before Clinton's short visit, screening El Paso for the usual bad actors and dimbulbs.

Say what you will about any president, the courage to dive into crowds over and over again is almost beyond comprehension in the secure lives most of us lead. You could feel the tension in El Paso, and it hung in the hotel like a leftover ringing in the ears when a fire alarm has been turned off.

Curiously, our Napa Valley Touring Society trip through the Ozarks had taken us through election night four years earlier, when Clinton was in nearby Little Rock, awaiting the results. When Clinton runs, we ride.

After a big steak dinner at the famous Billy Crews steak house, during which I accidentally ordered a T-bone about the size and thickness of a window air-conditioning unit, we had many toasts and said our goodbyes. In the morning we all flew home our separate ways.

Before my own flight, I had breakfast with Skip and Ken. Over coffee, I confessed that I hadn't known what kind of bike would be best for Mexico. Dual purpose? Pure dirt? Touring? Yet this trip had covered some of the best sportbike roads I'd ever ridden.

Skip smiled and nodded. "We do eighteen rides a year down here, all over Mexico, and almost any bike works. But many people think the pavement ends at the border, and they're afraid to come down here. 'What about banditos?' is another question we hear all the time. Half of our job is simply to dispense with anxieties. We do this mostly by taking care of the paperwork at the border crossing, and after that giving people some history and a feel for the place.

"Mexico is a remarkable country to tour, "he added. "Three hundred miles from an American shopping mall, you can ride curving mountain roads through country populated by primitive Indians in loincloths. And mile for mile, dollar for dollar, these roads can match anything in the world. Once people discover this, they keep coming back. They want to go deeper into the country and see more of it."

He had that right, at least in my case.

When I got home, the driveway was drifted with snow, and the right front tire on my snow blower was flat. Also, the garage door was frozen to the concrete floor and had to be broken loose with a crowbar. No big deal, really. I've learned to live with seasonal darkness and cold.

But without Mexico, I'd go crazy.

BASIC BLACK

A Brief Social History of the Black Leather Jacket

IT WAS AN EMBARRASSING MOMENT FOR ME. A couple of years ago, I went out to lunch with a bunch of employees at the rock 'n' roll station where my brother used to work. One of the younger DJs came with us, wearing a black leather motorcycle jacket of *The Wild One* variety. Without thinking, I asked what kind of motorcycle he had.

"Motorcycle?" he said, looking at me, blinking. "I don't have any motorcycle. Why?"

Foolish question on my part.

Nonmotorcyclists take the black leather jacket for granted now, as a mere fashion accessory. Everyone from the Ramones to Madonna has appeared publicly in some version of the Brando-style "Eric von Zipper" motorcycle jacket, so that it has become as harmless a cultural cliché as carhops on roller skates or the 1957 Chevy.

We live in the age of prefab charisma, where mere money can buy you an artificially aged (right at the factory) Fender Stratocaster or a prestressed fifty-mission flight jacket. Buy the stuff, share the life. And with a black leather jacket, the spurious risk-image of motorcycling can rub off on you without the inconvenience of learning which is the clutch lever or ever getting wet. Or crashing. Everyone wants a piece of the danger, but no one wants to get hurt. We want authenticity to come easy, without too much stress or conflict.

It was not always so.

There was a time in America when symbols had real meaning, and the black leather jacket was a potent one. No one dreamed of wearing a motorcycle jacket without owning a motorcycle.

Why?

Well, for one thing, wearing a black leather motorcycle jacket into the wrong bar could get you beaten up. It could also get you kicked out of school, shunned by "nice" girls, turned down for jobs, and stared at by cops with mirrored sunglasses. Style choices used to come with unpredictable and amazing consequences. Sadly, I am just old enough to have lived through this strange era.

Where did it all start? And why?

Logic certainly had a role. Leather has traditionally been—and remains—the best antiabrasion material for motorcycle clothing. The uniquely intertwined corkscrew cells in leather will not tear or rip along a faultline as most fabrics do. Also, leather is windproof and, when lined, warm. And it's long wearing and good looking.

Okay, but why *black* leather?

That's easy. It's the same color as dirty chain lube, seeping Harley gear oil, old Indian wheel-bearing grease, the underside of your Triumph, and the blacktop upon which you knelt to examine the gaping connecting-rod hole in your BSA engine cases. Doesn't show the dirt, as Mom used to say. If we could breed flies and junebugs without yellow-green innards, it would be perfect.

I've looked through a lot of my old motorcycle books for the first appearance of the black leather jacket, but it's hard to tell where the tradition begins. From the earliest days of motoring and flying, people realized leather's advantages in fighting off this new form of machine-generated wind, and I have photos from the 1911 Isle of Man TT showing riders in full black leathers—often with neckties worn underneath. American racers, for the most part, wore wool jerseys and looked like rugby players.

Nonracing riders seem to have gone for natty woolen-and-tweed suits, with the occasional use of sheepskin-lined leather coats with big wool collars.

But the first photo of a street rider in the classic black leather motorcycle jacket doesn't appear—in my files—until just after World War II: the age of the restless, existential rebel hopped up on Bop music and bongo drums. Or just someone who needed a warm, practical jacket.

Typically, this was the short "Cycle Champ"–style jacket, usually of horse-hide, with a bottom belt, overlapping front, snap-down collar, and countless zippers—some with rabbits' feet attached. Sort of a leather Eisenhower jacket, with good-luck features.

Racers and sport riders generally shunned all of the self-snagging appurtenances and stuck with an unadorned black leather jacket with a mandarin collar, tight-fitting sleeves, and two simple zippered chest pockets. A racing-striped version of same may be seen on Peter Fonda in *Easy Rider*. This has always been my favorite type of motorcycle jacket. I still have my original Buco version and just had a less-battered replica of it made by Bates.

Both styles were around in the 1950s, and they soon became emblematic of British rockers, serious American riders, and various brands of rebel in the motorcycling substrata. Elvis had one. So did James Dean, Eddie Cochran, Gene Vincent, and Marlon Brando. (How's that for unpaid star endorsement?) And before the Beatles were cleaned up by Brian Epstein, they had 'em too.

It didn't take Middle America long to connect these jackets with rock 'n' roll, overstimulated hormones, greasy ducktails, big sideburns, loud pipes, and the sort of trouble that rode into Hollister, California, one fine day and tore up the town. Ordinary citizens had seen the photos in *Life* magazine, and they were Not Happy.

You could almost say they were violently, homicidally unhappy. A wave of revulsion for all things motorcycle swept over the country, and the black leather jacket was its arch symbol.

By the time I was a freshman in high school in the early 1960s, wearing a black leather jacket was an invitation to be ostracized by all but the toughest elements in your hometown. Even the hoods in my high school quit wearing black leather jackets. They were afraid some older, unemployed biker with three teeth would kill them with the broken-off neck of a beer bottle, just on principle.

Anyway, where would they go? No café would let them in the front door, nor would anyone's parents. Nor the school. All they could do was stand on the street and draw contempt. Black leather was powerful medicine.

The country slowly got over that phobia as things loosened up in the 1960s, but when I took my first cross-country motorcycle trip in 1967, I still had to park half a block from a motel and leave that black leather Buco roadracing jacket on my bike each time I tried to get a room. Otherwise the "No Vacancy" light came on.

I usually took it off and folded it before I walked into restaurants, to prevent icy stares, stalled conversation, and very slow service. Or none. The movie *Easy Rider* in no way exaggerates the anti-biker/hippie/beatnik/long-hair mood of the era. It could be very chilly out there. Dangerous, even.

For the most part, we don't even have to think about this stuff anymore. It would surprise a black-clad motorcyclist to be discriminated against now—at least in any nonformal setting.

America has learned to live and let live a little better than it used to, and we can probably thank the Ramones and Madonna—and my brother's DJ friend at the radio station—for turning motorcycle jackets into a relatively benign, standard fashion item, so the rest of us can wear this practical gear in its intended place without drawing flak.

I think it has also helped that Harley-Davidson, with its charity rides and fundraisers, has managed to portray even leather-clad bikers as basically nice people. Who'd have thought you'd ever meet the nicest people on a Low Rider?

But that's a fairly easy message to get across these days, especially to a generation of aging rockers. Society has learned to be remarkably tolerant, now that we are them and they are us.

And Brando is seventy-three.

TO RIDE A VINCENT

**We Know the Vincent Black Shadow Is a Beautiful
Thing to Look at, but How Does the Legend Hold Up
After an All-Day Ride in the Texas Hill Country?
Our Editor-at-Large Heads South to Investigate**

IT WAS THE FASTEST BIKE IN THE WORLD the year I was
born, 1948, introduced just two weeks after my birth. I heard about it in
gas-station bull sessions when I was growing up, read about it in Floyd
Clymer's *Cycle* and later in *Cycle World*, and heard the legend passed by
word of mouth. The Vincent Black Shadow. The fastest production motorcycle in the world. A stock one was supposed to do 125 mph, at a time when
most large-displacement street bikes could barely stagger to 100. And modified
Shadows went even faster. Much faster.

Look at the pictures: Rollie Free in his swimming suit and bathing cap,
streaking (almost literally) across the Bonneville Salt Flats, prone on his modified, stripped-down, straight-piped Shadow prototype of the competition Black
Lightning—breaking the record for a naturally aspirated motorcycle at 150.313
mph. *Life* ran the photo on October 4, 1948, and this picture and others of the
record attempt have appeared over and over again in motorcycle books and
magazines ever since.

"That engine was put into the frame with a whip and a chair," someone
wrote, and the phrase stuck in everybody's mind. A sinister-looking black bike
full of external plumbing and raised oil lines standing out from those early
B-Series engine cases like veins in a bat wing. The Black Shadow. When I
was a kid it sounded menacing, like a combination of black widow spider and
masked movie-matinee phantom, everything exciting and dangerous packed
into one machine.

I grew up trucking all this lore around in my small, young brain. The Vincent
as ultimate.

So naturally, I have lusted after Vincents these many years, in both heart
and mind. I have gradually accumulated a small library of books and magazines
on this illustrious marque, whose history stretches from 1927, when Phillip

Vincent bought the respected but insolvent HRD motorcycle company, until another insolvency closed the factory in 1955. The bikes I like best, the 1,000cc V-twin Series B and C Rapides and Shadows, were all made after World War II.

The Rapide was the "regular" version, the Black Shadow the high-performance model, hot-rodded with higher-compression pistons, bigger Amal carbs, and hand-polished internals, good for a whopping 55 bhp—10 more than the Rapide. It also had fins on its dual 7-inch front brake drums and, of course, black-enameled engine cases and cylinders.

The Rapide is, perhaps, more beautiful with its polished-aluminum cases, while the Shadow is . . . well, more legendary and even more romantic, if that's possible. Also about $10,000 more expensive, these days.

But I have not bought either one.

And why not?

Well, as I mentioned in a recent column, these bikes have always stayed just ahead of my income and/or frivolity level, much like the carrot on the stick dangled in front of the donkey. When Vincents were $5,000 back in the early 1980s, you could buy a brand-new 900SS Ducati for that. Now Vincents are anywhere from $15,000 to $35,000, depending upon model, history, and condition, and you can buy a Ducati 916, slightly used, for $14,000. You see the problem.

But none of this has stopped me from wanting one. I mentioned this lifelong fascination to editor David Edwards over dinner at Daytona this year (while showing him J. P. Bickerstaff's new book, *Original Vincent Motorcycle* which now goes everywhere in my luggage or under my arm), and he asked, "Have you ever ridden one?"

"Yes," I replied. "Jay Leno kindly let me ride his Vincent Rapide about ten years ago. We went to breakfast, riding up a winding canyon in the Hollywood Hills to a café. It was a great experience, but we didn't really get out on the highway. I guess before I sell everything I own and shell out $15,000-plus for a motorcycle, I'd like to ride one for a full day on the road, spend a few hundred miles in the saddle."

David raised one eyebrow and said, "You know, I'll bet that could be arranged. We just did a story on the Rollie Free speed-record bike; it belongs to an avid Vincent collector named Herb Harris, in Austin, Texas. Herb has several Vincents, including a Shadow he rides on the street. He said if we ever wanted to come down to Texas and take a long ride out into the Hill Country, he'd love to have us visit."

I looked at David and grinned like a person showing off a new set of extremely white teeth.

"I'll call Herb and ask if we can do it. Probably have to wait until spring, when it's a little warmer and the bluebells are blooming in the Hill Country."

God, I love this job.

Austin, Texas, the green Hill Country, and Vincents. Three of my favorite things and places on earth, all in one trip. As Jelly Roll Morton used to shout while banging away on the piano, "Somebody shoot me while I'm happy!"

Nobody did, so a few months later my plane landed on a hot, sultry late-spring day in Austin, where I was met at the airport by a cheerful Herb Harris and his good friend and Vincent co-restorer, Stan Gillis. Herb owns a law firm in Austin, and Stan is a former Dallas banker who gave it up to restore motorcycles and work part-time for the law firm. *CW* photographer Jeff Allen flew in from California; we checked into a nearby hotel and then drove to Herb's home in suburban Austin for a look at the bikes.

Herb has a nice brick home that is my idea of perfection—large garage and six motorcycles parked in the living room: three Vincents, a BSA Gold Star, and a Manx Norton, a testament to the good nature of his wife, Karen. The Rollie Free bike was being shown in England, but Herb has another famous racing Vincent in the living room, the 1949 Reg Dearden Lightning, converted at the factory to use a Shorrock supercharger. I told Herb that if I had this room in my house, I would never go to bed. I'd just sit up all night long with a drink and look around.

The garage collection is not bad, either. Out there, he has a BMW R100RT, a 1927 Brough Superior 680, an immaculate 1965 Triumph Bonneville, an unrestored-looking 1936 Vincent HRD Comet Special 500, and—the object of our trip—a 1951 Series C Black Shadow, flawlessly restored.

And what a sight. All engine, set off with glistening black paint, gold-leaf trim, and stainless steel.

Philip Vincent and head engineer Phil Irving ("the two Phils") designed these bikes to use the engine as a stressed member. Like a modern Ducati 900SS, the triangulated swingarm pivots on huge bearings in the back of the unitized engine and transmission cases. Dual spring boxes and single hydraulic shock are up under the seat, where they push against the "UFM," or upper frame member. This is nothing but a long rectangular box that serves as the oil tank, bolted securely to the cylinder heads. There are also two friction dampers, tightenable with lovely knobs, attached to the seat stays.

The steering head bolts to the front of the UFM. Front forks are girder-type "Girdraulics" with long spring boxes behind them and a single hydraulic shock behind the headlight.

In other words, you essentially have the front and rear suspension bolted to a great big V-twin engine, with a little help from the oil tank. Add seat and gas tank, and there's your bike. Brilliant and simple.

But the mechanical detail of the bike is anything but simple. The two Phils made everything adjustable—or "infinitely maladjustable," as Stan points out. There are tommy bars and knobs everywhere. Wheels can be removed, like those of a racing bicycle, without tools, and all the footrests and levers can be adjusted to fit the rider or passenger.

The engine itself is notable for several innovations. It had (a) unit construction when most bikes did not and (b) rocker shafts that operate on collars on the centers of the valve stems, rather than on top, with separate upper and lower valve guides. This allows shorter pushrods for less reciprocating weight, shortens overall engine height, and keeps the valve springs high and cool in the heads. It also lowers the rocking friction of the valves against their guides.

Vincent called this a "semioverhead cam" engine, which is something of a stretch, as a thing is either overhead or it isn't, and these aren't. But it's a clever design.

The angle between the cylinders is 50 degrees, and the heads are hemispherical, with two valves each. A magneto handles the sparks, and a Miller generator the lighting current. And above the headlight sits one of the most famous talismans in all motorcycling, the gigantic 5-inch "Shadow clock," a 150-mph Smiths speedometer made especially for the Black Shadow. It's the size of a saucepan—which, in fact, was exactly what the early speedos were made from. Cookwear never looked do good. Or went so fast.

I ask Herb if the bike needed much work when he bought it.

He nods wearily: "The engine had supposedly been 'professionally rebuilt,' but it had many latent problems and needed to be rebuilt from the crankpin out. We sent it out to Dick Busby, a Vincent specialists, in Culver City, California, who does all our engine work now, working with Haig Altounian. Mike Parti did the crank. We started calling Busby 'Bad News Dick,' because every time he called he had bad news about the engine: 'Your timing gears look like they've been underwater for three years!' That kind of thing."

Gradually, it got done, though. The tank was repainted by Wayne Griffith in Los Angeles, and the original "loaf of bread" seat was restored to neat tautness by Michael Maestas in Sylmar, California. Herb and Stan did most of the assembly.

The Shadow, Herb says, was originally sold to Indian Sales Corp., USA (chassis number 5708), shipped in December of 1950 and sold in 1951. Its ownership lineage was lost after that, but Herb bought it in 1995 from a collector in Dallas. "He got rid of it when it spit him off," Herb says. "He went through a puddle that turned out to be more than a puddle. It was 3 feet deep. The bike somersaulted and bent the front wheel, but there was no other real damage. Those forks are made of forged-aluminum alloy, manufactured for Vincent by the Bristol Aircraft Company, and they are extremely strong."

"We restored it to pretty original and stock specifications," Stan says, adding that the only nonstandard touches are 8.5:1 "Kempalloid" pistons, replacing the original 7.3:1 pistons, and a 21-inch front tire from a Lightning rather than the stock 20-incher. Also, it has a Ducati 900SS dry clutch, from the current generation.

I pull in the lever, which feels about like my Ducati's. "Is this an easier clutch to operate?" I ask.

"No, the stock one actually has a lighter pull and is nicer to use, but the Ducati clutch is easier to clean if the engine breathes oil on it through the bearing seals, which occasionally happens," explains Stan.

So, riding would come in the morning, but first dinner.

Herb and Stan took us out to the Oasis, a great Tex-Mex restaurant built on a series of porches overlooking Lake Travis, like a big treehouse 1,000 feet above the lake. Over dinner, I learned that Stan and Herb have been riding since high school and, between them, have owned, restored, broken, or patched up just about every motorcycle ever made: BMWs, BSAs, Ducatis, Harleys, Hondas, Kawasakis, Laverdas, Nortons, Triumphs, etc. Motorcycle guys of wide focus, lifelong and hopeless, which we now know to be the best kind of person. They've got the disease.

In the morning we had a Mexican breakfast at the famous Cisco's Café in east Austin, under paintings of Willie Nelson and Texas humorist Hondo Crouch, of Luckenbach fame, then headed back to Herb's garage.

I put on my jacket, got my helmet ready, and Herb gave me the cold-starting drill:

1. Turn on fuel tap—or both of them, if you plan to go 70 mph or more.
2. Tickle front carb float chamber for three seconds.
3. Tickle rear chamber briefly, just until it admits fuel.
4. Kick engine over with compression release in.
5. Say small prayer.
6. Pull in compression release and kick firmly, releasing lever halfway through stroke.
7. Repeat again and again. (The bike tries to start on first kick, and actually lights off and runs on Herb's fourth kick.)
8. Open oil cap in center of tank and see that oil is returning. If it is, you are ready to ride.

Herb warns me it takes a while—at least 15 miles of riding—for the engine oil to be really warm, so the first few miles should be moderate.

I straddle the Shadow and listen to the engine's deep, steady idle. It's remarkably free of rattles and gear noise, yet I have read that Vincent twins normally sound like "a gas stove being dragged over cobblestones" at idle.

"They all come out different," Stan tells me, "no matter how you build them. This one is quiet. Dick did a nice job shimming everything."

I pull in the Ducati dry clutch (which, inexplicably, doesn't rattle as it does on my 900SS), click the right-side gear lever firmly up for the first of four gears in the famously stout Vincent-made box, and we are off. Herb is leading on his BMW R100RT, and Jeff, Stan, and Herb's son Brian follow us in a minivan.

As soon as we are rolling on the highway, memories of Leno's bike come back to me. You sit close to the tank on the Vincent, with a short reach to the semiflat bars. The bars, pegs, and controls are set up for Herb, who is 6 foot 4, but they fit me (6 foot 1) exactly right. This is just about the ideal sport-riding position for me, similar in layout to a 400F Honda or Ducati Monster. It is what I call the "alert Airedale" riding position—canted forward slightly onto moderately narrow, flat bars, feet just slightly back, head up.

A car pulls out on the highway in front of us and I get my first real surprise from the Vincent: the brakes work. Light, two-fingered pressure on the front lever hauls it down fast from 70 to 45 mph, though the rear drum is only fair. The front brakes feel almost modern, unless you have a really long, howling stop on the highway, and then they begin to fade a bit at the very end of the stop. In any case, they are vastly better than any of the mid-1960s drum-braked Triumphs I've owned.

Handling, too, is surprisingly modern: quick in slow corners, with a very slight tendency to fall into really slow turns (just above walking speed, as in a parking lot), and dead stable in fast sweepers, without a sign of head shake or fork deflection over bumps.

The bike loves to tick along at 70 to 80 mph in an effortless all-day canter. I've heard so much about Vincents with a "hinge in the middle" that I'm ready for anything, but there's no hinge anywhere on this bike. It's solid as a brick, unfazed by switchbacks, dips, roller-coaster hilltops, fast sweepers or bumpy midspeed corners. Not a bobble all day, and this is surprise number two. It is, honestly, one of the nicest-handling bikes I've ridden, neutral and instinctive on turn-in and lean. Grip is good, too, with the 21-inch Avon Speedmaster II front and 19-inch Avon Super Venom rear tires.

In both acceleration and handling, it's eerily close to the 1979 Guzzi 1000SP I recently bought, but lighter on the bars and a little more exciting and sharp in its upper-end rush. The road feel also reminds me somewhat of a Ducati 750GT; it's got that same easy gait, but with a shorter and more nimble chassis. Performance is far from eyeball flattening, but the engine pulls hard from almost any rpm and builds speed quickly. There's no tach, and little temptation to buzz the muscular twin—peak power occurs at 5,700 rpm—even though it's quite smooth at the upper end.

Sound from the engine is a rich, full thunder, but mellow and never headache loud. It's a lot quieter than the twin Contis on my old bevel-drive 900SS Ducati. The exhaust note is satisfying, but not quite comparable to anything else. You can't say it's like a Harley or a Ducati; as Stan says, it just sounds like a Vincent.

We stop at the little village of Driftwood to pose the bike in front of an old general store that is now a working silversmith's shop. Texas flag flying, old gas pump out front. I lean on a porch pillar to get my picture taken next to the bike and say, "How is a Vincent owner supposed to stand?"

Herb shouts, "Look superior!"

Next we head for Lime Creek Road, Austin's version of the Angeles Crest Highway, a wonderful winding river road full of dips, S-bends, and whoop-dee-doo rises. Great fun. The Vincent actually runs up the back of the BMW in many corners, even though Herb is riding fast and smoothly. The Vincent is simply lighter, lower, and easier to manage. It doesn't have to be wrestled as much as the tall, fairing-equipped BMW.

Ride? The forks and rear suspension are remarkably supple over small bumps, but they can deliver a pretty good jolt to the spine in a large dip or pothole because there's not much travel. Over the rough stuff, you learn to ride in the equestrian mode, standing up slightly in the stirrups and light in the saddle.

Vincent and Irving hated telescopic forks because of their inherent stiction and brake dive and insisted on girder forks after most others had abandoned them. On these roads, the men are largely vindicated in their shared opinion. Only the most recent telescopic forks (and BMW's Telelever suspension) feel as responsive over minor, pattering bumps or as settled under braking.

We turn out onto a long, empty stretch of road, and Herb hustles the BMW up to about 80 mph. I stay with him easily on the Vincent and then decide to open it up and pass. I hammer forward to 95 mph and breeze past, still accelerating steadily before I have to shut it off for a blind hill. There's lots left at 95, but I decide that's fast enough on a hot Texas afternoon (102 degrees) with a forty-seven-year-old British classic that doesn't belong to me.

Herb is laughing when we stop at a gas station for cold drinks. "What a wonderful sound that thing makes going by at speed! I never get to hear it from another bike!"

It amazes me how easy the Vincent is to ride in the company of a relatively modern big-bore motorcycle. Other than high maintenance and the archaic (but useful) rear stand, there's no real penalty for the bike's fifty-year-old design.

Over lunch (okay, candy bars and Gatorade) I tell Herb and Stan I've been reading for years what evil handlers Vincents are supposed to be, how nonexistent their brakes, how disappointing their supposedly legendary performance, etc. It's become practically a journalistic convention to ride Vincents and then try to take them down a notch, to destroy the myth. "It's obviously not a Honda CBR900RR or a Yamaha R1 in performance, but it's certainly a magnificent bike by any standard," says Stan. "And, for its age, it's spectacular."

"A lot of people want to hate Vincents," Herb says. "In fact they love to hate Vincents. I guess the bikes were on a pedestal for so long, and so few people actually owned and rode them, that it was comforting to believe they weren't all that good."

"You have to remember, too," Stan adds, "that the Vincent is a very complex bike, and if you work on one and don't know what you're doing, you can really mess it up. A badly assembled Vincent is a disaster."

"Handling is absolutely no problem," Herb says, "if the swingarm preload is correct and you keep the tire pressures right. Also, you can't have the front end adjusted to its side-car position, which a surprising number of people have done by accident. You have to get everything right, and then they're really nice to ride."

Stan grins and adds, "We've developed a saying while restoring Vincents: 'These bikes are monuments to unlimited funds, talent, and perseverance.' You can get them right, but it does take dedication."

At the end of the day, when we rumble back into Herb's driveway, we've covered just over 200 miles of hard riding on a very hot day. In that time, the only problem was a shift lever that loosened slightly on its shaft, and that was quickly snugged up with a wrench. Also, the clutch got just a bit grabby when I turned around (over and over again) in the road for photos. I killed the engine twice while maneuvering but both times started it with a single kick. Otherwise, the bike had been flawless.

Back in the dark air-conditioned coolness of Herb's living room/museum, we finish off the afternoon talking about the bikes. I put a question to Herb, one that has been much on my mind.

"It seems to me there are an awful lot of disaster stories out there about Vincents with engine trouble, like the problems your own bike had when you bought it. We know that Vincents are *great* motorcycles, in the sense of being legendary, but do you think they are *good* motorcycles? Are they honest?"

Herb nods, as if he's heard the question before.

"I think they are. The Vincent repays your efforts, and that makes it honest. And I like the special reward that comes from owning such a bike. Vincent achieved great things; it was on the absolute edge of the performance envelope, the highest performance of the postwar era.

"Also," he adds, "the materials used throughout the bike are absolutely first-rate. They used the best of everything they could find and cut no corners on quality. Every piece on the bike is nicely designed and beautifully made out of superior materials."

"No disillusionment after restoring these Vincents?"

Herb Harris smiles and shakes his head. "No. I'm always testing romance against the reality with motorcycles, and with Vincents the spell has not been broken."

Nor for me. I still want one.

HIGH FINANCE

NOVELIST D. H. LAWRENCE once asked himself how it was possible that so many young Englishmen were able to leave the green, pastoral beauty of their farms to work in the coal mines, living deep underground for all their daylight hours. His answer? Motorbikes.

Young men wanted motorbikes, he said, so they could return to their villages and farms, take their girlfriends for a ride, and generally Be Somebody.

Personally, I never worked in a coal mine to get money for a motorcycle, but I did plenty of other odd things. So did my friend Denny Berg.

Denny owns a motorcycle shop called Time Machine, only a couple of blocks from my office. I've been spending a lot of time over there lately, partly because it's a good place to hang out in the presence of Gold Stars, Harley XRs, Royal Enfield Interceptors, and other treasures that are being restored with meticulous care, and partly because Denny is building my Triumph engine.

The last Triumph engine I built myself inexplicably burned a quart of oil every hundred miles—on the left cylinder only. Two re-rings and a re-rehoning later, it improved slightly. But then I was always hearing sounds.

This time I decided to set aside an engine fund and let a true expert lay his hands upon the venerable Twin. Denny used to build flat-track Triumphs for fast guys like Eddie Lawson and Dick Lewis, so he knows where these engines fail, and why. The goal here is a long-lived Triumph engine that doesn't have to come back out of the frame for the foreseeable future, or the rest of my life, whichever comes first.

Other than watching the engine progress, the best part of hanging around the shop is just talking about bikes. Even though Denny is a few years younger than I am (like, it seems, most of the human race), we seem to have lived parallel lives in our early motorcycling, both having owned a succession of small-bore Japanese bikes.

When I dropped by the last Saturday, we got to talking about these early motorcycles, and the subject turned to the various financial hoops we jumped through to get our hands on them.

Denny told me that in order to buy his first bike—a Honda Sport 50—he took a job at a grocery store as a carry-out boy and put in long hours to pay

for the bike. This income was later supplemented with snow shoveling, a paper route, and working in a butcher shop.

In my own case, that first bike was a Bridgestone Sport 50, and in order to convince my doubting parents that I deserved this luxury, I had to agree to take on a second summer job. I was already working at my dad's printing shop, where I could usually be found running a hand-fed press, printing infinite millions of pink lunch tickets for the local school. Unfortunately, the proceeds from that job were slated for the dreaded College Fund. If I wanted something as frivolous as a motorbike, they informed me, I could find extra work, after hours.

Father Bernard Schrieber stepped in at that moment (deus ex machina) and offered me a job mowing the St. Patrick's Catholic Cemetery, evenings and Saturdays.

Father Schrieber took me out to the cemetery, opened the equipment she,d and said, "If you like machinery, you're going to love this. It's called a Turtle." He dragged out a big green mower with no wheels and a shape that really did look like a huge sea turtle with a 5-horsepower Wisconsin engine resting on its back. "It works on the hovercraft principle," he said. "You start it up, engage the clutch, and it hovers on a cushion of air created by its own blade. No wheels needed."

It really was a remarkable machine. You could swing its considerable bulk around effortlessly, like a floor buffer on waxed tile. I was in business.

The Turtle and I hovered religiously among the tombstones evenings and Saturdays (no Sundays: this is Church work, lad) through the summer and into the fall. Gradually, I paid off the $275 loan on my Bridgestone 50, at roughly $25 per month, including the exorbitant 6 percent interest charge.

It was actually a pretty nice job. I was out of doors, I got to ride my Bridgestone up through the green hills to the cemetery after dinner each evening, and when I was done mowing I would put the Turtle away, lean back against a tombstone, light up one of the Luckies I had hidden in the shed, and gaze upon my new motorcycle as the sun went down on the new-mown grass, with my hometown in the distance. Then, there was the pleasure of the ride home, with evening coolness descending into the low valleys, and a stop at the A&W root-beer stand for a cool one.

The only disconcerting part of these rides home was that there was something slightly odd about shutting down a lawn mower with a big four-stroke single and then firing up a motorcycle with a 50cc fan-cooled two-stroke that would have been right at home on a lawn mower. I felt, as Kurt Vonnegut would later say, that some terrible mistake had been made. Bigger bikes with Turtle-quality engines would come later, along with larger loans.

But then, as now, motorcycles were a powerful incentive to find a job. Or even two jobs. In fact, I've often thought that, in order to end the high youth-unemployment rate, the government need only develop a powerful psychological campaign to interest the young in small, affordable bikes.

Denny and I are living proof that a sixteen-year-old will do anything—mow anything, shovel anything, carry anything, or (dare I say it?) print anything—to get the money to for a motorcycle.

Nothing ever changes. We simply dream of better coal mines and faster motorbikes.

WHILE UNPACKING the last of our moving containers a few weeks ago, I found an old saltine-cracker box made of tin, filled with letters sent to me while I was in Vietnam, twenty-nine years ago. They were addressed to a Sp/4 Egan, MAC V Advisory Team 45, Phan Rang, APO San Francisco, Cal. 96381. Naturally, I stopped unpacking and started rereading the mail, most of which I hadn't looked at since the day it was first opened.

One of the letters was from my old college friend, Todd Saalman, who was still attending the University of Wisconsin the year after I quit and joined the army. Todd wrote funny, bleak, scatological, stream-of-consciousness letters—which almost everyone did at that time—full of disorder, uncertainty about the future, and unpleasant references to Nixon and Agnew. He also mentioned motorcycles in his letters.

Todd was an artist and early computer whiz who could play guitar and sing just like Paul Simon, and he bought the first Suzuki X-6 Hustler I ever saw. He brought it back to the dorms one day and did a smoky burn-out the entire length of the first-floor hallway as we all stood safely back in our doorways and watched. He flew through the open doors of Sullivan Hall at a high rate of speed with the David Crosby–like cape he was wearing fluttering behind him, leaving the hallway filled with acrid two-stroke haze. The handlebar ends cleared the doorway by inches, and everyone was quite impressed with his fearlessness.

This was the sort of thing people did in the 1960s when they were bored, and it probably explains a lot about our involvement in Vietnam. Excessive flamboyance and energy in all things, even self-destruction, was the disease of the decade.

Anyway, Todd would occasionally write me letters while I was stationed in what was then called The Armpit of the World. In retrospect, it was actually quite a beautiful country, a place whose reputation as a vacation spot was somewhat damaged by the stigma of death that clung to its green mountains and rice paddies like so much heavy fog. But back then, we enjoyed calling it The Armpit of the World and sat on sandbags reading our letters from home.

And there I was, in 1969, sitting on my particular sandbag, reading Todd's letter. It rambled on about the usual campus happenings, co-op living

problems, politics, and so on, but it ended with a rather key passage. In closing, he said, "Me and a bunch of crazies rode our bikes out to the Mississippi Cliffs last weekend and camped at Wyalusing State Park. Beautiful cold autumn night, huge campfire, guitars, etc. Stayed up all night. Wish you were there. Or here. Or somewhere else. Anywhere."

I could picture firelight reflecting off the spokes and pipes of the gathered motorcycles, see my sleeping bag laid out on the ground near the fire. And then there would be friends around, people with whom you shared beliefs, to talk and drink and smoke with. And girls.

Good Lord, girls. We didn't call them women then. Women were an older species who wore severe business suits and stamped your student registration card with a menopausal vengeance. Women who went on dates and rode motorcycles and camped out were called girls. Even now, it sounds friendlier. We were the boys and they were the girls.

What I felt most of all in Todd's letter, however, were the usual bohemian freedoms we all treasured so much. The freedom to own a sleeping bag of some color other than olive drab, to hike unarmed, to stay up all night or sleep all night, to get up when you pleased, to choose your friends, and let them choose you. Most of all, the freedom to get on a bike and go. That was the key.

I don't think I've ever had a moment where the image of personal freedom was as clearly etched in my mind as it was during the few minutes of reflection I spent with Todd's letter. The whole nighttime autumn camping scene was complete in my imagination, right down to the last detail, like the persistent memory of a landscape seen in a lightning flash. Or a trip flare.

What I also understood, grudgingly, was that without the army and its tiresome discipline, without the vast distance separating me from the Mississippi Valley, there would have been no vision at all. It was pure contrast that made Todd's weekend ride seem larger than life.

But it did loom large, and it's possible I remember that camping trip better than the people who were on it. I probably had more fun that night than anybody, and I wasn't even there. I was in two places at once, while they were only in one.

Sometimes, however, one is just the right number of places to be. Like last weekend. Barb and I woke up and discovered it was a beautiful golden late-autumn morning, a throwback to the previous month's sunniness and warmth. Indian fall, if not exactly Indian summer.

"Let's load up the Beemer and go camping," I said. "It's probably our last chance of the year."

"Where do you want to go?" Barb asked.

"Wyalusing," I said.

We got out our sleeping bags and tent, packed up, and headed southeast toward the river. Our friends Chris and Dana joined us on their reconstituted $750 Gold Wing, and by sundown we were camped on the cliffs above the mighty Father of the Waters.

It was a cool, rustling autumn night with a diamond-black sky and a million stars, and we built a great big campfire, around which we stood, talking and drinking Jack Daniel's. Firelight reflected off the spokes and pipes of our bikes, and the fire warmed our faces and hands.

It was a very good evening for me, and I drank a silent toast to Todd and his fine letter. And to the little-appreciated, nearly always motorcycle-related luxury of being in just one place at a time, and not wishing to be anywhere else.

GOODBYE, MR. HONDA

MR. SOICHIRO HONDA is no longer with us. I read in the papers he died on August 5th, in Tokyo.

The story said he was born in 1906, that he was eighty-four years old. That's eight years older than my father. Is this possible?

The overlap of generations—and the effect of one generation on another—is a strange thing. Those of us who think of ourselves as America's postwar baby boomers are, on the average, a good forty years younger than Soichiro Honda was, and yet somehow I can't help believing he really belongs to our generation. Before anyone else does, I think we should claim him for our own.

The simple fact is, his genius and his years of accumulated know-how really came into full bloom just about the time many of us became speed-crazed teenagers. (Or, in the case of the Honda 50, merely motion-crazed teenagers.) The invasion of Honda's small, well-engineered, and inexpensive motorcycles dovetailed perfectly with our coming of age and filled a great vacuum that no one else seemed to have noticed.

Many of us, now approaching our mid-forties, were already hanging around motorcycle shops and lusting after Harleys and Triumphs before we ever heard the name Honda. We wanted bikes badly, but our options were limited. Big bikes were out of the question, financially and parentally speaking (and boy, did they speak), but the traditional motorcycle companies just didn't offer much in the way of cheap, small-bore equipment.

So we high-school kids were largely stuck with such choices as (1) Whizzer conversion kits for old Schwinns; (2) minibike kits with go-kart wheels and lawn-mower engines; (3) used Harley Hummers with piston rattle; or (4) Cushman scooters with variable belt drive and styling borrowed from an ice-cream delivery truck.

Contraptions, in other words. Mostly cantankerous little devices that hugged the shoulder of the road while smoking heavily, balking at hills, and burning out their tiny centrifugal clutches, if they were lucky enough to have them.

Then, suddenly, there were Hondas. Word spread like wildfire, and so did the bikes, all through the early sixties.

The price range was $245 to $700 *new*, depending on the model. Most models (other than the 50cc step-through) had slick four-speed transmissions

HONDA

cademartori-'18

hidden inside engine cases, where they couldn't even snag your pants cuff and leave grease marks. Electricity actually reached the headlight, which in turn lit the road. Performance, per cc, was amazing. A Honda Super 90 would go about 60 on the highway while getting around 100 mpg. The CB160 was quicker than most of the old 250 British singles and cost less. The 305 Super Hawk was a giant killer. What's more, these bikes looked good. Someone in Japan understood. Goodbye, Cushman.

Until Hondas arrived, motorcycle technology seemed to have lagged well behind modern standards for cars and aircraft. It was assumed, for reasons I will never understand, that motorcycles had to be wrenched upon constantly, that they were destined to leak oil and vibrate excessively, scattering parts and vaporizing light filaments.

Perhaps I'm painting too bleak a picture of the pre-Honda era, as there were many fine and relatively refined bikes made earlier, but the majority of 1950s motorcycles had what seemed to me a World War I aircraft flavor to their mechanical innards—and outards. ("Advance the spark, Biggles! We've a Hun on our tail.")

My own first bike was not a Honda. After a brief fling with a semifunctional James/Villiers 150, I bought a Bridgestone Sport 50, mainly because we had a local dealer. A good little bike, but it was a two-stroke and had the usual oil-mix/plug-range hassles.

Shortly thereafter, I got a Honda Super 90 and decided I was a four-stroke kind of a guy. After that, I owned ten more Hondas of progressively larger displacement, sampling other brands of Japanese bikes only when they, too, converted to four-stroke engines (my old Yamaha RD350 being the only stray).

Through all those years of Honda ownership, the company—or maybe the old man himself—always seemed to know exactly what I wanted next, before the thought was fully formed in my head. Or, more likely, Mr. Honda simply built what he knew was right, and his ideas made sense when I saw them. In any case, I always felt as if I had a friend in Japan, a kindred spirit who could interpret mechanically what I could not express.

I never met Soichiro Honda. I know him only from his upbeat, candid autobiography, from his life's work, and from his portrait, which has hung on the wall above my desk for years, right next to that of Ducati's Dr. Taglioni. Like Taglioni, Honda belongs to that small pantheon of engineers who managed to bring both irrepressible character and expertise with them to the drafting table.

You have to have owned a motorcycle designed by an individual (or worse, a committee) where one of those two traits is missing to appreciate what we've lost.

What else can I say? Mr. Honda's bikes took me across Canada, through college, off to visit my girlfriend on a summer of weekends, around the track on my first season of roadracing, down Highway 61 to New Orleans, across the Mojave Desert, up Pikes Peak, touring with my new bride, and on a mad autumn dash to the USGP at Watkins Glen. And back. Always back.

Eleven bikes, and none of them ever let me down. Not once.

Thank you, Mr. Honda. They were good times, all.

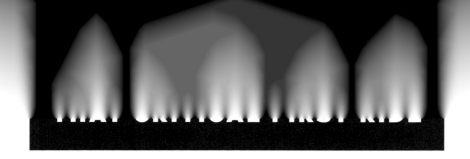

TRUE STORY. When my boyhood friend Pat Donnelly was in his early teens, he was invited to a birthday party on the family farm of his classmate, Conrad Shaker. Conrad had a horse and saddled him up so all the kids at the party could take a ride. Pat, who had never been on a horse before, climbed into the saddle and gave the horse a gentle prod with his heels. The horse took exactly two steps forward, exhaled loudly, fell over on its side, and died.

Pat, who was wearing a brand-new pair of extremely cool engineer boots just like James Dean's in *Rebel Without a Cause*, had his leg and boot trapped under the horse, but both were eventually extricated with minimal damage. The party was over. Pat gave up on horses and two years later bought his first motorcycle.

Usually it works the other way around.

A more typical first-ride story comes from my good friend Lyman Lyons, who grew up in Louisiana. A buddy of Lyman's had saved up all his paper-route money for several years and bought himself a new scooter, a Cushman Eagle. The friend insisted Lyman "take a spin," and Lyman complied with a display that only the masterful Buster Keaton could have orchestrated. He whacked open the throttle, froze at the controls (forgetting which way to twist the grip), rocketed across several front lawns, and finally blasted through a thick hedge, which probably saved his life by slowing him down before he hit the inevitable trees.

The brilliance of this physical comedy was lost on the Cushman owner, who quietly examined the crushed front fender and bent fork and simply said "My scooter . . . " over and over again.

Lyman, needless to say, did not rush right down to the Cushman dealer and plunk money down on his own two-wheeled fun machine. He was somewhat abashed and never really recovered his full measure of youthful enthusiasm for scooters—or motorcycles.

I have now lived long enough to have heard at least a hundred of these first-ride disaster stories, and I'm sorry to say that most of them involve motorcycles rather than horses.

Tell a group of people at a party you ride a motorcycle and at least one person in the crowd can produce a richly detailed, moment-by-moment account of catastrophe on a first bike ride. Usually the tale is quite similar to Lyman's and ends in a vow never to ride again, or to "stick to four wheels."

As nearly as I can tell, a typical sequence of events in most of these mishaps seems to be: (1) surprise at the abruptness or speed of forward motion combined with a poor sense of twist-grip modulation; (2) growing panic in realizing that the technique for stopping safely has not been adequately rehearsed; and (3) a total loss of steering control as the unnatural instinct to countersteer is replaced, through terror, by an attempt to physically turn the handlebars in the direction you want to go (which is effective only at very low speed), causing the rider to hit the very object he or she had hoped to avoid.

When you think how many times this has happened to first-time motorcycle riders, and how many of them have gone away dazed and confused, the worldwide effect on motorcycle ownership has to be phenomenal. A few minutes of simple training might have eliminated many of these accidents, and a course from the Motorcycle Safety Foundation would prevent just about all of them.

Those first few rides are clearly the most dangerous—as are the first few months of riding—so I'm all in favor of as much training as possible.

And yet . . . when I listen to these stories, there is a side of me that says perhaps not everyone is cut out to be a motorcyclist. My own first ride, for instance, was not a lot better than Lyman's, yet the effect was quite different.

I was trying to buy an old Harley 45 from a guy who ran a local gas station. I was fifteen and could not legally ride on the street, so he let me take it for a short ride in the pasture behind the station. I chuffed around successfully for a while, mastering (?) the foot clutch and tank shift, and all was well until I returned to the station. I looked down at the clutch pedal as I came to a stop and ran into a bunch of trash barrels full of scrap metal and old oil filters. The bike and barrels tipped over with lots of noise, but no real damage. I quickly scrambled up and got the bike on its stand, just as the owner came around the corner, wearing a flipped-up arc welder's mask.

"No problem," I said. "Just bumped into some cans."

He scowled and went back to work, welding.

A week later, when I turned up with the money ($100), he told me he'd decided to keep the bike. So I made a down payment on a brand-new Bridgestone Sport 50.

Strangely, it never occurred to me to shy away from motorcycling because I'd dumped the Harley on its side. I would no more have given up the idea of owning a motorcycle than Lyman—who is a good baseball player—would have given up baseball because he struck out his first time at bat. The incident was a small setback, but not a trauma. All the defense mechanisms in my brain closed ranks, made their excuses, and the event was quickly paved over, seamlessly, almost as if it had never happened.

The difference here, of course, is simply a matter of commitment. Lyman was merely curious, while I was absolutely fanatical. I had to have a bike, and nothing else would do. Most of us will accept a lot of hard knocks to fulfill some personal dream but are turned away rather quickly if we take a bruising in pursuit of a merely marginal interest.

Maybe that first ride is just a filter, a means to separate those of us who have to ride motorcycles—or horses—from those who don't.

THE RIGHT BIKE
FOR THE MAP

WITH CERTAIN MOTORCYCLES,** there is a defining moment when you know you are going to have to buy one, sooner or later. A gear suddenly locks to its shaft and the two spin as one, idea and destiny together.

That happened to me when I was at the Harley-Davidson plant in York, Pennsylvania, last fall, doing a story for *Big Twin* magazine, our all-Harleys sister publication. I spent an entire Sunday sitting down at the end of the motorcycle assembly line, interviewing H-D workers who build, ride, and modify their own Harleys.

The assembly line had been shut down for the weekend on Saturday at noon, and the last bike on the conveyer was a Mystic Green and black Road King, missing only a few bits of hardware to be complete.

All day long I looked at the thing, letting it soak into my brain, much the way a strong sauerbraten marinade works on chuck roast. Between interviews I would walk over and stand by it. By the end of the afternoon, a welder named Kevin "Smokey" Barley said, "I believe you better buy one of those."

And I said, "I believe I will."

Returning home, I ordered one from my local dealer, a gentleman named Al Decker, who, with his wife, Mary, has run a Harley dealership for fifty years. The bike is supposed to be here in about three weeks, theoretically.

I bought essentially the same motorcycle from Al four years ago, a 1992 FLHS. Not much different from the current Road King, except that it had a plastic instrument pod left over from the 1970s and the optional "pillow-look" touring seat with little puckered buttons all over it. On the positive side, it had better handlebars, a stock luggage rack, and was $4,000 cheaper.

But the Road King is more like the bike I was looking for in the first place, a functional, modern antique with a slightly closer resemblance to an early Hydra-Glide Panhead, the standard by which I judge all American Twins. Anyway, the FLHS is gone; the King is coming.

Quite a few of my sport-riding buddies, of course, have suggested any number of desirable bikes I might buy for the same price—a fine collection of them, even. But nearly all duplicate in some way the sporting virtues of my Ducati 900SS or my old Triumph 500. Which I already have.

What I miss having is a bike at the other end of the spectrum. A motorcycle for carrying two people and luggage across the vastness of America while exuding a certain historical charm and making great mortar-like thuds of combustion. The motorcycle equivalent of a Stearman biplane, if you will. For my money, nothing fills this bill better than a H-D Twin. Still.

Especially if you tweak about 20 more bhp out of its engine aftermarket-wise, which I'm fixin' to do *toot-sweet* upon delivery.

Anyway, I've noticed an interesting change in my life since I ordered the Road King: I've found myself looking at a whole different set of maps.

Big ones. National maps, with large, distant places like Kansas and New Mexico on them. It's been a while.

Before taking a Sunday-morning ride on my Triumph 500, I tend to get out small maps. Usually from my highly detailed DeLorme Atlas of county maps, with lots of thin gray roads named Shady Hollow Lane or Dogbite Ridge. Short-range stuff.

I know people like our friend Ted Simon in *Jupiter's Travels* went around the world on a Triumph 500, and there's no reason not to if you don't object to the extravagant consumption of pistons. But in my own mind, the Triumph T100-C was made for trails, farm roads, and local exploration. Its agile, lightweight talents are wasted on the big open highway; the meter is always running toward rebuild time.

On Ducati rides, a state map comes into play. On top of the Ducati's tank bag I have a Wisconsin map, usually folded to one quadrant or another. If I get up early enough on the weekend, I'll usually plan a trip of several hundred miles. As with the Triumph, you can obviously ride a 900SS farther than that, especially with a Corbin seat. In fact, I'm planning to take mine to Sturgis next week.

Still, when you look at a 900SS in your garage, you don't think of cross-country travel. That's not what it's for. You *can* ride across Texas, but you don't *dream* of riding across Texas.

And the Road King?

Here, all the state borders come tumbling down. The fine focus goes away (along with a little finesse), and you roll a big map of North America across the dining-room table, like a Persian rug merchant showing his wares.

Suddenly you would pay good money and use valuable vacation time to ride to Texas, and then go all the way across it, just for fun. Visit your good friends in Blanco and Archer City, then drop down to Big Bend Park and maybe take in the Terlingua Chili Cookoff. No problem. America is at your feet.

As it should be. Most motorcycles, after all, have evolved to work best on their native roads.

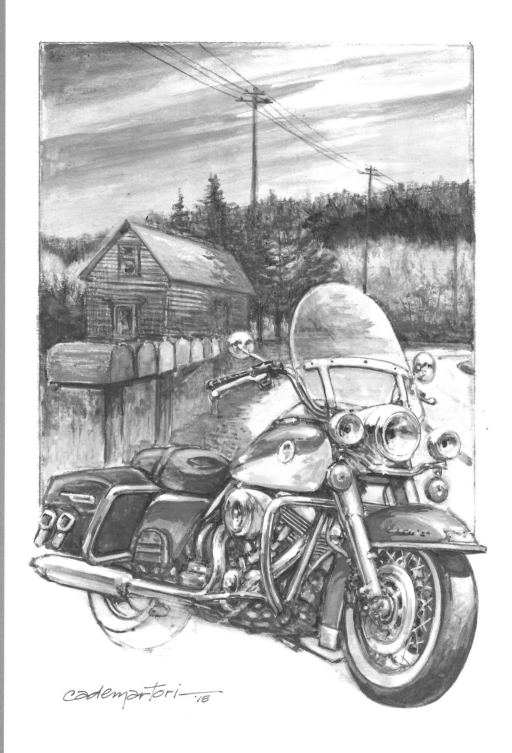

cademartori '18

Triumph 500s, for instance, may have won the Jack Pine Enduro here in the US, but I always feel they were actually built for a quick spin down a country lane between two small villages in the Cotswolds. Or a run to the pub.

Ducatis can cover a lot of ground anywhere, but they seem happiest in those pockets of the US that most resemble the twisting mountain roads of Emilia Romagna or the open sweepers of Tuscany. It's what they were born to do.

And Harleys? To me, they seem to have been built with the Great Plains and deserts in mind . . . the American West. Big Sky bikes.

Thudding down some long, lonesome highway in Nebraska or Wyoming, you can easily imagine that Bill Harley long ago took one good look at the map of America, let out a low whistle, and said, "we're going to need bigger pistons. Two of 'em, with a slow, lazy heartbeat."

FOR RICHER AND EVEN POORER

OVER THE PAST TWENTY-SIX YEARS, I would estimate that upwards of one hundred people have said to me, "I'm surprised your wife lets you have a motorcycle."

This statement is occasionally made by men, but most often, I'm sorry to say, by rather well-dressed, conservative women whose husbands stand in the background looking as if they've been hit across the side of the head with a 2×4. More than once.

Aside from the dismal connotations of the word "lets" in a marriage, I always find this statement more amusing than offensive. Why?

Well, for one thing, my wife, Barbara, had her own motorcycle when I met her—a Benelli 125—but there's more to it than that.

Let me explain, begging your patience here for a short tale.

Late on a winter afternoon in 1973, an old Econoline van with ladders on the top dropped me off at the corner near my house in Madison, Wisconsin. My fancy new journalism degree had failed to get me a writing job anywhere in town, so I had taken up the rain-gutter and downspout trade.

Our crew had been out on the rooftops all day, installing rain gutters on a new housing project in the town of Sun Prairie, which had much more prairie than sun and a stiff north wind raking across the plains. "Nothing between us and the North Pole but a barb-wire fence," as the radio weatherman said. We wore hooded parkas on the job but were pretty well frozen.

I crunched through the snow to our place on Chandler Street, where Barb and I rented the top floor of an older house. Yellow light shone warmly from the upstairs windows, meaning Barb was already home. She had a "real job" (i.e., in her chosen profession), working as a physical therapist at the nearby Madison General Hospital.

On the way in, I noticed an old red Chevy pickup truck parked in front of our house, with a camper on the back. The camper was one of those homemade deals, with a roof of real wood shingles. It looked like a trapper's cabin on wheels.

While Barb and I made dinner, I mentioned there was a strange truck out front. Barb was silent for a moment, then said, "I know. I borrowed it from someone at work. We have to use it to pick up your birthday present tomorrow." She smiled cryptically.

That night a blizzard hit, and I lay awake listening to the wind and snow howl against our windows, wondering what kind of gift required a truck. Our only car was a rusted-out 1968 VW Beetle with almost no cargo space, so the gift could be just about anything larger than a necktie.

Toolbox? I needed a good toolbox. I was still storing my tools, at that point, in something that looked like a fishing-tackle box. And smelled like it, too. Maybe we were going to Sears for a new Craftsman tool chest that didn't reek of bluegills.

I hoped she hadn't spent too much. We didn't have much money. It was a time of "justs." I was just out of the army, we'd just married, and I had just finished my last few semesters of college. Barb was still paying off her student loans.

How poor were we?

We were so poor I didn't even have a motorcycle. My parents had sold my Honda CB160 when I was in Vietnam. I'd been trying to save for a bike but had made very little progress—almost none, actually—what with rent and groceries. My Bell 500TX helmet and Buco leather jacket hung in the closet like a silent remonstrance.

In the morning it was still snowing and drifting, but we shoveled our way to the truck, then shoveled out the truck as the first snowplows went by. I got behind the wheel of the pickup and said, "Where to?"

"Take Highway 18 out of town."

Hmmm. Not the way to Sears. Too bad.

Spinning our tires and drift-busting down the highway, we pressed on through the dark morning, half blind from blowing snow. Past the outskirts of the city, through the towns of Verona and Mount Horeb. Whatever we were picking up was *way* out of town.

When we passed Dodgeville, 37 miles from Madison, I was advised to press on, westward. Suddenly, I knew where we were going.

"We're headed for Prairie du Chien," I said.

Barb smiled.

Prairie du Chien, a Mississippi river town, was famous (among guys like me) for having a large-volume Honda dealership called Stark's Sporting Goods, which undersold nearly all other Honda dealers. It was, perhaps, not very loyal for buyers to go out of town to buy bikes, but at Stark's you might pay $869 for, say, the new Honda CB350 I'd been lusting after, when the same bike was $969 everywhere else. And you have to remember that $100 in those preinflationary, poststudent times meant as much to most of us as $1,000 might now. Huge difference.

As we slid into the drifted main street of Prairie du Chien and headed down toward the river bridge, Barb said, "Why don't you park over there?"

Sure enough. Stark's. A red Honda sign glowed in a dim halo of light.

Inside, mixed with fishing lures, hip boots, rifles, and shotguns, were rows of new 1973 Hondas. And one of them, pulled out from the row, had a tag on the handlebars that said "SOLD: Egan."

It was a Honda CB350—first year with the disc brake—in a beautiful dark green.

I looked at Barb, who was watching my face to see if she'd done the right thing.

"How did you do this?" I asked quietly.

"I saved a little every month in the credit union at work."

Back in business, after three years without a bike. Reborn.

Almost ten years later, Barb bought me yet another motorcycle for my birthday. An elaborate set of clues led me to a gleaming black Kawasaki KZ1000 MKII parked in our neighbor's garage. Another quiet wish fulfilled, unexpectedly.

Anyway, when someone says, "I'm surprised your wife lets you have a motor-cycle," I never get annoyed. I just reflect for a few fond moments and reply, "Yes, I am too. Every time."

THE GREAT DYLAN CRASH

JUST LAST WEEK I found myself on a cross-country trip in my ancient 356 Porsche, driving along the southern edge of the Catskill Mountains in New York, right through the famous village of Woodstock. Sharing the driving with me for a few days of the trip was my old motorcycle touring buddy, Mike Cecchini, from Bethesda, Maryland.

Woodstock, of course, is best known for the great rock festival of 1969, which actually took place on a farm near Bethel, New York, about 35 miles away. The Woodstock title stuck, however, because (a) that's where the festival was originally planned to be, and (b) the name had a certain magic.

Why magic?

Well, mainly because Bob Dylan lived there, having discovered the place while visiting the country retreat of his manager, Albert Grossman.

Also, Dylan's backup band (who later named themselves, simply, the Band), rented a little pink-shingled house nearby, a place they christened "Big Pink," composing the songs there for their first album: *Music from Big Pink*. With the Band and Dylan in town, lots of other musicians moved into the area, so the place became a kind of counterculture hotbed.

But, besides its abundance of famous residents, Woodstock was also known for another event in pop-culture lore: the Dylan motorcycle crash.

As every reasonably hip high-school and college student knew in those days, Bob rode a Triumph. He was pictured on the cover of his *Highway 61 Revisited* album in a Triumph T-shirt, and he'd been photographed sitting astride his Triumph 500. I still have this photo in a book, and the bike looks to me (on close inspection with a magnifying glass) to be a 1964 Speed Tiger T100SR. Or maybe a 1963. In any case, you can see that the left front fork is drooling oil from the upper seal, just as my own 1968 Triumph 500 is doing at this very moment. Nice to know nothing ever changes.

I was working that summer on a railroad section crew, just about to start my freshman year at the University of Wisconsin, when news came over the radio of Dylan's crash on July 29, 1966. My friends and I were both stunned and not surprised at all, in equal measure. This, after all, was the Age of Disasters. Assassinations, the war in Vietnam, race riots, drug overdoses, and motorcycle crashes seemed to be claiming lives of the famous and nonfamous at a rate almost too fast to calculate. None of us, in fact, thought we would live to be very old.

Still, Dylan's motorcycle accident was sad news. I think I can say without contradiction that he was simply *the* man, the music legend of the era. He was held in the same high artistic regard as the Beatles, but with all of it poured into a single individual. If nothing else, he wrote more songs that I took the trouble to learn on my own guitar than any other songwriter before or since.

Anyway, he crashed his motorcycle, and the underground rumor mill went wild: Dylan is paralyzed; Dylan is so badly disfigured he will never appear in public again; Dylan has a head injury and cannot speak, etc., etc.

Then in 1968, he came out with a new album, *John Wesley Harding*, and we all examined his photo on the cover for signs of damage. Scars? Stitches? He appeared to be standing upright under his own power. The album sounded good. Apparently he was okay.

The accident is still somewhat shrouded in mystery, but biographers seem to agree that he indeed had a motorcycle accident, locking up his back brake while swinging into a corner just south of Zena Road, about a mile east of Woodstock, where the road takes a tight S-bend near the site of an old mill. Some visitors to his home reported him wearing an arm sling and a neckbrace. In any case, the accident seems not to have been too terrible, and it appears Dylan used the mishap as an opportunity to quit touring for a while, stay at home with his family, and get some much-needed rest.

So, against this background, Mike and I came driving into Woodstock on Highway 212, on a late fall afternoon, thirty-one years later, and there, just out of town, was Zena Road. We turned off and, sure enough, found a severe S-curve just past the site of an old mill. I got out and walked around in the late-afternoon sunlight.

Bad curve, all right. Beautiful spot, right next to the mill creek, with yellow autumn leaves falling lazily onto the water and whirling downstream. But easily a place where you could go in a little too fast. Maybe brake too hard too late, lose confidence, fail to countersteer or just plain run out of traction. I walked through the corner and thought, "Yes, I could crash here myself. No problem."

Mike, who is not so steeped in rock lore as I, smoked a cigarette patiently and leaned on the car, soaking up the sun rays while I walked around. I hoped he didn't mind the little detour, my dragging him here for some kind of quiet contemplation of historical vibes and private meaning. He kindly left me alone and said nothing, as he had two days before, when we visited the Vietnam War Memorial.

Hard to explain what brings us to these places. What are we looking for? My friend George Allez has visited at least three times the Iowa baseball diamond where *Field of Dreams* was filmed. He can't explain the allure, but every time he drives west, he stops there for a while and just takes it all in, as though the ghost of Shoeless Joe might still walk out of the cornfield.

We all have our own ghosts, I guess, and we like to pay them homage. Triumphs and the songs of Bob Dylan meant a lot to me at the time of his crash, and they still do. So it was just a place I had to go, to see for myself, as if to visit an incident from my own past at which I had somehow failed to be present. Such is the power of music—and motorcycles—to move us around in time. Pure transportation.

After a while, we got back in the Porsche and drove off in search of Big Pink. As we headed up the road, a line from a Band song ran through my head: "If I thought it'd do any good, I'd stand on the rock where Moses stood. . . . "

FOREVER YOUNG

WHILE DRIVING THROUGH a light snowstorm to see my dad at the nursing home this weekend, I happened to be listening to *A Prairie Home Companion* with Garrison Keillor on the radio.

For those of you who are unfamiliar with this program, it's a variety show broadcast live from St. Paul on National Public Radio, generally highlighting humorists and musicians whose work is not tedious enough to land them a slot on easy-listening stations. It often features blues, Cajun, bluegrass, folk, and genuine country music. My kind of stuff: hard listening.

Anyway, at one point in the show, host Keillor sang one of the great old Bob Dylan songs, "Forever Young." He sang it with a clear, moving simplicity that made it sound almost like a traditional church hymn.

Which I guess it would be natural to do. It's written almost as a psalm or a prayer anyway, each verse ending with the wish, "May you stay forever young ... "

I have to admit, it made me feel pretty sad. I was going to visit my father, who remains cheerful, with a sharp sense of humor, but cannot remember being in the navy during World War II, nor where his children now live. He can't remember owning his 1966 Mustang, either.

He's forever young in some ways—mostly in his easy wit and our family's recollections—but not in other ways. Time marches on. Even Bob Dylan himself is not looking like a kid these days. It's mostly his music that keeps him fixed in time.

Later that same evening I found myself out in the garage tinkering with the Vincent, doing a midwinter oil and filter change (why not?). When I stood up, my back was in partial spasm. "Jeez," I muttered, stretching and twisting to take the kinks out, "this bike's in better shape than I am."

And, of course, it is. Laughably so. We are close to the same age—the bike was built in 1950 and I was manufactured two years earlier—but the Shadow was fully restored a couple of years ago, and I was not.

Nor is it likely I will be. (For sale: one 1948 Caucasian male; still able to feed self, but needs full restoration ... ") Yet the bike looks like it came off the assembly line only about an hour ago. With proper care, it might even be immortal.

I sat down and gazed upon the Vincent for a while, sipping some post–oil change antifreeze (otherwise known as a Jim Beam Old Fashioned) with

subzero winds rattling dry snow against the windows outside, and wondered who the original owner of my bike might have been.

Who brought it home in early 1951—when the bike was actually sold—and sat in his or her garage (we'll assume *his*, with this kick-start ratio) and did exactly what I was doing now?

It was probably not bought by a teenager. Vincents were not normally a beginner's bike, so if we assume the owner had a real job and was, say, twenty-one years old, that would make him sixty-nine today. If the first owner were thirty-five, he'd be my dad's age, eighty-three. And if that mystery purchaser were the same age as I was when I bought the bike last fall (God forbid), he would now be ninety-nine.

In other words, it's unlikely the first owner of the bike is still riding, and it's entirely possible this same person, without a modicum of good luck and sound genetic heritage, has gone to that great café-racer hangout in the sky. Some hale and hearty people are still riding at sixty-nine, but many are not.

Still, the Vincent endures, looking to be in the prime of life.

This phenomenon of the ageless machine was first pointed out to me about twenty years ago in an essay by aviation writer Richard Bach. He noted that old machines—antique aircraft like his 1929 Detroit-Parks biplane, for instance—keep getting rebuilt and rejuvenated, while their pilots slowly turn gray, ultimately to hand over their aircraft to a new generation of pilots.

Which may, of course, be one of the very reasons we like to restore these things.

Everybody wants to be remembered for something, and most of us have devised some small strategy for leaving behind a moderate legacy, whether it's in the green eyes of our children, a house well built, contagious kindness, oak trees planted along the driveway, or just a perpetual trust fund for disadvantaged motojournalists. Along those same lines, motorcycle preservation is not such a bad way of projecting ourselves forward in time, and it seems more worthwhile with each passing year.

After all, these are good bikes we've got on our hands. I don't know if craftsmanship and clarity of vision will ever again intersect with the same mood of hope, innocence, and sincerity that created our best twentieth-century motorcycles. Motorcycles will definitely continue to improve (almost weekly), but I'm not sure they'll ever become more beautiful or more important to history—or to their owners—than were the bikes we saw last year at the Guggenheim.

In other words, those old Triumphs, Ducati Singles, Super Hawks, and Knuckleheads in our garages are probably at least as wonderful as we always suspected they were, well worth caring for and passing along. These bikes are talismans of a lucky accident—the overlapping of our short lives with an era that produced an unusual and exquisite craft.

It's become fairly common these days to note that we are just transient "curators" of the worthwhile things around us, but not too long ago my friend Greg Rammel put a more original spin on it, I think, at least for our own closely focused purposes.

When he and a bunch of riding buddies were standing around in his motorcycle shop near Detroit one evening, tipping beers and talking about the relative costs of classic old bikes, Greg shrugged and said, "It doesn't matter. We don't own these things, anyway. We just rent them."

Greg should know. He's had many years of motorcycles and customers pass through his shop, and he's seen more than a couple of leases expire. Usually on bikes that look better than ever.

THE SEARCH FOR ROBERT JOHNSON

I **DIDN'T HAVE A HELLHOUND** on my trail, but my bike was leaving a pretty good rooster tail of rainwater. Mounted atop a brand-new Triumph Bonneville, I was cruising down Highway 100 through the hills of western Tennessee in a cold, steady rain. Pockets of ghostly fog drifted through the hills, causing moments of sudden blindness.

A shame, really, because Highway 100 is a nice, curvy road, full of forested dips and rises and old bridges over rivers with romantic Chickasaw Indian names. It was a wonderful road for an agile bike like the Bonneville.

But as I neared Memphis, the country began to flatten out and the deep forest melted away. West of the Loosahatchie River Canal on Highway 64, I began to see cotton fields. The sky cleared, a warm sun dried the roads, and I stopped to take off my rain suit at a gas station. A crop duster swept over a nearby field.

Out of the Appalachians and into the Mississippi Delta. Goodbye, curves.

But then, I hadn't come here for the curves. I was looking for the roots of that uniquely American musical phenomenon, the blues.

For reasons that have never been adequately explained, this 200-mile stretch of rich southern bottomland between the Yazoo and Mississippi Rivers has been home to about 85 percent of all the great blues musicians who ever lived—Charlie Patton, Son House, Howlin' Wolf, Muddy Waters, B. B. King, Sonny Boy Williamson, John Lee Hooker, Mississippi John Hurt, and a hundred others. Many of them moved north to Chicago or Detroit, but the sound they took with them came right out of Mississippi.

And, I must confess, this sound is my favorite kind of music. Has been since I was first exposed to its haunting tones and lyrics by the Rolling Stones as a young northern white boy back in the early 1960s.

So, when editor Beau Pacheco called and said he'd like someone to pick up a new Triumph Bonneville in Nashville and take it down to the Delta on "a search for Robert Johnson," I signed on approximately at the speed of light.

"A search for whom?" you say.

Robert Johnson, for those not baptized in these deep, mystical waters, is to the blues roughly what Hank Williams is to country music. He was a thin, handsome black musician who died at the age of twenty-seven, back in 1938,

when a jealous husband at a juke joint supposedly poisoned his whiskey. He did only two recording sessions but managed to lay down such classic tracks as "Cross Road Blues," "Love in Vain," "Come On in My Kitchen," "Hellhound on My Trail," and twenty-five other songs that have been recorded by everybody on earth.

Legend says that Johnson went to the crossroads at Highways 61 and 49 one midnight and sold his soul to the Devil in exchange for his extraordinary musical talent. (I've tried this trick several times myself, but no one ever shows up.)

There is much controversy surrounding Robert Johnson's final resting place—several books and film documentaries have been made about the search for Johnson—so I thought it best to add to the confusion by heading south to see if I could straighten things out. And maybe hear a little live music at the same time.

On a cold Wisconsin October morning, I climbed on my Harley Electra Glide, rode to Nashville in fourteen numbing hours, and swapped for the Triumph at a place called Castle Motorsports.

I hadn't ridden a modern Bonneville for a couple of years and had forgotten what a delightful, all-purpose standard motorcycle it is. It has a perfectly flat seat, so you can move anywhere on the saddle; there's plenty of legroom, and the bars and pegs put you in a slight forward lean, ideal for a road bike with no fairing. The gas tank is really the gas tank, the replaceable handlebar is tubular, and the styling has not been contrived to prove that the designer is an avant-garde genius. It's a compact yet roomy bike, flickable and fun to ride.

Late in the afternoon, I hit the four-lane blacktop into Memphis, making my way to the famous old Peabody Hotel. I had deemed this a good starting point because the Mississippi Delta, it is said, "begins in the lobby of the Peabody Hotel in Memphis and ends on Catfish Row in Vicksburg."

The Peabody is also just one block off Beale Street, the traditional blues-club row of Memphis. It's a grand old hotel, even if they charge $175 per night and have neither coffee makers in the room nor free coffee in the lobby.

This shortcoming was quickly pointed out to me by Keith May, our caffeine-addicted photographer and art director, who flew in from California. Keith and his camera-packed rental car would be meeting me along the route to snap pictures of whatever scenic locales I would happen to blunder upon.

That evening, we walked down Beale Street looking for food and drink. We ambled in to the Blues City Café for some of the best seafood gumbo I've ever had and later heard a good guitar player named Earl the Pearl and his band.

As we stepped out into the warm night, I looked down Beale Street at the bright neon lights, tourist-crowded bars, shops, and cafés and said to Keith, "You should have seen this place when I rode through here twenty-five years ago on my Honda CB400F. It was bombed out. Vacant lots, broken glass, closed-down bail-bond stores with bars on the windows. But they've brought it back from the dead."

We passed under the crown-shaped neon sign for B. B. King's club, and I thought maybe the street finally looked more like it did when B. B. himself came here to seek his fortune. Half a century later, the exact same music was bringing people back again.

The next morning, we rambled a few blocks east to the little brick building that houses the famous Sun recording studio.

Sam Phillips, founder of Sun Studio, once remarked that if you could find a white singer who had a "black feel," you could make a million dollars. Lo and behold, young Elvis walked in. As well as Jerry Lee Lewis, Carl Perkins, Johnny Cash, and Roy Orbison. A magical place, from the very dawn of rock 'n' roll, and the original recording studio is still there, apparently unchanged, with its perforated white acoustical tile. Musicians still come to pay homage and record. U2 did a session there a few years ago.

When you stand in the studio, you can see why. There's still a vibe to the place, a distant thrumming in those walls, a time-machine sense of suddenly finding yourself in a simpler era. And Sun still draws true believers.

On our tour of the studio were two young German-speaking guys with well-greased Gene Vincent ducktails, big sideburns, skinny belts, and rolled-up cuffs on their blue jeans. One of them looked just like the guy who took my sister to the prom in 1958.

Here was a whole new 1950s twist on William Faulkner's famous comment that in the South, "the past is never dead. It's not even past."

I climbed on the Triumph and cruised down Second Street, to Huling, and found myself suddenly confronted with the chilling edifice of the Lorraine Motel, where Martin Luther King Jr. was gunned down. There's a wreath on the second-floor balcony to mark the spot.

The motel is closed now, the original structure having been absorbed into the larger National Civil Rights Museum. Before leaving, I pondered that balcony for a while and marveled at King's courage. It's a risky business being hated by J. Edgar Hoover and every homicidal maniac in America just because you would like to vote. Or stay at a better motel.

On a slightly lighter note, I cruised down the famous Elvis Presley Boulevard and parked at Graceland. Keith met me there, and we took a guided tour, visiting the graves of Elvis and his parents.

One thing that immediately strikes you about Graceland is that the mansion is not very big, compared with the ridiculous palaces perfectly ordinary Americans are building for themselves these days. You get the feeling that Elvis just wanted a comfortable place to hang out with his friends and family, rather than to show off his wealth. A nearly lost concept.

I cut across to Highway 61 and motored south past bail-bond offices, used-car lots, and liquor stores. At the Mississippi state line, the new four-lane highway suddenly exploded with huge, garish signs for huge, garish gambling casinos. Bally's! Harrah's! Seafood Buffet at Sam's Town!

Gambling came to the northern edge of the Delta about ten years ago, and it has transformed the landscape. The new gambling resorts dwarf the old cotton plantations, shacks, and warehouses, making them look like quaint, sepia-toned leftovers from another century. Gigantic casinos sit uncomfortably in the middle of cotton fields "like space ships filled with money," as author Peter Applebome once remarked.

Just south of Highway 304, however, the gambling stops and the Delta returns to its old self. I pulled into the tiny village of Robinsonville for lunch and found a charming old restaurant called the Hollywood Café, famously mentioned in several John Grisham novels. I wanted to see Robinsonville because Robert Johnson had grown up nearby on the Abbay and Leatherman Plantation. While Keith and I were eating the catfish lunch special, we started talking with the people at the next table and found out one of them was none other than Bobby Leatherman, heir to and owner of the plantation.

"Yes, Robert Johnson's house was just down the levee from our place," he told me. "The house is gone now, but it was just kitty-corner from the Exxon station down the road. My father knew him very well. He worked for our family."

I rode down to the station and found that the place where Johnson's house once stood is now nearly buried under the entrance road to Sam's Town Casino.

As I rode away, a sign along the highway said Kenny Loggins was coming to one of the casinos. Delta showbiz, old and new.

Swinging back onto Highway 61, I cruised down to Clarksdale, population 19,717, Ground Zero for the blues. Every black musician in the Delta seemingly was born in Clarksdale—or on the nearby Dockery Farms or Stovall Plantation. The Delta Blues Museum is located in the old train station in Clarksdale. There are record shops there, too, as well as a recording studio and several clubs—one of them called Ground Zero, no less.

There's a blues-theme "motel" just east of town on Highway 49 called the Shack Up Inn, where Keith and I found rooms for the night. It's essentially a row of artfully restored old sharecropper shacks lined up behind the cotton gin and seed houses of the old Hopson Plantation. They look like the real thing but have carefully hidden amenities for the modern traveler, such as hot running water, air conditioning, and VCRs. It's just the kind of place at which Robert Johnson would have stayed, if he'd had a cell phone to make reservations. It's a friendly, laid-back place that bills itself as the Delta's "oldest B&B—Beer and Breakfast." So we ordered a beer and joined a group of other guests sitting around in a circle of lawn chairs outside, watching the sun go down over the cotton fields.

The next day, I visited the Delta Blues Museum—notable for having Muddy Waters's boyhood log cabin assembled within its walls—and then rode south to Highway 7 and the metropolis of Quito. This is just a wide spot in the road with a derelict garage, a few houses, and a neat little church called the Payne Chapel next to a cemetery. One small block of granite has a guitar engraved in the stone, and it reads, "Robert Johnson, May 8, 1911–Aug. 16, 1938, Resting in the Blues."

Except, of course, no one knows if he's resting there, blue or otherwise. He was murdered at the Three Forks Store, a juke joint just a few miles up a side road, and quickly buried somewhere nearby—most people think here, or at the Zion Church a few miles south. A fan put this headstone over an unmarked grave sometime in the 1970s.

There was a Hohner Blues Harp harmonica lying on the grave, with the initials "J.H." drawn on it in Magic Marker.

I paid my tentative respects to this probable monument, then rode down the highway to a junction where the old Three Forks juke joint used to be.

Alas, since I was here last, the very building in which Johnson was poisoned had been bulldozed into a nearby swamp to make a turnaround spot for trucks. Too bad. If I'd known the building was worth so little, I'd have bought it myself. Maybe started a blues bar.

From there, I rode 3 miles south to Zion Church, which is just east of the road. This cemetery has a much larger headstone, an obelisk with an engraved portrait of Johnson and a list of his great songs. It reads, "King of the Delta Blues Singers, his music struck a chord that continues to resonate. His blues addressed generations he would never know and made poetry of visions and fears."

Nicely put. And there was another Blues Harp on the grave, with "J.H." on it. Also a bottle of Beam's Eight Star Kentucky Whiskey.

If Johnson—or any other real bluesman—were still around, I thought to myself, that bottle would be history. Yet out of respect—or fear of poison—I did not drink it.

Instead, I headed back to Clarksdale for a drink and some live blues. Keith and I stopped for a rib dinner at the junction of Highways 61 and 49, reputed to be the place where Johnson sold his soul. These days, he'd be run over by truck traffic and muscle cars with rap music pulsing from their doors at nosebleed volume. I guess it was quieter in the 1930s.

We went over to Ground Zero, had a few beers, and listened to a phenomenal Texas guitarist named Catherine Denise, then walked back to our lodgings for the night, the famous old Riverside Hotel. This slightly weather-beaten place is a former black hospital, the place where Bessie Smith died after her car accident in 1937.

As the only black hotel in town, it was the natural stopping place for all the traveling bluesmen—Sonny Boy Williamson, Robert Nighthawk, Ike Turner, and others. The owner, Frank "Rat" Ratliff, gave us a tour and showed us Bessie Smith's old hospital room. Our rooms, just down the hall, were clean, plain, and neat. I read somewhere that there's still a morgue in the basement, but I didn't ask to see it. Such places give me the blues, which are possibly related to the creeps.

In the morning, I rode southeast to the little town of Tutwiler on Highway 3. Tutwiler is famous for two things: The famous bandleader W. C. Handy waited here for a train one hot night in 1903 and heard a black man playing slide-guitar blues with a jackknife and was quite taken by "the weirdest music I had ever heard." It was the first time this music had ever attracted the attention of a professional, big-time musician.

Tutwiler is also famous as the final resting place of Sonny Boy Williamson II (AKA Aleck "Rice" Miller), who I think was the best blues harmonica player who ever lived. He recorded with Eric Clapton and others during the blues boom of the 1960s and died in 1965—about the time I discovered his music. There's a map painted on the Tutwiler train station showing how to reach his grave, which is next to an abandoned church a few miles from town.

The church is gone now. Recently burned down. But the grave is still there, neatly kept, with a list of Williamson's great songs chiseled in stone. My favorite is "One Way Out," which my own garage band has in its vast repertoire of bad imitations. On Williamson's grave was another harmonica left by the ubiquitous "J.H."

I checked out of the Riverside Hotel the next morning, said goodbye to Rat, and swung south under a dark, rainy sky for one last day in the Delta and two more holy shrines to visit. Following Highway 1 down the river, I rode to the little town of Rosedale, which I wanted to see only because it's mentioned in one version of "Cross Road Blues."

Rosedale is a little town with neat, shaded suburbs and a crumbling Third World downtown slumbering beneath a vine-covered water tower. I walked up onto the nearby levee in a pouring rain for a view of the river, but it was entirely invisible through the trees, as it often is. I suspect that many Delta dwellers live for years at a time without ever seeing the Mississippi unless it floods. Then they see it in their kitchens.

So, I had finally seen Rosedale. Big deal, you say, but now I could die happy.

Almost. I still had to find the grave of another musical hero, Mississippi John Hurt. When I was in college, every guitar player I knew was trying to fingerpick like John Hurt. He was said to be buried in the St. James churchyard, in Avalon.

But when I got to this little roadside settlement on Highway 7, no one seemed to know anything about him, or the church. The local mail carrier and several local farmers shook their heads and looked blank. A tractor driver finally told me that there was a small church on a dirt road along the creek.

When I turned onto the dirt road, I found no church, but rather a black family disembarking from an SUV to go fishing. I asked the man of the family about St. James Church.

"Why do you want to go there?" he asked.

"I'm looking for the grave of Mississippi John Hurt."

The man looked surprised. "I'm his great-grandson!" he said. "My name's T. Kimball," he added, shaking my hand.

Kimball's wife shouted from the car, "Who's he looking for?"

"Grandpa John!" Kimball shouted back.

She made a face. "He'll never find that grave," she said. "It's way back in the woods." They gave me complex directions to the cemetery nonetheless.

And find it I did, after many missed turns and much backtracking. The cemetery was nowhere near the church but in a small, mosquito-infested clearing in the woods, high on the bluffs overlooking the Delta. The cemetery looked like a stage set from a John Fogarty concert, and the road to it was a single-lane dirt trail, overgrown with vines and forest. Any bike larger or less nimble than the Triumph wouldn't have made it. Shades of my Triumph Trophy 500—a bike that can go anywhere.

A simple headstone between two trees said, "John S. Hurt, born Mar. 8, 1892, died Nov. 2, 1966." There were some faded flowers on the grave—and a harmonica from J.H. again. A true and hard core blues fan, J.H. I was beginning to like the guy, and I'd never even met him. Or her. We had the same heroes.

It was a little sad, I suddenly realized, how much our homage to the blues had become mostly a series of visits to gravesites. A bit macabre, perhaps, but then I suppose culture is mostly a matter of honoring the dead. In every generation, there are only a few people who do really great work, and if you don't keep their memories alive, you have no history and no standards to lean on or learn from. These men buried in the Delta had changed my life, and they were all long gone. Only the songs and legends remained.

And they'll outlive us all. Especially those of us who died of West Nile virus from all the mosquito bites we got while standing around old cemeteries in Mississippi. Time to go.

As I climbed out of the Delta and into the hill country, it turned cold and began raining harder. I found myself humming "Hellhound on My Trail" inside my steamed-up helmet, though there was nothing in my mirrors but that big rooster tail of rainwater again, and those same eerie patches of fog moving over the highway. "Got to keep on movin'," I sang quietly to myself, heading inexorably north toward winter. "Blues fallin' down like hail."

A THOUSAND MILES FROM NOWHERE

IT WAS ALMOST HALLOWEEN, and the baggage handlers unloading our plane in San Diego were wearing clown masks. A little unsettling in this age of terrorism and bad chainsaw movies, but our luggage arrived unmolested.

We quickly hoisted our three huge duffel bags of riding gear from the carousel and lugged them out into the warm California sunshine.

Palm trees rattled in the light ocean breeze. Deeply tanned women who'd stepped right out of a fitness video were flagging down cabs or climbing into Mercedes convertibles with guys who looked like Kid Rock or Prince Bandar.

Simultaneously, we all put on our sunglasses.

About five minutes later, a spotless white Chevy pickup towing a double-axle trailer loaded with bright red motorcycles came skidding to a stop in front of the baggage claim. The truck said "GoBajaRidin" on the door.

"I think that's our ride," Pat Donnelly said. Jim Wargula and I picked up our bags and headed toward the curb.

This was more like it.

Only two years ago, my buddy Donnelly and I had done a 700-mile, off-road loop through northern Baja on our own Suzuki DRZ-400s. It was a great trip, but more than half of our vacation time was spent hauling our bikes across the United States in my Ford van. By the time we got home, our off-roading adventure had almost become a dim memory, like trying to remember your exact bank balance right after a bad plane crash.

"Next time," Pat said, as we pulled into his driveway, "I think we should fly out to California and rent some bikes. That tour group we met at Mike's Sky Ranch seemed like the way to go."

So last summer, Pat, who is a lot more computer savvy than I am (which is also true of our senile dachshund, Tuffy), got on the Internet and tracked down the folks whose path we'd crossed at Mike's, an outfit called GoBajaRidin Tours (www.gobajaridin.com). The owner of the company, Bruce Anderson, said he would be happy to organize whatever kind of trek we had in mind.

"Here's the deal," Pat told me, after gathering all the facts. "You pay your money, fly into San Diego, and they drive you down to a hotel in Ensenada.

You start riding the next morning. They provide Honda XR400s, hotels, fuel, and meals. Everything's included except your drinks and airline tickets. They have a support truck for tools and spares, and to carry your luggage to the next hotel. Most of their guided tours are three- or four-day loops in northern Baja, but Bruce said they could take us on a five-day run down the whole peninsula to La Paz because they want to prerun this year's Baja 1000 route."

"Perfect," I said. "Now all we have to do is get Jim to go along."

The Jim in question was Jim Wargula, a trail-riding buddy who, like Pat and me, had just gotten back into dirt riding a couple of

years ago. We went way back, Jim, Pat, and I. We'd all played in the same clueless loud garage band back in the 1960s, and we were still playing together now, in an only slightly quieter version of the same group. Three guitar players, three motorcyclists, three old gringos: the Tres Amigos.

"I'll have to put the pressure on Jim," I told Pat. "He won't want to spend the money because he just bought a Honda XR650 and some new motocross boots. Also, he's cheaper than ten Scotsmen."

So I called Jim and used what I call the Mortality Argument.

"I really shouldn't go," Jim said. "I can't afford it right now."

"Well, look at the bright side," I said. "We'll all be dead soon and then we won't have to decide whether to go on THE RIDE OF A LIFETIME WITH OUR BEST FRIENDS or not."

A few days later, Jim called and said he'd go. Terror of the void works every time on people over fifty-five.

So we maxed out our credit cards (GoBajaRidin prices range from $1,750 per person for the four-day loop of northern Baja to $3,700 for a six-day run to Cabo San Lucas), packed our riding gear, cashed in our frequent-flier miles, and flew into San Diego. Minutes after arrival, that white Chevy pickup drove into view, towing its trailer load of Hondas.

Bruce "Bruno" Anderson, a big, hearty guy who looks vaguely like Kris Kristofferson (but can probably hold a note more accurately), bounded out and shook hands with us. "Let's throw your luggage on the roof rack and head for Mexico," he said.

We cleared customs at the border and drove across into Mexico. Small clusters of young men were sitting on earthen embankments next to the highway, tying rubber tubing around their biceps and shooting up in broad daylight.

"Look at all these guys shooting heroin," Bruce said.

"Why here?" I asked.

"Because it's cheap, and the cops don't care."

We cruised out of the sunbaked border-town tackiness of Tijuana and down 60 miles of scenic highway to Ensenada, where the Pacific was glistening under sunny skies. We passed the seaside Fox movie studio where nautical scenes from *Titanic* were filmed. The icebergs, apparently, had melted.

At Ensenada, we unloaded our bikes and met two of Bruno's assistants, Manuel Santana and Ricardo Lopez, who would alternatively be riding sweep and looking after our bikes. We checked into rooms at the San Nicolas Hotel and walked to dinner. The town was jumping, and a big Tecate sign over the street said, "Welcome SCORE 1000, Nov. 17–18."

Over a plate of great fish tacos, Bruce said, "Larry will be joining us in the morning, just before we leave."

This was none other than Larry Roeseler—ten-time overall winner of the Baja 1000, six-time ISDT gold medalist, and twelfth-place finisher in his first Paris–Dakar race last year. One of the greatest off-road motorcyclists on earth. In recent years, he'd started racing off-road trucks for the Terrible Herbst team, and was doing just as well in those.

Larry would be riding with us partly for fun and partly to scout this year's Baja 1000 route, which he, Bruce, and Santana would all be running in a few weeks. Bruce had run the race four times on bikes and won his class twice with four-wheelers, while Santana had done it twenty-five times, finishing third in class on an XR600.

This was a fast bunch we were riding with. Especially considering the almost tragically limited dirt experience of the Tres Amigos.

On our walk back to the hotel from dinner, Bruce pointed out the traditional starting point of the Baja 1000, a city street that immediately hooked down into a river valley and headed up a wide, shallow riverbed. He explained that we would be skipping this immediate baptism in the crystal waters of the Arroyo de Ensenada and hitting the trail just east of town in the morning.

"Get some sleep," he said at the hotel. "We've got a big day tomorrow." It was not the last time we'd hear that phrase.

We congregated at our bikes in the morning, suited up, and got ready to go. Bruce requires full body armor for all participants—motocross boots, knee protectors, chest protector, elbow pads, full helmet, goggles, etc. A good idea, as it turned out.

Larry Roeseler showed up and unloaded his personal mount, a KTM 625 EXC. I'd never met Larry before, and he turned out to be a great guy—articulate, funny, and very sharp, but also modest and self-effacing. Funny how the best people in motorsports almost always turn out to be this way.

We learned the starting drill on our XR400s (choke when cold, ease just past TDC with the compression release, then kick like you mean it, all the way through), pulled our goggles down over our eyes (or trifocals, in my case), and hit the road in the direction of San Felipe on the eastern, Sea of Cortez side of the peninsula.

A few miles later, we turned off the highway onto a rocky, rutted two-track road through the mountains. Time to get it on, as they say in old *Shaft* movies.

And Bruce, who was leading our group, did just that. The pace was fast.

It took me about five minutes to warm up and wish I hadn't worn my enduro jacket. "This ain't no disco," I wheezed into my helmet while standing on the pegs and leaping around a rock-infested puddle. "This ain't no foolin' around."

Larry went by me with his rear tire occasionally touching the earth in a sort of wheelie dance, and he disappeared into the distance. I gripped the bars, sucked in, and cranked on some more throttle. "Only about 992 miles to go," I noted cheerfully.

That day followed a pattern repeated often during the trip. I'd feel old, slow, and useless in the morning, then get into the rhythm of riding and feel more energetic in the afternoon. Some days were better than others. (I have hepatitis C, and my energy level takes wild swings, like the laugh meter in a cheap sitcom.) But by the end of the trip I felt great and was ready to ride to Tierra del Fuego. If you don't break your leg, dirt riding is always therapeutic.

Meanwhile, Jim would ride like a bat out of hell in the morning, then he'd tire in the afternoon, and I'd pass him. Pat rode fast all the time. Being a good, natural powder skier, he was very comfortable in loose, deep sand—of which we would have many, many miles.

Regardless of position, we rode most of the fast, straight sections about ⅛ of a mile apart to stay out the previous guy's dust cloud—good for both lungs and air filters. We were a long dust train, burning up the open space.

We looped upward into the pine country of the Sierra de Juárez, through El Coyote and Santa Catarina, then hit a short stretch of paved Highway 3 before dropping into sand whoops (where Jim crashed in a deep sand wash, saving me the trouble) leading onto the mirage-ridden expanse of Diablo dry lake. More miles of sand and dirt road, through the existential city dump, and into San Felipe on the Sea of Cortez. We pulled into a nice motel called George's with a protected courtyard for parking and climbed off the bikes. I was wringing wet with sweat from the last 10 miles of sand whoops.

"I'm glad I didn't put this trip off until I was seventy-two," I told Pat.

We cleaned up, came out at dusk, and found ourselves surrounded by little ghosts, mummies, witches, pumpkins, and zombies. No baggage handlers. It was Halloween night in San Felipe, and the town's parents had gone all-out on their kids' costumes. We had a beer on the boardwalk near the beach and watched these apparitions trick-or-treating in all the stores and shops. To see families interact in Baja is to go back to the 1940s and 1950s in the United States—the kids are respectful, unspoiled, and a little shy around adults, not encouraged to see themselves as royalty.

We had our own Halloween treat—dinner at the famous old El Nido steak house. There we met Jim Dickinson, a three-time GoBajaRidin client who had flown in from Maryland and was just joining our intrepid troupe. He turned out to be a lively, high-energy guy and an excellent rider, adding a whole new element of fun to the trip. Arriving with Jim was another guide, a tall, easy-going surfer/skier/rider (what season is it?) named Clark Hudson. Now we were nine.

"Gotta leave early in the morning," Bruce said. "We've got a really big day tomorrow."

During the night our bikes had magically been fueled, cleaned, and lubed by the crew, and we headed south out of San Felipe just as the first sun rays were breaking over the Sea of Cortez. At the edge of town, Bruce suddenly cut left over a huge sand dune, and we all followed him, sliding back down onto the highway.

The coast highway south of San Felipe starts out paved, then gets steadily worse all day long, until you are riding on a mixture of loose gravel and rocks held together with potholes, seismic faults, igneous extrusions, and Permian hogbacks—not too many lava flows. The Honda XR400s, I must say, handled all this in stride.

Bruce and Clark prepped the bikes with bigger plastic IMS 4.3-gallon gas tanks, taller gearing, heavy-duty tubes, O-ring chains, much richer jetting (160 main), K&N air filters, and tall Moose seats with heavy racing foam from Guts. Forks and shocks were reworked by Precision Concepts and revalved with "way stiffer" springs from Eibach.

And their bikes did take a beating, mile after mile of it, without complaint. They were a little less flickable than my KTM 525, and somewhat wound out on paved highway, but they handled the dirt with good stability and poshness of ride and had nice power delivery on the trail. Kick-starting and air cooling keeps them simple, basic, and tough. Great Baja bikes, they built more respect with each passing mile.

Morning sun helped to warm us despite an eerie 35-mph gale that blew our dust clouds away in small horizontal twisters. We stopped to take a break at the only ugly spot on the coast, a little godforsaken concrete-and-rebar village called Puertecitos. There were no humans to be seen, and the broken sign in the closed Pemex station creaked in the wind. Somewhere a cat ran away. The place gave me the creeps, like a postnuclear town from *On the Beach*.

We climbed on our bikes and hammered south, fueling up at Gonzaga Bay, a fly-in fishing village. We stopped for lunch at a famous (only) restaurant called Alfonsina's. The owner told us they had just stopped serving lunch.

But, as we were their only customers, he started again. Good business plan. Good fish tacos, too.

We struck inland toward the mountains, climbing to a place called Coco's Corners at a remote junction of roads. Coco is a notorious character, a wild man who runs a little snack stand and campsite decorated with tin cans, hubcaps, Baja 1000 stickers, women's underwear, goats' heads, and dead scorpions. Picture a Mexican John Belushi in a high-desert version of *Animal House*.

We had a Coke, and I asked Coco if there was anyplace to take a leak. He waved his arm at the great outdoors. "Everywhere the ground needs water." I looked around and saw that he was right.

Another 40 miles of scenic bliss, up canyons and riverbeds, brought us to the highway and a short distance from our destination, the famous little fishing town of Bahía de los Ángeles. We hit our friendly little motel right at sunset and met up with our late-arriving, hard-riding photographer Jeff Allen, who'd brought his own Suzuki DRZ400S. We all kicked back for a few beers in the courtyard, then walked to a beachside restaurant called Guillermo's—great fish.

In fact, nearly everywhere in Baja has great fish. The Sea of Cortez is one of the richest fisheries in the world, a fact that didn't elude the great author and sometime marine biologist John Steinbeck, who came to Bahía de los Ángeles in 1940. Even then, he noted, there were a lot of Americans in town, fishing. He didn't mention dirt bikes.

"Better get a good night's sleep," Bruce said on our walk back to the motel. "We've got a really long day of riding tomorrow."

In the morning we looped inland along a mountain ridge, then descended a steep valley to Punta San Francisquito for lunch in a little seaside outdoor café under a palm-covered roof. The afternoon was spent climbing back through the mountains, up beautiful valleys washed by creeks and surrounded by stunning Sonoran desert plant life—big cardon cactus, ocotillo, and the famously weird boojum trees of Baja, which look like twisted, 20-foot-tall candles. In one of these valleys, we stopped for a breather and were passed by none other than Robby Gordon in his prerunner truck, scouting for the upcoming 1000.

At El Mujica we hit Highway 1 and "burned pavement," as Bruce would say, for the last 30 miles to the La Pinta Hotel in San Ignacio. This little town is one of my favorite places in Baja. A green oasis in a deep valley, it has a lovely old mission church and a quiet little square with shops around it, like something in an old Peckinpah Western. When I retire, I just might move to San Ignacio.

As we headed back to our rooms after dinner, Bruce said, "Get a good night's sleep. We've got a really big day tomorrow, and we have to leave before sunrise." I turned on the TV in my room, where votes were being counted in the Kerry–Bush race for president. No results yet. Good. I needed sleep. And ibuprofen.

We met by our bikes in chilly pitch-darkness, fired up, and headed out of town. Before the trip, Bruce had recommended clear-lens goggles. I neglected to buy any before the trip and brought tinted goggles. Big mistake. For the first hour out of San Ignacio, I had to ride through the darkness with my goggles off, squinting through the dust clouds to see where I was going. By the time the sun came up, my eyeballs felt like they'd been on loan to Erwin Rommel.

Southwest we rode, toward the Pacific coast, on endlessly long sandy roads flanked by cacti, turning south at the coast through a series of small, remote fishing camps. Lunch found us at San Juanico, eating under a palapa (thatched hut) at the famous surfer's camp called Scorpion Bay, a stunning spot surrounded by blue water and drenched in sun, like something from a Jimmy Buffett album cover.

An American in surf baggies sat at a nearby table, clacking away on a satellite-linked portable computer. "Well, it's final," he said. "Bush has won the election."

The news caused quiet elation in some of our group and speechless despair in others. I won't tell which camp I was in, except to say that I had voted for a candidate who I believed was *not* dumber than a pail of mink food. You'll have to draw your own conclusions.

From there we rode south along the hard-packed sand beach—an exercise in pure elation and freedom—then cut toward the other coast on rugged sand and dirt roads toward Loreto. With shadows long, we descended to the coast through one of the most beautiful canyons I've ever seen—mystically deep and misty green. It had an ancient colonial road hacked into cliffs (by Indian slaves) on the opposite wall, so the Spanish padre and soldiers could cross the mountains. To build more roads. To find more Indian laborers whose souls needed saving, and so on. Most of the Indian population of Baja was wiped out by smallpox, so the missions here were left with few parishioners but large graveyards.

The canyon opened up to the coast, and we found our hotel—a big seaside golf-course resort, just south of Loreto. This was the most swanky hotel of the trip but my least favorite. Too removed from the gritty reality of Baja for my humble soul. I like the mom-and-pop places, where your bike is just outside your room.

In the dark, early morning, we backtracked up that same spectacular canyon and forked south to the beautiful San Javier mission, nestled in the mountains like a jewel lighted by the rising sun. On the gate of the mission was a business card from Larry Roeseler, who'd left earlier to do some scouting. On the card he'd written, "What took you guys so long?"

From San Javier we zigged to the Pacific coast, then headed across the peninsula's narrow waist to our final destination, burning some highway toward the Bahía de la Paz.

This was the best day of the trip for me. I felt good and finally started feeling relaxed with the throttle wide open on deeply sanded roads with the bike squirming queasily but harmlessly across the endless miles of desert and beach sand. This is what it takes to go faster in Baja: confidence under conditions of disconnected looseness, but without losing your concentration or readiness to deal with sudden surprises. Of which we had several that day—washouts, buried boulders, sudden turns over blind rises, etc.

When we got into La Paz, just at dark, we'd covered 274 miles that day. This, folks, is a long way to go on a dirt bike. We'd averaged well over 200 miles a day and covered just over 1,150 total miles, what with all our backtracking to hotels at night.

How far is that? Well, it's like riding from my home in Wisconsin to Daytona Beach, off-road, or twice the length of Florida. I don't know how anybody does it in one continuous ride, or even splitting the Baja 1000 into halves with a co-rider. If you ride at racing speed—especially at night—the opportunities to crash are endless. These guys have my undying admiration and respect.

Even at our more sedate pace, Jim and Pat had each gone over the handlebars once in spectacular fashion—getting only minor bruises—while blitzing through deep sand whoops, and Jim had done a couple of minor get-offs in deep sand wallows. I got through the trip without crashing but had more than my share of "moments" when I'd abandoned all hope. How Larry Roeseler could *win* this thing year after year without crashing his brains out is beyond me.

As Jim said, "That's why he's Larry Roeseler and we're not."

La Paz, when we finally got there in the gathering darkness, turned out to be a large, rather cosmopolitan city—with lots of good restaurants, upscale shops, and hotels—on a huge blue bay. Our hotel, a beautiful, friendly beachside place called La Concha, sat on a white sand beach just on the edge of the city.

The crew from GoBajaRidin loaded up and left in the morning, hauling the bikes back up to Los Angeles. The rest of us took a day off for beach lounging, then flew home the next day.

Before he left, Bruce shook my hand and said, "Well, you guys all made it."

I laughed and said, "There were a couple of days when I wasn't so sure we all would."

Bruce nodded. "It's a tough ride, but we do everything we can to make sure no one gives up. People who finish this trip will always remember it and feel like they've really done something, but a guy who quits is ruined forever."

As we flew north along the Sea of Cortez, I looked out at that 1,000-mile coastline and thought to myself that riding here in the dirt is not so much a sport as a parable.

NEW FRANCE AT LONG LAST

IT WAS AN OLYMPIAN ENTRANCE into the old French Canadian city of Trois-Rivières on the St. Lawrence River. Thunder clapped and lightning struck hills on both sides of the highway. But as we followed signs for the Centre Ville, the clouds parted and the sun came out, bathing the tall church steeples and the slate roofs on the old stone houses in soft evening light.

We turned left near the river on a street called the Chemin du Roy.

"What does that mean?" Barb asked over my shoulder as we paused at a stop sign.

"It means 'Way of the King'", I replied.

"I thought *king* was spelled r-o-i in French."

"It is," I replied authoritatively, "but in this case they are referring to Roy Rogers, King of the Cowboys. French Canadians love Westerns. They consider Dale Evans to be their queen."

This would not be the last time my masterful command of college French came in handy on this trip. In fact it was a college course, taken thirty-six years ago, that prompted this trip in the first place.

It was all Dr. Loudon's fault.

Loudon was my freshman Geology 101 professor at the University of Wisconsin, a guy who might have been the prototype for Indiana Jones. He taught college in the winter, but in the summer he was a highly paid oil geologist who worked for Sun Oil and traveled all over the world in search of this vital black fluid. He'd canoed down the Yukon River, paddled into the jungles of British Honduras, and flown his own float plane into the wilds of northern Canada. And he had the Kodachrome slides to prove it.

In one of his lectures, he showed us images of rock formations on the shoreline of Québec's Gaspé Peninsula, that lobster claw of land that follows the St. Lawrence River northeast and juts out into the Atlantic. His pictures showed a rustic land of sweeping coastal roads, lonely stone cottages, and small fishing villages that looked like something from Brittany or the north coast of Scotland. The people, he said, spoke only French and were descended from the earliest European settlers in North America.

I was stunned.

Here was a chance to exercise your pathetic French skills and visit a place that looked like Europe without actually buying an airline ticket and flying to Europe—something this starving student couldn't begin to afford. And you could ride there on your motorcycle!

My roommate, Pat Donnelly, was equally thunderstruck by the irrefutable logic of this concept.

So in the autumn of 1968 we loaded our two motorcycles (mine a Honda CB160, Pat's a Honda 305 Dream) and headed for the Gaspé. Barb, who was then my girlfriend, knitted me a warm scarf to take along. I still have it.

Pat and I rode for days in the cold autumn Canadian rain—with no rain gear, because that wouldn't look cool—and slept on the ground in a leaky tent. We made it as far as Montréal before we ran out of time, money, calories, and body heat simultaneously and had to turn around. We arrived home in Wisconsin like prodigal sons: wet, cold, and broke.

No Gaspé Peninsula. A failed quest.

And all these years, I have nursed an unfulfilled desire to see the place, partly out of curiosity and partly out of revenge on the past, to let the other shoe drop, as it were.

So when Barb and I were looking for a touring destination last summer, I said, "Let's go see the Gaspé Peninsula. Limber up our rusty French, see Québec, eat some seafood in small fishing villages, and come down through New England on our way home."

Barb looked at the map and said, "Wow! It's way out there! That's a long way to ride. . . ."

I nodded and said nothing. Now, as back in 1968, I didn't want Truth to interfere with Destiny.

We loaded up our BMW R1150RT and on a hot, sultry Wednesday morn headed north into threatening skies toward upper Michigan and the Canadian border at Sault Ste. Marie.

By lunchtime that first day, four equipment failures had occurred.

First, we discovered that the stock BMW seat that felt so good in the showroom was almost unbearably uncomfortable after four hours in the saddle. By noon, we were both standing up on the pegs every few minutes.

Barb made me stop at a Wal-Mart, where she bought a small child's pillow festooned with stars and moons and planets. It looked like artwork from *The Little Prince*. Very cosmic.

Then it started to pour, and I discovered that my trusty old Gore-Tex touring jacket—perhaps a victim of one too many washings—had suddenly decided to soak up water like a sponge. Also, my plastic rain pants leaked in the crotch. So did Barb's. We looked like poster children for incontinence. Backtracking to Nick's BMW near Green Bay, we Master charged about $200 worth of new rain gear.

Suitably pillowed and waterproofed, we thrummed up the Lake Michigan coastline as far as Manistique and then hit Canada the next morning, crossing the bridge at Sault Ste. Marie. The border crossing was friendly and easy, a far cry from the one Donnelly and I had endured in 1968. Fearing the endemic draft desertion, drug culture, and motorcycle hooliganism of 1960s youth, the border authorities had run us through the mill, checking our police records, patting us down, pawing through our duffel bags, and sniffing our toothpaste.

No such trouble this time. We are old and respectable. We have hard luggage, credit cards, and bifocals. It's hell not being a threat to anyone.

On Canada's Highway 17, we soon discovered a pleasant fact. Canadians drive like bats out of hell. Their roads are seriously underposted (90 kph, or about 55 mph, even on four-lane segments), but no one pays any attention. They all go 70 to 90 mph, speeding along politely without aggression, keeping right except to pass. And you never see a cop. Pure heaven.

We made it through the north woods and lakes to Mattawa that night, a pretty little town on the steep banks of the Ottawa River. Our view from the Valois Motel could have been a painting from the nineteenth-century Hudson River School, except for the satellite dish and the oil-head Beemer with ABS in the foreground.

Early daylight found us descending the river valley on winding scenic roads through Pembroke. I looked for a place called Wright's Cabins, where Pat and I had pooled our dwindling money for a cabin one night so we could avoid shivering to death in our soggy sleeping bags. Old Mrs. Wright had made us tea, dried our clothes, and brought extra blankets. A miraculous find, fondly remembered. But now I couldn't locate the place. It was either bypassed with the new four-lane around Pembroke or buried under a shopping center. Everything looked different. Time marches on, while memory simplifies and condenses. Also, brain cells are killed off by tequila.

Barb and I cruised through Ottawa and then up the freeway to Montréal, where we hit rush hour. Montréal has a beautiful old city center, but the surrounding suburbs are what I call a Ruined Zone. Too much traffic, too many people, houses, franchises, malls, and car dealerships. You look around and say, "Lord, get me out of here."

We zoomed northeast on increasingly more rustic two-lane roads along the St. Lawrence and soon found ourselves in Trois-Rivières, a picturesque city that is still human in its size and scope. Motoring straight into the old downtown on the Chemin du Roy (Rogers), we found a beautiful bed and breakfast called the Auberge-Gîte le Fleurvil', right on the river.

Barb checked on a room while I waited outside, fearing rejection. We were wet and dirty. The owner, a Monsieur Yves Adams, came out, shook my hand enthusiastically, and directed me to park our bike in the family garage, next to his Harley Springer Softail. He had a copy of *Hog Tales* on the antique coffee table in the living room.

Sometimes you stop for the night and drive right into the dead center of Nirvana. Other times, the bear eats your tent.

We walked around town in the evening, and suddenly everything was very French—menus, signs, and architecture. The houses in Trois-Rivières are right out of France, a curious mixture of ungainly proportions, wrought-iron porch railings, and metal roofs of bright red or green. As in Paris, all old architecture is charming, while nearly everything modern is hideous beyond all comprehension, as if two different races of humans had inhabited the country, before and after World War II.

Cruising up the St. Lawrence on the river road the next morning, we began to see a lot of touring motorcycles and bicycles. Things were getting more scenic and vacationish by the mile.

Using our proven method of following signs that say Centre Ville, we rode steeply uphill into the lovely old city of Québec, which was originally built as a mountaintop fortress to protect French Canada from the ambitions of British, Indian, and Yankee marauders. It was here, on a high plateau called the Plains of Abraham, that the British under Wolfe defeated Montcalm's French forces and ended France's power in North America.

If the battle had gone the other way, people in Winnipeg would be eating snails and drinking decent wine at this very moment. Both Montcalm and Wolfe were killed in this battle, incidentally, and never saw the outcome of their struggle.

Old Québec is a wonderful city, full of great restaurants, charming old hotels, narrow streets, and sidewalk cafés—a Paris in miniature, easily walked. I was right in my suspicion that Donnelly and I could have visited Europe right here in North America. Too bad we never made it.

On the other hand, we couldn't have afforded it anyway. Cities—even beautiful ones—can be hostile to young people without money. When Pat and I left

198 // DECADE ONE OF THE 21ST CENTURY

for Canada in 1968, we each had $60 to last us for two weeks. Québec would have eaten us alive. We'd still be there, washing dishes.

Barb and I, however, had a paid-up credit card, so we checked into the Hôtel Le Clos Saint-Louis, parked our bike in the courtyard, and chatted with our friendly concierge, who said she used to tour all over Canada on a Gold Wing. You have to love a country where hotel managers don't stare sullenly at the bugs on your jacket while you check in.

Climbing the narrow stairs to our antique-rich second-story room, we kicked back to wait for photographer Brian Blades to join us for dinner. He was supposed to fly in from California and call us when he got to the hotel.

At 7:30 in the evening, Brian still hadn't called, so we phoned California to find out when his flight was arriving. His wife, Wendy, answered and said, "I'll let him tell you. He's standing right here."

"Hi, Brian," I said. "I guess this means you'll be late for dinner."

"I couldn't get a Saturday flight," he said, "so I'm taking the redeye. I'll be there tomorrow around noon."

I was secretly delighted because this gave Barb and me a leisurely morning to look around Québec City and enjoy Sunday breakfast at an outdoor café, where the chairs were a lot better than our BMW seat and there was no helmet buffeting.

We met Brian at the airport, where he snagged a rental SUV the size of Idaho and followed us up the highway into the fabled and much-imagined Gaspé Peninsula.

I'd made it at last.

For the first few miles, however, this was not the cliff-hanging shore road I'd expected, but rather a busy highway through rolling farm country. It was still quite populated until we got to Rimouski, where the road narrowed and finally began dipping in and out of small villages and harbors on the shoreline. The St. Lawrence River starts out narrow at Québec (which means "a narrowing of waters" in Iroquois) and gets wider, like an opening funnel, as you head toward the Atlantic. By the time you get to Cap-Chat, the opposite shore has disappeared.

It was Cartier who first charted this shore, in 1534, looking for that elusive western route to the Far East. Europeans were desperate for a way to bypass the steep trade markup imposed by Islamic potentates. An urge that persists to this day, as anyone filling up at a gas station will tell you.

In the United States, I'd been keeping track of our mileage, which was always between 48 and 50 mpg on the big Beemer, regardless of speed. In Canada, trying to figure out mileage using liters and kilometers proved difficult for a person of my math skills, so I gave up computing our mpg at every gas station and ate a Butterfinger instead.

From 5:00 to 6:00 p.m. we started scanning the small coastal towns for a motel and finally lucked out at a place north of Rimouski, called the Auberge Marée Douce (Hotel of the Gentle Sea). Yet another discovery, a nice old hotel with big porches and quaint cottages on a hillside overlooking the coast. At night the place was lit up like a Mandarin palace, and it had a fine dining room with excellent food.

Funny how the French preoccupation with good cuisine made the transition to the New World and is still in force, more than three hundred years later. I always wonder why the English never noticed all this highly edible stuff, right across the channel. Or north of Maine and east of Toronto.

Incidentally, the couple who ran this hotel, Marguerite and Fernand, spoke very little English, so we got a chance to exercise our rusty language skills. You don't need a lot of French in Québec Province, but it helps to know a few common phrases, such as "Have you a bottle of absinthe and two glasses?" or "The shaft of my blue umbrella is afflicted with doleful malfunctionings."

As we headed up the coast in the morning, the road was alive with touring motorcycles, mostly bearing Québec provincial plates. A loop around the Gaspé Peninsula seems a popular getaway for Canadians, just as circling Lake Superior is for midwesterners. And I would say that 85 percent of the bikes you see touring now are big V-twin baggers—Harley Road Kings and their imitative Japanese brethren. Black beanie crash helmets rule.

The central spine of the Gaspé Peninsula is a heavily forested mountain ridge, and as you go northeast, the foliage changes from central Eastern to North Woods, and it starts looking like Sergeant Preston or Nelson Eddy country. There are few internal roads on the peninsula, but at Sainte-Anne-des-Monts we turned inland to see the Parc de Conservation de la Gaspésie, a camping and hiking area in the mountains.

Alas, we had no hiking boots or tent, so after lunch at a costly and strangely sterile little hotel complex in the park, we headed back down a scenic valley full of sweeping roads and turned right. As we headed east along the shore, the towns got more remote, the coastline prettier, and the road curvier. The place was beginning to look like Doc Loudon's old Kodachromes.

Late in the afternoon, the road began to turn southeast along the cliffs, and I realized we were suddenly at the farthest end of the peninsula. My odometer said we were exactly 1,900 miles from Wisconsin. Twice as far east as Donnelly and I had gone with our little Hondas. At Montréal, we were only halfway here. What were we thinking back then?

And even now, as we stopped at a scenic lookout to gaze at the Atlantic, Barb said, "It feels like we're a long way from home . . ."

Truly, as you turn away from the St. Lawrence and along the Atlantic cliffs, the ocean suddenly looks vast, with nothing but Europe out there somewhere.

Even the road feels lonelier, and there's less traffic and tourism. The roller-coaster pavement makes steep climbs and descents, sweeping down on the coast and briefly inland at small bays, like California's Big Sur. The curves are all sweepers—no scorch-the-edge-off-your-tires stuff. Everything can be taken at 70 mph. Symphonic riding, with the cymbal crashing of waves.

With the sun setting, we finally turned into Gaspé Bay, where Cartier first set foot on North America, 471 years ago. We looked around the slightly seedy (but lively and jumpin') town of Gaspé and found an old, partly restored hotel called La Maison William Wakeham at the edge of town. The place was still being renovated but had Norman architecture and a beautiful wood-paneled lobby and dining room (closed Mondays, wouldn't you know).

After dinner at a good local restaurant called the Café des Artistes, we returned to our hotel, where I think we were the only guests. As we made our way through the silent, dimly lit lobby, Barb said it felt slightly creepy, like a scene from *The Shining*, so I thoughtfully resisted the temptation to shout "Here's Johnny!" as we entered our room.

In the morning we found a man wandering around the lobby, inspecting the place. He was a French Canadian named Jacques who had rented one wing of this hotel forty years ago as a family dwelling and had returned to look around. He told us he now worked for a government agency that promotes Gaspé development. I asked him how the economy was doing.

The fishing industry, he said, was essentially dead, what with the near extinction of cod from overfishing. "But we're doing okay with tourism," he said. "Still, the peninsula is big and far from any urban center. Far flung. It's a commitment to come here."

I nodded. "I tried to come here thirty-six years ago myself and didn't make it. It was too far."

As we rode away I was troubled by a recurrent thought. Everywhere we go now, the traditional local economy is half ruined by some environmental meltdown, but there's always said to be tourist or real-estate money coming in from "the outside." I worry about shrinkage of the outside.

We crossed the York River and swept down a coast studded with lighthouses to the tourist town of Percé, so named because it has a huge Gibraltar-like rock off the coast with a hole pierced in it by waves. Just off the coast sits Bonaventure Island, famous as a sanctuary for thousands of wild seabirds and no good place to sit down.

Percé is a beautiful spot, with lots of seaside motels, restaurants with porches on the ocean, gift shops, etc., but it was absolutely swarming with tourists. We had lunch on a sun deck and then left before terminal claustrophobia uncorked my penchant for sudden violence. As we crawled out of town in bumper-to-bumper traffic through a sea of pedestrians, I turned to

Barb and said, "Never underestimate the power of a rock with a hole in it. Erode it, and they will come."

We rounded the peninsula and headed back west along Chaleur Bay into increasing population, prosperity, and farming along the shore. More meadows and fields, less forest. The coastline was still pretty, but the wild part of the Gaspé was behind us.

It had taken us three days to round the peninsula, and our last stop for the night was in Carleton. We stayed at the Hôtel Baie Bleue, a clean, modern place with an upstairs dining room overlooking the bay, where we sat down to the best seafood stew I've ever had. Every tour has its Meal of the Trip, and this was it. After dinner we said goodbye to Brian, who was getting up early to head back around the peninsula for Québec City and home.

Barb and I left early in the morning, too, rolling down into the forests of New Brunswick on Highway 17 through pockets of ghostly morning fog. Suddenly the signs were in English again. We crossed into Maine at Van Buren and began a wonderful back-road journey diagonally across New England, upstate New York, and western Pennsylvania.

We passed Maine's Mount Katahdin, the state's highest peak, and then spent three days crossing the White Mountains, Green Mountains, Adirondacks, and Alleghenies, winding through one lovely old colonial town after another, across stone bridges, around white-painted churches, and pausing to explore Revolutionary War cemeteries, Fort Ticonderoga, and Watkins Glen.

Riding pleasure? For endless curves and sportbike roads, this was the best part of the trip. The northeastern United States doesn't have the exotic French flavor or the lonely, edge-of-the-world atmosphere of the outer Gaspé, but it's great riding in a setting of deep antiquity and charm.

Maybe this is where Pat and I should have gone. It was closer to home, was cheaper to get to, and had more curves. We also understood the language and the money.

But that wasn't the point, really.

Back on that first motorcycle trip, we wanted desperately to go somewhere else, somewhere that didn't look or feel or sound like the place we lived. We were driven onward by those exotic Kodachromes, images of ocean and fishing villages, of stone huts and slate roofs, of a place where people spoke French and had menus filled with things that were new and hard to pronounce. We had to go there.

Or at least try.

And now, thirty-six years later, on the last day of our tour, Barb and I found ourselves in a fast-food joint along the Indiana Toll Road, making tracks for home and drinking iced tea to rehydrate ourselves from the suddenly crushing midwestern summer heat.

Barb looked tired. She'd come a long way—4,000 miles in twelve days of riding without a day off—while sitting on that cosmic little Wal-Mart pillow with nary a word of complaint. She gazed out the tinted window at the passing traffic and said, "Well, was the Gaspé Peninsula what you expected?"

I thought about it and shook my head. "No," I said. "It's not as poor and remote as I pictured. It's greener, more vast and mountainous. Still rustic and beautiful, but more prosperous and complex. Also, much farther away. From our place, it's like going to California and back."

Barb nodded. Apparently she'd noticed.

As we rode toward home I pondered Barb's question further and realized that no place I'd ever been turned out to be exactly as I'd imagined it while sitting at home. Not Vietnam, Paris, Katmandu, or Yellowstone Park. Nothing is ever what you expect. Maybe that's why we travel.

RIDE A CROOKED ROAD

NO WONDER THERE ARE SO MANY Bluegrass references to fog," I mumbled, wiping off my visor with one hand and peering blindly into the pure whiteness. "'Foggy Mountain Breakdown' . . . the Foggy Mountain Boys . . . these mountains are full of it."

A gas station and convenience store loomed out of the ether as I crested a ridge, and I pulled in for a warming cup of coffee. "What's the name of this village?" I asked an old boy who was climbing out of a nearly invisible pickup truck.

"Whitetop," he said.

I nodded approvingly. "Good name."

On the downside of the mountain, things got better. My Buell Ulysses suddenly dropped out of the clouds on a steep, winding road along a beautiful valley with small pockets of pure white fog stuck in its hollows like balls of cotton. Rays of sunlight broke through the overcast, and suddenly you could see one of those views that only Appalachia offers, a descending vista of increasingly distant mountain ridges in shades of gray and green, all bathed in soft light. Corners came at me one after another on the valley road, and the Buell flicked through them effortlessly.

If this road were a drug, I thought to myself, it would be illegal.

The road, in this case, was a route put together by the State of Virginia to stimulate tourism in the backcountry. Dubbed "The Crooked Road," it looped through the pointy western end of the state, linking all kinds of famous musical sites in Appalachia.

Some alert member of the state tourist board sent a map and brochure to *Cycle World* in California, and the equally alert Editor Edwards called me in Wisconsin and asked how I felt about doing a musical tour of Virginia on the just-released Buell Ulysses.

"You live close to the Buell factory in East Troy," he pointed out, "so you could pick up one of their early test bikes and ride down there. Also, you know a lot about Bluegrass and traditional music."

Well, sort of. I'm not exactly a mountain-music scholar; my expertise is pretty much limited to a veneration for Bill Monroe and Ralph Stanley, along with a deep suspicion that Patty Loveless and Alison Krauss secretly wish they'd met me in high school.

And, like millions of other Americans, my interest in old-time mountain music was reinvigorated by the soundtrack from *O Brother, Where Art Thou?* And, before that, *Bonnie and Clyde* and *Deliverance.*

But to a hardcore Bluegrass fan—the kind who plans his vacations around the annual Bean Blossom Festival—I'm just a piker. I have, however, squandered lots of money on books and exploratory CDs, so I guess you could say I'm a student of the art form.

And what better thing for a student than a class trip like this one? Also, I was keen to put some road miles on a Ulysses, as it's one of a small handful of new bikes on my ownership radar.

Off to East Troy.

I picked up the Buell with my van, brought it back home, packed the voluminous saddlebags and a duffel bag with enough riding gear to theoretically survive all the variations of mountain weather in October, said goodbye to Barb, and rode south at sunrise on a Tuesday morning.

It took me two days of steady riding to reach Virginia. I left Wisconsin, blitzed down the Interstate to Bloomington, Illinois, and then headed diagonally across Indiana on two-lane roads. I stopped for the night in Madison, Indiana, a beautiful old town on the Ohio River. After checking into a hillside hotel, I walked downtown for dinner and a movie.

The theater was showing the highly acclaimed documentary *March of the Penguins* in one auditorium and *The Dukes of Hazzard* in the other. A recent review of the latter in our local paper had called it (and I quote here from memory) "a really bad movie made from one of the dumbest TV shows in history."

I looked at the posters in front of the theater and noticed there were no '68 Dodge Chargers or girls wearing short shorts in *March of the Penguins*, so I naturally went to *The Dukes of Hazzard.*

It wasn't as bad as I expected, and it had Waylon Jennings in the soundtrack. Some things you have to do for art.

On a foggy morning, I crossed the Ohio and climbed into the warm, sunlit hills of Kentucky. Farm stands along the road were laden with Indian corn, yellow squash, and pumpkins almost the same color as the airbox cover in front of me.

The Buell was booming along nicely, the 1,203cc Twin cranking out tons of easy torque. The engine shows its Harley heritage at idle, shaking up and down in its rubber mounts, but transforms itself into a smooth runner when you start rolling. It revs freely and easily to its 7,500-rpm redline but seldom needs to be revved past 5,000, with all that midrange wallop. And the sound is deep and throaty.

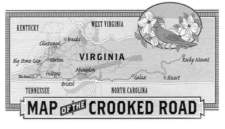

Gears are well spaced, but you rarely have to shift and can dial speed on and off with the throttle in fourth or fifth on a twisty road. When you do shift, clutch pull is light, and the thing changes gears with quiet, well-oiled precision. Nice gearbox. Superb brakes, too.

Typical of most Buells, the Ulysses's handling is quick, effortless, and reassuring. Erik Buell makes much of his engineering efforts at mass centralization (short exhaust canister under the engine), low unsprung weight (perimeter brake rotor on a very light wheel), and weight-saving cleverness (oil reservoir in hollow swingarm), but it all pays off in agility, handling, and ride. This is a really fun bike that works with you on a back road. The ride is compliant, well damped, and civilized.

It ain't bad on the Interstate, either. The bike is a little windy at 70 to 80 mph with its short snap-on-and-off windscreen (a larger optional one is on the way), but the roomy riding position is just about perfect for all-day travel. So is the seat, which may be the best-designed, most comfortable perch available on any modern motorcycle. I spent seven days and 2,200 miles in this saddle and never gave it a thought.

Note to BMW, Ducati, and KTM: quit fooling around and just copy this seat.

The Buell carries its 4.4 gallons of premium unleaded in the perimeter frame/gas tank, and range can vary widely depending on how and where you ride. On

the Interstate, I averaged about 41 mpg, and the fuel light came on around 155 miles. Following coal trucks through mountainous West Virginia on the way home, I averaged 57 mpg.

Any downsides?

Riders with short inseams will find the bike tall and a bit clumsy at stop signs and in slow maneuvers. Also, a noisy electric fan that cools the rear cylinder stays on for about a minute after you shut off the ignition. When you stop to ask for directions, it roars away.

The engine probably needs it, though. On a hot day, the frame/gas tank gets quite hot to the touch, particularly on the right side, even with the fan running.

And the weather stayed warm and beautiful all the way into Kentucky on Highway 421, a zone of old cabins, deep valleys, and tobacco barns. I turned onto Highway 460, and the state morphed into horse country, with huge estates and miles of white fences. Places where big pillars and gates say, "Hey, look over here! I'm rich!"

That evening I crossed into Virginia to the official starting point of the Crooked Road. This was a mountaintop park that straddles the Kentucky/Virginia border, called Breaks Interstate Park. I stayed at the park lodge and took advantage of its deck looking out on a gorge with rock chimneys and a river far below. In the morning, I was supposed to meet Brian Blades, our photographer, who had flown in from California and rented a car at the Bristol airport.

The steep mountains precluded cell phone service—which was lucky, because I don't own a cell phone and Brian's was broken—so we agreed to meet at the Breaks village post office at noon. Brian was a little late, so I got to talk to dozens of people who came to pick up their mail.

One older gent by the name of Tom Blankenship told me he'd been a coal miner for twenty-four years until the local seams played out, then built Cadillacs and Chevys in Detroit. Now he was picking ginseng in the forest for a living. He asked where I was heading, and I said, "Down to Clintwood, which is Ralph Stanley's hometown."

He nodded. "I know old Ralph. Everyone here knows him. He's kin to my wife. Her mother was a Stanley. Ralph and the Clinch Mountain Boys are playing tomorrow night at the theater in Clintwood. You might want to see 'em."

Good tip.

Brian hove into view with his rental car, and soon the Ulysses was descending into legendary Dickenson County on tight, winding Highway 83 in a light rain. I rumbled into the small town of Clintwood and stopped on Main Street at the Jettie Baker Center, which had "Ralph Stanley and the Clinch Mountain Boys" on the marquee. Friday night.

This was only Thursday, so I decided to continue south and somehow backtrack the next night for the show. I took a wrong turn leaving town and did an accidental 70-mile loop through Appalachia and ended up back in Clintwood two hours later. It's hard to sense your direction in these mountains when the sun's not shining. I'm surprised Daniel Boone didn't end up in Newark.

I finally rode into Norton, the next star on Virginia's Crooked Road map. Outside of Norton was a famous old place called the Country Cabin, built in the 1930s as a community recreation center for dances, music, cakewalks, hoedowns, box suppers, and other entertainments whose allure has been partly lost to youth since the invention of the Marshall 100-watt stack and the reign of Sid Vicious.

Across the street from the original site is Country Cabin II, a larger log hall that holds more people. Unfortunately, the place was closed until Saturday's Bluegrass night, so I looked in the darkened windows, hoping that bad timing would not turn this into the Closed Building Tour.

On the door were rules of behavior for music nights: no drinking, guns or other weapons, unruly behavior, harassment of others, vulgar language, etc.

This train don't carry no gamblers, this train. Bluegrass is essentially a culture of modesty and good manners, the flip side to Rock's experiments in sullen nihilism. You'd be just as likely to see a space launch at a Bluegrass festival as to hear the F-word spoken.

Near Norton I motored down a deep valley behind a coal truck and suddenly realized the road was covered in fine coal dust. Along the highway I saw my first big coal-processing plant and stopped for a look. Glancing in the mirror, I saw a face with a raccoon mask of carbon looking back at me. You could get black lung here just reading the fine print on someone's bumper stickers.

As I headed through the valley, a small drive-in movie theater appeared (*Bad News Bears*), tucked into a small parcel of flat land. On both sides of the road, old houses and mobile homes clustered in deeply shaded hollows and ravines, and it occurred to me that opportunity here is pretty much proscribed by valleys, channeled by ridges. That isolation is a good part of what made—and preserved—the old music.

It being too dark and late to search out rustic charm, Brian and I got generic hotel rooms on the highway outside Norton and ate at a generic steak house. Other than that, I remember nothing. Another case of amnesia through modern comfort.

The next day the Ulysses threaded its way through old coal towns around Big Stone Gap, then headed for the next big star on our route, the little village of Hiltons, Virginia. Home of the Carter Family Fold.

You might call this spot the cradle of modern Country music.

A tall, thin man named A.P. Carter lived here with his wife, Sara, and they sang songs with Sara's guitar-playing cousin, Maybelle. In 1927 they got into their car and drove down to Bristol for a trial recording session in an old warehouse with a talent scout named Ralph Peer. He discovered, to his amazement, that this "hillbilly" music was immensely popular with record buyers all over the country. Their songs, "Wildwood Flower" and "Will the Circle Be Unbroken," are the dual anthems of Country music.

Maybelle's daughter June married Johnny Cash, and A.P. and Sara's daughter Janette still emcees music nights at the family home. The Carters are the Royal Family of Country music, only without the tweeds, Wellingtons, and big ears.

Peer also recorded a guy with a bluesy yodeling style named Jimmy Rodgers, "The Singing Brakeman," and he too became a star. I still listen to his records myself. These sessions are called "The Big Bang of Country Music."

Anyway, the old Carter family home and grocery store is still there on a quiet rural road in Poor Valley near Hiltons, at the foot of the Clinch Mountains, and there's an open-sided music theater built next door. I got there on a drizzly afternoon, and there were workmen renovating part of the theater.

One of them was a *CW* reader and avid motorcyclist. He said Janette Carter usually performed with Bluegrass groups on Saturday nights, but she'd been in the hospital and probably wouldn't be there that weekend. Once again, I'd have to backtrack the next night to make the show. I'd see.

Motoring into the big town of Bristol, Brian and I got motel rooms for the night. We then jumped in his rental car to retrace our route back to Clintwood to see Ralph Stanley. It was a dark and rainy night, and I didn't feel like riding over the mountains again on the Buell. I like to pay my dues, but only once.

When we got to Clintwood, Stanley's tour bus was in front of the theater. As we stood under the marquee to keep out of the rain, Dr. Ralph Stanley himself climbed down from the bus, and I got to talk to him for a while. A nice man, alert and quick for his seventy-eight years. Now that Bill Monroe is gone, he is really the last performing legend of mountain music, one of the greats.

Before the show, I wandered across the street to the Ralph Stanley Museum. I got there ten minutes before they closed, but that didn't keep me from loading up on rare bluegrass CDs and DVDs. I got a feeling the Buell's luggage was going to get heavier on this trip, perhaps approaching black-hole density.

The show that night was terrific. Stanley has a high, lonely ache in his voice that Dwight Yoakam once called "ancient, in the most flattering sense of that word, and timeless." It really is the sound of the mountains. He sang "O Death" in his haunting a cappella, a performance that brought him national fame in the soundtrack of *O Brother, Where Art Thou?*

I should mention, too, that the opening act, the Reeltime Travelers, was one of the best bands I've ever heard, and they all looked to be under thirty. They had a stunning woman fiddle player who blew everyone away, as did the woman who played guitar. I think there were also some guys in the group.

Brian and I careened back down the mountain to Bristol in the fog and rain. In the morning we headed to the Birthplace of Country Music museum, which is located on the basement level of the huge and modern Bristol Shopping Mall. As we crossed the parking lot, I said to Brian, "This is where the Carter family did all their shopping during the Depression. They'd come in here and pick up calico and biscuit flour and then get a latte at Starbucks."

The museum, however, turned out to be well worth the risky mall exposure, and the woman running it told me the mall had been kind enough to donate space until they could move into a larger and more appropriate site. Also, the place was full of music fans, even at 10:00 in the morning.

I unholstered my Visa card and spent a small fortune on more CDs and DVDs. The Buell saddlebags quaked in the parking lot; flocks of birds took flight in alarm; Alan Greenspan tossed in his sleep.

Winding roads, all day long. Beautiful roads with endless corners along Highway 58. We stopped first at Abingdon, a rather upscale town full of beautiful old homes and architecture, to look at the famous Barter Theater, then swung on to Galax, Virginia (pronounced "Gay-lax," like an over-the-counter medication). This is a pretty town in a broad valley, famous for its Old Fiddler's Convention, held each August since 1935, and the Rex Theater, home to a nationally popular Friday-night radio show called *Blue Ridge Back Roads.*

There was no bluegrass at the Rex that night, but something completely different: a gospel celebration to raise money for Hurricane Katrina victims, organized by the local fire department. Performers and audience were mostly black, from nearby churches, and it was one of the best nights of music I've ever heard. Everybody sang and clapped and swayed. The local talent was amazing; Aretha Franklin meets Percy Sledge.

With volunteer work and personal donations, these small-town citizens raised hundreds of dollars and presented the money to a young white family from New Orleans who'd lost their home. Meanwhile, American oil companies raked in billions of dollars in profits from high fuel prices after Katrina and got an enormous tax break from our government.

Nice to know part of this country is still great.

From Galax, Highway 58 just got better and better. The music may hold this route together, but it needs no such justification to the motorcyclist. It's all curves, scenery, mountains, ridges, and subtly changing landscapes, down to Stuart and all the way up to the hilltop town of Floyd, where a famous record shop and the Floyd Country Store (home of the Friday Night Jamboree) were both closed, as you might expect on a Sunday afternoon.

And that's the main problem with this tour. You need at least two weekends to do it right, rather than just one, and most things happen on Friday and Saturday nights. You have to be too many places at once. Regardless, you still hear a lot of good music, as we did, and to a motorcyclist the music is just a sidelight anyway. The Crooked Road is exactly that, and you'd have a great ride if you didn't know Bluegrass from Shinola.

Brian and I motored up to the end of the Crooked Road at Rocky Mount, had lunch at a good Italian restaurant, and split our separate ways for home. He was driving back to the Bristol airport, and I was 1,100 miles from home, mostly by winding two-lane roads through Appalachia. The return trip took me two and a half days.

I rode through the stunningly beautiful and rugged mountains of West Virginia, more raw and wild than Virginia's and studded with gritty coal towns. While passing a coal truck on a mountain road, my Check Engine light came on. The engine was running fine, but I pulled over and checked the oil, which was okay. I noticed the rear-cylinder cooling fan hadn't come on, as it usually did. Maybe it was running hot, and this fan was the Achilles's heel of the Buell. (Achilles's heel on a Ulysses from East Troy? Isn't this too much Greek literature in one paragraph?)

But the engine didn't feel hot, and the Buell continued to run well all the way home. Still, the engine light came on intermittently, giving me one of those dull headaches of doubt. Erik Buell later told me the first forty bikes left the factory with defective threading on a screw that opens the exhaust system's power valve, and this tripped the light. Didn't hurt anything; just reduced horsepower slightly above 5,000 rpm. Now I know.

Except for that, the bike never gave me a moment of trouble. It was a good partner on this trip: quick, agile, and comfortable, with an engine that pulls like a truck—but much better than the trucks you pass in the mountains. Every morning, I looked forward to getting on it. Which is the big test of an adventure-touring bike.

Is it a dirt bike as well?

Not really. I ran up some rutted dirt-and-gravel roads (to look at a cabin for sale) and found the 17-inch front tire too easily deflected for serious off-road work. You can make it through, but it's not all that much fun. What we have here, really, is a roomy, comfortable, and charismatic sportbike that lets you travel long distances and carry luggage while you sit up and enjoy the scenery.

And there was plenty of that on the Crooked Road.

If you showed the public some good color photos of rural Virginia and said they were NASA pictures from a distant planet, people would sell everything they owned and pay a million dollars for a one-way ticket on a space ship. Their hearts would ache with a desire to move there. It's that beautiful.

But it's not on a distant planet. It's right here on earth, in a quiet corner of Virginia, haunted with old cabins, half-forgotten villages, brooding forests, and the echoes of ancient Celtic music with a high and lonesome sound. And the occasional motorbike on some kind of odyssey. You can ride there from your home.

DUCATIS AND CIGARETTES

BACK WHEN I WAS a full-time tech editor at *Cycle World* during the early 1980s and lurking in the roomy but windowless office now occupied by Editor Edwards, I had a small quote from a British bike magazine taped to my door.

It read, "Ducatis are like cigarettes; you may quit for a while, but you always come back to them in the long run."

This little gem of wisdom struck a chord with me because both addictions seemed related in some strange way.

I was then trying, with only limited success, to quit smoking and had several times ceremoniously thrown my last pack of Camels (a fine blend of domestic and Turkish tobaccos) into the trash, only to have the urge for a nicotine hit return at the least opportune time. Usually while I was working alone in the office over the weekend.

I'd be sitting there typing my deathless prose about rejetting a Honda 400 Hawk with midrange stumbles when, suddenly, a red message would light up in my brain saying, "You must have a cigarette." And I couldn't concentrate until I did.

Well, I've long since stopped smoking—quit cold turkey on my fiftieth birthday—but the instinctive urge to own a Ducati has remained as persistent as that old cigarette habit used to be. I've owned nine of Borgo Panigale's finest over the past twenty-eight years, and the occasional gap in ownership has always set off a motorcycle variant of that same red message light: "You must have another Ducati."

The problem goes back quite a few years.

While I admired the small Ducati Singles that hit our shores in the 1960s (even if they weren't Triumphs), the first stirrings of genuine desire came with the arrival of the exquisite round-case 750 SS V-twins. These were expensive, however, and seemed virtually unobtainable, as any Ducati dealer lucky enough to get one simply kept it. They were always on display in showroom windows, but I never saw one on the street.

It was the square-case 900SS, built in much larger numbers, that finally made the sleek desmo Twins available to mere mortals. And it was here that the real addiction took hold.

It started about the first week I worked for *Cycle World*, early in 1980, when I arrived in California from Wisconsin just in time for the Los Angeles Motorcycle Show. A bunch of us rode up there from the office, and when we walked through the doors of the main pavilion, the first thing we encountered was a black-and-gold 900SS rotating on a raised, round platform under the lights. It looked like a wedding cake with a black widow perched on top.

Except the Ducati was better looking than any deadly arachnid. Equally dangerous, but much better looking. It had gold wheels, an anodized chain, and bodywork in ebony black with discreet gold trim to stir the Anglophilia of those of us who misspent our youths lusting after Vincents, Velocettes, and AJS 7Rs.

But this was no dusty old British classic. This was the most potent production track weapon of the moment, its immediate antecedents having recently won (in variously tweaked forms) both the Isle of Man and the Daytona Superbike races. And the bike was cleaning up everywhere in production club racing. Spartan, purposeful, and uncluttered.

While the other *CW* guys wandered off, I stood there transfixed by the beauty and rightness of the design, sort of like Wayne (or was it Garth?) staring at that white Stratocaster in the window of the music shop. Anticipating that movie by a couple of decades, I said aloud, "Oh yes, it shall be mine!"

As luck would have it, a few weeks later I won a $5,000 editorial prize from CBS Magazines (which then owned *Cycle World*) for a story I'd written about my Triumph Bonneville. It was clearly a case of mistaken identity or some bizarre corporate foul-up, but I wasn't about to ask any questions.

The check arrived at 11:45 on a Friday morning, and at noon I ran down the block to Champion Kawasaki-Ducati and bought a used 1978 900SS from shop owner Lee Fleming. When I signed over the check, the money had been in my hands for exactly fifteen minutes.

This bike was a runner. It had been Lee's personal streetbike, and he was then the AFM Open Production class champ on his racing 900SS. The compression was up slightly, and Jerry Branch had reworked the cylinder heads.

I remember my own first ride as being somewhat disorienting. Compared with, say, a Honda CB750F or Suzuki GS1000 of the day, the Ducati was slightly harsh and uncomfortable, with a severe shortage of steering lock. Your feet were tucked up behind you in a full racing crouch, and the exhaust note sounded like Muhammad Ali working a speed bag with forceful, rhythmic deliberation. You looked down at the engine and wondered if it had enough aluminum around the cylinder bores to contain all that violence.

Getting off my Honda 750 and climbing onto the Ducati was like leaving the Hilton and entering a Trappist monastery, a dark place lighted by torches where you slept on a stone floor.

No minibar in this room, pal. We're looking for salvation through austerity.

But out of the crowded city and on the back mountain roads of California, the bike transformed itself. Fast, composed, and easy to ride, it clicked smoothly along like a runaway freight train compacted into a highly precise instrument of speed. Pure pleasure, a mechanical drug that seemed to mix some kind of opiate with an equal amount of caffeine.

Nearly every Sunday morning my buddy John Jaeger (on his R90S Beemer) and I would take a ride over the Ortega Highway to Lake Elsinore for breakfast. The road was nearly empty in those days and largely unpatrolled.

Or so we thought. On a long downhill straight coming out of the mountains toward San Juan Capistrano, we got side by side and held our throttles to the stops. We'd just hit an indicated 135 mph when two cop cars materialized out of the rapidly approaching distance and turned on all their lights and sirens. We pulled over, feeling suddenly busted and financially ruined, but the cop cars kept going. I think they were on their way to investigate a minor fender-bender we'd passed earlier and were too busy to turn around.

John and I looked at each other, shrugged, and split for home. We spent the rest of the day hiding out in our respective garages, staying away from windows.

After a couple of years, I sold the 900SS to buy something more practical (a category that includes nearly all other objects in the universe), then started twitching like a dope fiend and bought another 900SS in the late 1980s.

Since then, I've owned a long string of Ducatis, old and new, including yet another bevel-drive 900SS. I sold that last bike to a friend in Colorado seven years ago and just bought it back last summer. It is now sitting in my garage, and here it will stay.

I guess I've finally reached the age where I'm not looking for anything more practical. I have a couple of modern bikes that work better for normal daily use, but I've come to realize that Ducatis are important not just as great machines but as symbols of a healthy resistance to compromise.

In a world where everything gets dumbed down, fattened up, or overcivilized, Ducati has managed to keep a focus of purpose—what my friend Jeff Craig calls a "core idea of what they do best." They don't try to be all things to all people. Ducati makes racing and sportbikes that are light and charismatic, and that's it. We don't want Eric Clapton doing the best of Justin Timberlake, and we don't want Ducati making cruisers or 800-pound touring rigs.

Also, if you like Italy and things Italian—which I do, despite being largely Celtic, from a family that was notoriously undemonstrative—Ducatis are a way of celebrating everything distinct about the Italian approach to life, as filtered through a spare-yet-flamboyant mechanical sensibility. Motorcycles project a cultural force field upon your life, and Ducatis do it better than most. The bikes have Emilia-Romagna written all over them and seem to have been made for narrow Apennine roads lined with Lombardy poplars and old stone buildings. Which is why you don't want to go off the road in that country. And why Ducatis generally don't have floorboards.

Another key quality in Ducatis is presence. Whether you're riding along on a 250 Mach 1, an old 900SS, or a new 1098, you never forget for one moment what you're riding. You keep looking down at the tank and instruments and thinking consciously about where you are—both literally and in the flow of history. Remaining oblivious to my 900SS while speeding down the highway would be difficult indeed, like sitting across the dinner table from Hilary Swank and trying to forget who she is, or that Clint Eastwood may have taught her how to box. The mind doesn't wander much.

But enough of these show-business analogies. Back to smoking.

Like those cigarettes I gave up a decade ago, Ducatis also carry with them a bracing touch of fatalism. The owner has to be somewhat willing to dive into the unknown (or at least be willing to endure a desmo valve adjust) in order to make life more interesting and less predictable. The bikes serve as a kind of compensation for putting up with everything safe and mundane in this world, a thumb in the eye of caution. All motorcycles do this to some extent, but Ducatis are the image on the recruiting poster.

I took my black 900SS for a long ride this weekend (maybe the season's last, as it's supposed to snow tonight) and sat in my workshop, warming up and looking at the bike for a while when I got back.

I happened to glance over at my glass trophy case, where I keep memorabilia—odd souvenirs, old tank badges, models, etc.—and noticed that I still had a spare set of silver velocity stacks left over from my first 900SS, as well as a $\frac{1}{12}$-scale Tamiya model of the black Ducati, carefully assembled years ago by my late father-in-law, Fred Rumsey.

Behind the velocity stacks, on the middle shelf of the trophy case, was an ancient pack of crumbling Camels. They'd come out of the zippered tail compartment of my 900SS seven years ago, when I sold the bike to my friend in Colorado.

I always carried them there—for scenic roadside stops and reflective episodes of bike appreciation—along with two spark plugs, a tool roll, and a Zippo lighter. The Zippo, which I'd purchased at a military PX in a place called Phan Rang in 1969, was in the trophy case as well. Right near the cigarettes.

A small red light came on in my brain, but I ignored it—for the time being—and opened a Diet Coke. The kind with caffeine.

RIDE HARD, RIDE SHORT

IT WAS ONE OF THOSE MIDWESTERN autumn weekends you'd like to frame and put up on the wall so you could look at it all winter. Balmy and clear, with the maples nearing full color and the wind "counting its money and throwing it away," as Carl Sandburg put it so nicely, scattering golden leaves across country roads. The wind smelled like dry leaves and grain dust from corn harvesting.

Which is a good thing, because I did not. I reeked of wood smoke from sleeping in a tepee all night, next to a campfire.

Yes, we recently acquired an actual Plains-style Indian tepee and have erected it on the lower pasture overlooking our creek.

We camped in it this past weekend with a bunch of our friends, roasting hot dogs and marshmallows on sticks, much as Lakota warriors might have done if they'd had a grocery store nearby, instead of ten million buffalo.

Good times, but when I got up in the morning and walked out the east-facing door into the first rays of sunlight, it was time to shift back into the present century and ride. A big day around here: the seventh-annual autumn Slimey Crud Motorcycle Gang Café Racer Run.

As I've noted in previous years, this and the spring run are essentially semi-disorganized affairs in which interesting bikes in the café-racer tradition are encouraged to show up at a country bar in Pine Bluff, Wisconsin, and then randomly ride about 60 miles to another country bar called Sprecher Tap in the village of Leland, for an afternoon of bike appreciation. Not a real long ride, but then the Slimey Crud motto is, "Ride Hard, Ride Short."

This year, I looked over my meager four-bike "collection" and decided to ride my black 1977 Harley XLCR. What could be more appropriate, after all, than a motorcycle that actually has the words "Cafe Racer" in its official factory designation? It's as easy as picking out clean underwear with "Wednesday" stamped on it.

A nice assemblage of bikes showed up again this year, approximately five hundred of them. My favorite was a café-racerized "Black Bomber" Honda CB450, looking very Dunstall-period correct, with upswept pipes, a long, low tank, and a bum-stop seat. None of this prepackaged stuff, like mine.

Motorcycle Performance of Madison brought a Kawasaki drag racer they started up for the crowd. It revved with an unearthly, eardrum-shredding

cademarTori-'18

bark and filled the air with exotic fumes that made everyone's eyes water. It was wonderful.

Late in the afternoon, our Slimey Crud President for Life, Dr. Kenneth Clark, mounted the front steps of the Sprecher Tap to thank all the riders for being there and not crashing their brains out on the way. He said people had been calling all week to ask if the unpublicized run was being held as usual, and he said, "Of course it is! This event has taken on a life of its own. We couldn't stop it if we tried!" Much cheering.

Then, on a more somber note, he reminded the crowd that one of the founders of the Café Racer Run, Bruce Finlayson, had died of cancer this past summer.

"We Cruds all took up a collection and dedicated a park bench to him," Ken explained. "It's at Brigham Park, up in the hills near Blue Mounds where we all used to ride together. It overlooks the valley, at the place where we scattered his ashes. If you ride past there, you should stop and rest awhile. The bench has a plaque with his name on it."

It suddenly occurred to me, while looking out at the crowd, that you could see the faces of nearly all the people who took care of Bruce when he was sick.

Like so many families, his was widely scattered around the United States, so it was friends who looked after him when he became ill. An old friend from Michigan named Kathy did most of the hardest work, but the Cruds helped, too. We all drove Bruce around, ran errands, and put on rides and gatherings to try to condense the pungency of life as best we could. Another old friend, Phil Schilling, the former editor of *Cycle*, flew all the way out from California to visit and help out, then returned a few weeks later for the funeral.

Bruce knew everyone in the motorcycle world. He raced at Daytona in the 1960s; restored Ducatis, BMWs, and old Hondas; and wrote articles for motorcycle magazines. He was a fast guy of almost magical smoothness, who could ride like the wind.

And in the end, it was mostly just other riders who looked after him. People in leather jackets; the other family.

Odd how that happens, I thought. All but a small handful of my own good friends, after fifty-two years of life, are motorcyclists. The effect, no doubt, of some unspoken agreement on how life should be lived.

I rode home alone that afternoon and took a little detour, the XLCR hammering up the winding valley roads out of the Wisconsin River Valley, climbing County Highway F to Brigham Park, which stands on Military Ridge in a natural grove of sugar maples.

It didn't take me long to find the new redwood park bench. The bronze plaque on the backrest reads:

BRUCE M. FINLAYSON
1945–2000
SLIMEY CRUD MOTORCYCLE GANG
RIDE HARD, RIDE SHORT

I sat there for a long time, taking in the view. You can see all the way back down to the Wisconsin River Valley, and beyond, to the bluffs at Devil's Lake. It is, to my mind, one of the finest views on earth.

Late in the afternoon, a wind came up and began to blow steadily, rustling the trees. There's something about a warm autumn wind in this part of the country that's a little unsettling. It sounds like the audible passing of time, the hidden clockwork behind the scenery, moving way too fast and sweeping another season away.

I rode home on the back roads, taking the long way around, listening to the beatific sound of those siamesed pipes until it was almost dark.

A TOWN TOO FAR

WHEN I RODE INTO TOWN about two hours before sunset, it occurred to me that Jackson, Wyoming, had everything a touring rider could want at the end of a long, hot day.

Motels, movie theaters, Mexican restaurants, invitingly cool bars with invitingly cool drinks, camping and fishing stores to browse in, bookshops full of books on Western history, and a large number of mixed tourists to gaze upon while eating an ice-cream cone on a park bench. The place was jumping.

Not that I'm normally drawn to places with hordes of tourists, but it is nice to be able to walk around town at night and get some exercise without being followed by the police car because you're the only guy who isn't home.

I cruised the entire length of Jackson to scope out the motels, riding all the way to the western city limits and noting that several inns still had "VACANCY" signs burning. I pulled into a parking space and looked at my watch. It was only about 6:30 p.m., a little too early to stop, but I had been riding my old R100RS Beemer for about ten hours and was feeling a little buzzed.

The best way to gauge your touring-fatigue level, I've found, is to get off your bike for a minute and shut it off. If your head is humming like a tuning fork and you can't put change in a parking meter, it's probably time to stop. Dropped gloves are a bad sign, too. The brain is switching over to its menu-contemplation mode (appetizer and beer-list phase) and doesn't want to be bothered with basic motor skills.

I should have turned around right then and gone back into town. But I didn't. After all, there were nearly two hours of good riding light left. I looked at my watch and uttered those terrible words, "One more town."

Seemed like a good decision at the time. The ride out of Jackson was stunning. I swung up through the southern end of the Teton range on Highway 22 toward Teton Pass (8,429 feet), a curving mountain two-lane with only moderate traffic. Pulling off at a scenic overlook, I flipped up my face shield and looked at the map on my tank bag for a minute.

Hmmm. Not many big towns out there. If the motels were full in the tiny villages of Wilson or Victor or Swan Valley, my next sure bet for a hot meal and a bed would be Idaho Falls. About 85 miles away. The cars were already turning their headlights on, and in the dark shadows of the mountains my face shield

THE RAMBLER

MOTEL

DIRECT DIAL PHONES
QUEEN BEDS
WI-FI

NO VACANCY

cademartori '18

was beginning to shimmer with the halos of many departed bugs. Road signs warned of deer and elk. Maybe I should go back.

Yeah, that was the ticket. Mexican dinner, movie, walk. Buy a book. Have a margarita nightcap. Stop a little early for once and live like a human instead of a forward-progress machine. I turned around and rode back to Jackson, now more glittering than ever in the warm dusk.

Trouble was, much of the glitter came from newly lighted neon that said "NO" in front of the former "VACANCY" signs.

I cruised all the way back to the other end of town before I saw one lone vacancy sign, in front of a nice log-cabin-style lodge. But when I walked into the lobby I heard the desk clerk say to a family of four, "Sorry, we just gave away our last room. And absolutely everything in town is full. I've been calling around for the past half hour, and there's nothing."

The family looked hollow eyed and tired. So did I, one would suppose.

I had ridden right through town during that critical window of time another motorcycle journalist long ago (I can't remember who) referred to as "the witching hour." It's that fleeting period every evening when motels suddenly fill up, restaurants begin to run out of their prime-rib special, and movies start. If you don't stop then, you will probably be out of luck. An hour later, you've missed the boat. One more town is a town too far.

I have ridden through the witching hour and aced myself out of a perfectly idyllic stopping place so many times I hesitate to admit it. I generally ride through some scenic little town that's so perfect Walt Disney might have designed it and then end up sleeping at some bleak motel out on the highway with a diesel idling outside my window and dining on the last piece of fried chicken from a convenience store where they are just mopping up and their last customer looks like he's waiting for me to leave so he can rob the place.

I should make a little sign and put it on the inside of my fairing that reads, "On the other side of Paradise is a great abyss."

It was almost dark when I headed for Idaho Falls, and I made it a few hours later.

Luckily, Idaho Falls is anything but a great abyss. It's a lovely little city right on the Snake River, with a nice park right around a real set of waterfalls (hence the name, I suppose). Unfortunately, all the motels were full.

Well, not quite. A helpful clerk at a big chain motel called all over town and found one room left, a cancellation at a remarkably inexpensive place across the river. "You'd better head over there right now," he said. "This is, literally, the last room in town."

"Tell them to hold it for me," I said, slamming on my helmet without bothering to fasten the chin strap. It was starting to rain when I found the motel.

Seldom have I been so glad to see a flat bed, a roof, and four walls. I ate that night at a nearby restaurant that was just closing but let me in anyway, then had a beer at a brewpub that was also just closing but let me in anyway.

Perfect timing, once again. Another big victory for intrepidness and the Western concept of linear progress.

And nothing so warms the heart of the weary, wayward traveler as the sight of chairs stacked upside down on tables, the quiet clack of salt shakers being refilled by a tired waitress, the reassuring sound of the night manager locking doors from the inside, and the shriek of a vacuum cleaner picking up bread crumbs left by customers who dined much, much earlier.

LOST SUMMERS

IT ISN'T EVERY DAY you get a letter on cast-off official stationery from the palace of Saddam Hussein, but it happened to me last month.

I have been corresponding, you see, with one SP/4 Darrell Pacheco, who is an MP patrolling the streets of Baghdad. Some of you may recognize the Pacheco name, as Darrell is the brother of Beau Pacheco, editor of our sister publication, *Adventures*.

Like Beau, Darrell is an avid lifelong motorcyclist, but he hasn't been riding much lately because of his job in Iraq. His story is an interesting one: he's a forty-nine-year-old veteran of the first Gulf War who stayed in the army reserves afterward and then retired two years before the September 11 attack.

On September 12, he did what many of us felt like doing but did not have the means or the strength of will to accomplish—he rejoined the army and went back to the Middle East.

He's been there for about nine months now, and he isn't sure when he's coming home. "Just get me home in time for Daytona," he writes. "That'll be one year."

Despite dealing with the constant threats of ambush and land mines and the intense heat ("Woke up from a nap this afternoon and it was 132 degrees . . ."), he writes letters that are remarkably free from the sort of grousing and complaining in which I, personally, would be tempted to indulge. Still, you can tell, reading between the lines in Darrell's letters, that he misses his motorcycles back home.

He has a 1978 BMW R80 with R90S fairing and cycle parts on it and a Kawasaki ZRX1100 with the Eddie Lawson–replica paint scheme, both of which he rides on the Blue Ridge Parkway near his North Carolina home. He's also owned a Sportster and a VFR750 ("Wrecked it at Deal's Gap") and is an avid roadracing fan. He's hoping to buy a Springer Softail when he gets out, to do some traveling.

Though we aren't that far apart in age (I'm just six years older), it's funny how the content of Darrell's writing reminds me of my own letters from Vietnam in 1969 and 1970. When we can't ride motorcycles, the dream of doing so fills our plans and sustains us.

My little army stint in Southeast Asia was the one period of my adult life when I didn't ride any bikes at all. Although the country was crawling with

millions of Honda 50s and Super 90s, we troops had no opportunity to own motorcycles, and I was never seriously tempted to borrow one from our Vietnamese interpreters because these guys had most of their life savings tied up in their Hondas. They were not toys to the Vietnamese, but their only means of transportation. You didn't mess around with these bikes.

So in lieu of actually riding, I simply dreamt of riding. I sent away for Triumph and Norton brochures and had them taped on the inside of my foot locker, and I'd spend hours off-duty staring at those pictures and trying to decide which bike to buy when I got out and where I would go with it. I also sent for brochures from a company in London called Elite Motors Limited, checking into the possibility of foreign delivery of a new Bonneville when I got out. A trip through England on a new Triumph sounded like an ideal way to quickly dispose of fourteen months of overseas combat pay. Still does!

Then I hatched a new plan: I would get out of the army on October 8, 1970, at the Oakland, California, replacement center, buy a new Bonneville or Norton Commando from a San Francisco dealership, and ride home to Wisconsin. I wrote my parents and informed them of this scheme.

My dad, who seldom wrote letters, responded almost immediately:

"You will <u>not</u> (underlined three times) buy a motorcycle in San Francisco and ride home in October. Your mother is worried sick and has hardly slept since you left for Vietnam, and she doesn't need one more thing to worry about. Have a little mercy. You will get on an airplane and fly home as soon as possible."

I was twenty-two years old and free to do what I wanted, but when my dad used this tone, you didn't cross him unless you wanted to be swatted to death with your own hat. So I gave up on the San Francisco idea and flew home. A few weeks later, it snowed in Wisconsin, and I bought a rusty old Volkswagen instead of a bike. Triumphs and Nortons would come later, in better weather.

Still, those bikes in the brochures had done their job, which was boosting morale about the future. I think with my friend Darrell in Iraq, they are serving the same function.

As they are for me, even now.

Last spring, I was diagnosed with hepatitis C, an unpleasant little virus whose eradication requires six months of injections and pills that make you too queasy and tired to do much but lie on the sofa and stare at the ceiling. (I should really do something about that cobweb and those plaster cracks.) As of this writing, I have five weeks of this delightful treatment left, and, though the prognosis is good, the past summer was an almost total write-off for motorcycling. I was simply too tired and dizzy to ride most of the time. I took a few short rides into town but didn't have the stamina to go very far.

If you look carefully at the sofa where I spent the summer, however, you will note that it is surrounded by stacks of motorcycle magazines, sales brochures, US road atlases, and maps of Europe, England, and Mexico. Somewhere in the pile is a book about the Isle of Man . . .

I may not have ridden much this summer—a few hundred miles total, on the handful of days when I felt okay—but I have lived what is possibly the richest imaginary motorcycle life since my days in Vietnam. Never have I had so many plans.

It'll be winter when I'm done with this medication, but I'm already plotting a "Payback for the Lost Summer" tour in the Deep South with my new Triumph Bonneville.

I'll probably hit Daytona this year, too. Maybe finally get to meet SP/4 Darrell Pacheco, whom I know only from his letters. With any luck, we'll both be home by then, back on our bikes.

FLYING ON THE GROUND

LATE AUTUMN is usually the best time for riding in the upper Midwest—dry, clear, and sunny. It's cool enough to enjoy wearing a leather jacket, but not so cold that great sheets of ice cover the North American continent and drive our local mastodon herds relentlessly south. It's a time of ideal balance.

Not this year, though.

October was pretty much a washout for riding. Granted, we had a beautiful first weekend for the Slimey Crud Motorcycle Gang's fall Café Racer Run—about one thousand bikes showed up—but after that things went downhill fast.

On Monday morning, low clouds moved in like an armored division and brought with them an endless convoy of bad weather—wind, cold, freezing rain, and snow showers. Nearly four unbroken weeks of it. I parked my bike and, until yesterday, didn't ride at all. Pretty grim.

Luckily, I found a novel way to make it through those dark and difficult weeks without giving up my usual quota of banked turns, skids, slips, hair-raising miscalculations, and grateful homecomings.

I took flying lessons.

Yes, after a fifteen-year absence from flying, I'd decided to get back into it, to see if I could be taught to fly again and update my license. I took an FAA physical (alarmingly thorough, it seems, when you're fifty-eight) and signed up for flying lessons at a place called Morey Field in Middleton, Wisconsin. My instructor, an unflappably calm and patient man named Richard Morey, is the grandson of the airport's founder. A third-generation flight instructor. His grandfather, an aviation pioneer and barnstormer, flew with Lindbergh.

It may have been too cold for riding—at least by my exacting and self-indulgent standards—but not for flying. Airplanes don't mind a little sleet or dry snow blowing around. They have heaters. So I flew twice a week for four weeks and finally finished up last Tuesday.

On this final lesson, we flew to nearby Sauk Prairie Airport so we could take advantage of the fierce crosswinds and see what I was made of. Never a good idea, but we somehow survived my crosswind landings without serious injury. So Rich—in a mood of life-affirming gratitude, no doubt—signed off my ancient and crumbling log book (first entry, 1964). I was good to go. A pilot again.

And the next day, as if by magic, the bad weather skulked off to the east, high pressure moved in, and our classic fall riding weather returned. It was a sunny 65 degrees yesterday, and I took my big KTM 950 out for a good back-road flog through the russet-colored hills with leaves swirling across the road and the dry smell of corn-harvester dust in the air. Carved pumpkins grinned at me from farm porches. Glorious stuff.

And, while riding again at long last, inevitable comparisons crept into my partially trained journalistic brain, and I started thinking how closely related motorcycling is to flying.

Okay, they aren't exactly the same. When you climb out of a Cessna after an hour of crosswind landings, driving anything on the highway at moderate speed seems absurdly easy, and you wonder briefly how anyone ever manages to have an accident—especially in a car.

There are no critical instruments to scan (other than your speedometer, if you so choose). No rate of climb or stall speed to worry about. Your altitude and heading are predetermined by the road. You don't have to radio ahead to Barnes and Noble and tell them you're coming into the parking lot from the west on a heading of zero-niner-zero. There are no other vehicles above or below the road surface. If your engine quits, you pull over.

Another difference is that flying—once you've mastered the basic motor skills—is more of a cognitive process than riding and less of an athletic act. You always have to think about where you're going, where you'll be twenty minutes from now, and how you're going to make it all happen. The actual steering is not so crucial, except in landing.

Riding, particularly dirt riding, roadracing, and fast back-road riding, is more physical and immediate. Your plans are much shorter in range and duration, corrections more frequent and imperative. Expletives of doom arrive with greater regularity.

But the two sports are still related. You tilt the horizon, and forces act through your own personal vertical axis. Bank, accelerate, zoom. Grin. Your inner ear is hard at work, as it is nowhere else. In full flight, with either bikes or planes, all your senses are engaged and you become hyperalert.

Maybe that's the link: the thing flying and motorcycling have most in common is that you simply must pay attention. Your life depends on it. Both sports, you might say, are naturally riveting.

Of course, the same may be said of mountain climbing, whitewater canoeing, skydiving, bicycle racing, downhill skiing, and mountain biking. (Notice how all these sports involve a rapid elevation change. A form of falling, as it were, skillfully arrested.)

In any case, it's that paying attention thing I like best.

Winston Churchill once remarked that nothing is more exhilarating than to be shot at and missed. Well, pilots and motorcyclists are shot at quite often, figuratively speaking, and called upon to arrange their own near misses.

Which is a good thing, in my opinion. Life is full of perfectly nice activities that don't require this kind of concentration, but most of them seem to me only half interesting.

As I've discovered at many parties and social gatherings over the years, I'm never really comfortable—or completely awake—around people who are unacquainted with the invigorating joys of mild panic.

THE LOCUS OF KARMIC PERFECTION

"I 'LL MEET YOU IN MARFA, TEXAS," I told my friend Mike Mosiman, "if I can ever get out of Wisconsin."

It wouldn't be easy. We'd had two blizzards in three days, and my driveway was sculpted in drifts and hollows like some frozen treat from Dairy Queen. Nevertheless, I fired up my Suzuki DR650 and slithered through the deep snow into the van. Success. I was on my way to Texas.

And after that, Mexico. We'd cross the border at Presidio, then down to Copper Canyon, for seven days of mostly off-roading through old mining towns in the rugged deep valleys.

But first I had to get to the border.

So on that wintry Thursday afternoon I drove south to Pekin, Illinois, where I transferred my bike onto a trailer belonging to Mike's brother, Bob, and tied it down alongside his big new BMW R1200GS. We then climbed into Bob's new Toyota Highlander hybrid (which had lots of power but got an unremarkable 12 mpg) and towed both bikes all the way to Texas in two long days of fast driving and fast food.

At Marfa—famous as the place where the 1956 movie *Giant* was filmed—we hooked up with Mike and his buddy Dave Scott, who drove down from Fort Collins, Colorado. Mike brought his KTM 640 Adventure, and Dave had a BMW R100GS Paris–Dakar model, the one with the huge 9.3-gallon tank. We would soon be calling this the "Mother Ship." And many other things, as well.

After the usual border hassles—tourist permits, vehicle permits, Mexican insurance, etc.—we rode into sunny Mexico at last. Warm weather and clear skies. Blooming jacaranda everywhere. Nice people, great food, surprisingly good paved roads, and a different sense of time. I love old Mexico. Don't expect both faucets to be hooked up in the men's-room sink, though.

We rode through the big city of Chihuahua and on to Cuauhtemoc, where we found a good motel along the highway just before dark. The motel was owned by Mennonites, part of a large colony that moved to Mexico from Germany. Mennonite farms are responsible for most of the great Mexican cheeses we sprinkle on our tacos. We ate at a Mennonite restaurant, which, sadly, served no beer or margaritas. Or tacos. Still a nice place, though. I told Mike the

Mennonites are so helpful and friendly, they're in danger of giving organized religion a good name.

We had lunch in Creel the next day, then finally turned off the pavement and headed down into the canyons for four long days of off-roading.

And two things immediately became apparent: (1) The roads were steeper, rougher, and rockier than we'd been led to believe; and (2) unless you're some kind of Paris–Dakar superhero rider, BMW GS Twins are way too big and heavy for serious off-roading in Copper Canyon.

We had one bad day in the wilderness. Picked too long and difficult a route—with one pretty deep and wide river crossing—and found ourselves after dark having to cross a mountain ridge with miles of rocky switchbacks.

Dave ran flat out of energy on his P-D, so we traded bikes and then I ran out of energy an hour later as we crested the ridge. One of those new, street-legal KTM 525 EXCs was looking pretty good at this point. Dave crashed my DR650 twice getting to the top. Bob hammered his way to the crest with his massive R1200GS, then parked the bike and said, "I quit. I'm walking the rest of the way down to Batopilas."

We had been riding for thirteen hours and were very, very tired. Not to say a little brain-dead.

This energy crisis was resolved when a Mexican pickup truck pulled up and offered us a ride down the mountain. We found a hotel and then hired another pickup the next day to take us back up the mountain. Our motorcycles were still there—despite silent prayers that certain large, well-insured bikes might be stolen—and it was a much easier ride down in daylight, after some sleep and a good breakfast with plenty of chorizo.

The rest of the trip was great—and even the hardships added their charm, retrospectively. They don't call this "adventure" touring for nothing.

And there was one strange moment on this trip that was so right, it probably qualified as one of those personal epiphanies you hear so much about.

We were winding down a cliff-hanging road above the town of Urique, motoring through a canyon of huge rock spires, falling streams, and green foliage, when the road opened up on a spectacular view of the chasm below and the distant mountains. On a spur of land in the foreground was a small farm with burros roaming and apple blossoms blooming. The beauty of the spot was surreal. We shut off our bikes and just sat for a while.

Then I had one of those odd shifts of focus and looked down at my bike and my dusty, worn gloves on the handlebars. We were in the greatest place in the world, but what had it taken to get here?

Quite a bit.

Learning to ride, getting a drivers license in high school. Acquiring tools, learning to change flat tires and clutch cables. Gaining dirt experience and going to dealerships to shop for the right bike. Installing knobbies and hand-guards and a skidplate. After years of youthful indigence, moving through a series of jobs that finally allowed you to afford a truck or a bike trailer. Learning to read maps and cross rivers in deep water. Finding helmets and enduro jackets and motocross boots that fit. Getting a passport, paying your bike registration, learning a smattering of useful Spanish. . . .

And living long enough to have friends who were crazy enough to do all these things, as well. People you could count on who'd gone through the same lifetime of motorcycle connections that had brought us to this perfect spot in time.

As I put my helmet back on, it occurred to me that you are never more completely the sum of everything you've ever been than when you take a slightly difficult motorcycle trip into a strange land. And make it back out again.

THE CURIOUS CASE OF THE BLACK VENOM

ARE YOU DRIVING OUT TO CALIFORNIA to pick up that Velocette?" my friend Mike asked over the phone.

"No," I said. "That would take at least a week, plus all the mountain passes between Wisconsin and California are closed with heavy snow right now. And one of them is named after the Donner Party. I had the bike shipped by truck. It should be here in about a week."

"Oh man, you broke your vow!" Mike said.

"Which vow was that?" I asked. "You mean the one about not buying another bike with magneto ignition?"

"No."

"The one about Lucas electrics?"

"No, not that one."

"Ah, you're thinking of the vow about no more old British bikes. . . ."

"Nope."

"You mean that one I made in Mexico, about not making important decisions when I've been drinking mescal with no label on the bottle?"

"No! You swore you'd never buy another vehicle sight unseen!"

"Oh yeah, that one . . ."

I'd made this declaration a few years ago, shortly after buying a '53 Cadillac on eBay. I won't say the seller was dishonest, but he omitted many details that might have caused me to call in an air strike on the car instead of buying it.

"This deal's different," I told Mike. "The owner is a retired gentleman who used to work for Rolls-Royce in England. His name is Derek Belvoir, and we have mutual friends who speak highly of him. The bike looks good in pictures, too, and the price seems fair."

"Uh huh . . ."

"Also," I added by way of self-assurance, "the bike was restored by a Velocette enthusiast named Ellie Taylor, who used to make prescription goggles. Years ago, I wrote a column mentioning my interest in Velocettes, and Ellie wrote me a nice letter. He said if I ever got serious about looking for a Venom or Thruxton, he'd help me find one. And now, twenty years later, I'm buying the Venom he owned when he wrote that letter. It's a small, strange world. . . ."

A week later a big box van came slithering up our icy driveway, and two guys got out and opened the back of the truck in 5-below-zero weather. They unhooked four tie-down straps from a wood pallet and rolled a black-and-gold 1961 Velocette Venom out onto the hydraulic rear lift. They lowered it to the ground and then drove away.

The bike sat alone in the cold winter sunlight, looking great. I carefully rolled it down the shoveled snow path and into the welcome shelter of my heated workshop. My neighbor Chris Beebe (Norton Commando, Ariel Square Four, Honda GB500 owner) came over to have a look.

"Can you imagine what this bike has been thinking?" he asked. "It spends its life in sunny California, then gets loaded onto a truck and spends a week in the dark with the temperature getting colder and colder and frost forming on the inside of the truck. Then the door opens and it's here in the frozen north, getting unloaded in your snow-covered driveway...."

I didn't know whether to commit suicide, move to Florida, or just feel bad for the bike, so I walked over and kicked the thermostat up another 2 degrees. When Chris left, I did a light cleanup on the bike and then sat back with a can of Guinness (no tapper in my workshop, alas) to look at the Velocette.

My first British single, ever, after a lifetime of admiration from afar. And up close as well.

I've always loved the architecture of these beautifully finished 500s from Hall Green—classics, to my mind, right in there with the BSA Gold Star or the AJS 7R. Among these, the Velocette is somehow the most "British," as if the music of Sir Edward Elgar or the novels of Thomas Hardy had been transformed into metal. If Holmes and Watson had lived long enough, they would have owned Velocettes, the motorcycle counterpart of the Webley revolver. Like Morgan cars, Velocettes held on to their conservative styling long after the world around them moved on, making no changes for change's sake.

I have no personal experience with these bikes, but friends who've owned them say they're surprisingly stout, maybe the most durable of the old singles. A Venom did set a twenty-four-hour endurance record at Montlhéry in 1961, averaging just over 100 mph. Another one, in high-performance Thruxton tune, won the Isle of Man Production TT as late as 1967.

So why a Velocette single at this stage of my life? (The bike arrived a few days after my sixtieth birthday.)

Timing and opportunity, I guess. I've been keeping an eye open for a decent 500 Velo ever since I missed out on a beautiful Thruxton in the mid-1970s. Had a photo of it taped above my desk for years. Then, last fall, I drove back to visit my friends Jeff and Nancy Craig in Pennsylvania, and Jeff has four Velos in his garage. This got the gears turning again.

When I got home I called our own resident CW Velocette nut, Mark Hoyer, and told him the hunt was officially on.

"I'm buying a KSS from a man named Derek Belvoir in Grass Valley, California," Mark said. "He's also got a Venom for sale. I'll give you his email address."

Derek emailed me photos of the bike, and I was stunned. It was exactly the combination I would have put together, had I built the bike for myself. Thruxton tank, rearsets, clubman exhaust pipe, twin gauges, flat early-1960s seat, alloy rims, low sport bars . . . I was instantly smitten.

Still am. I've started the bike up twice in my garage, and it sounds great. While waiting for spring, I've been polishing the bike and listening to Elgar's *Serenade for Strings* on our big garage-band PA system, which hardly knows how to handle such refinement.

Nice music, but not as good as the geese I heard honking overhead this morning, headed north. I can't wait to ride this thing and see if all those old vows were really meant to be broken. Simultaneously, by just one machine of considerable beauty and extreme Britishness.

THE LONG SHADOW OF CLOUDS HILL

A Visit to *Lawrence of Arabia*'s Last Home—And Last Stretch of Road—After All These Years

DRIVING DOWN A SURPRISINGLY WIDE (more than 6 feet!) English lane through a green tunnel of shade trees, I suddenly spotted a clearing along the road, so I pulled over and parked our Vauxhall Corsa rental car. Barb and I got out and walked over to a man who was exercising his tiny dog in the grass.

"Excuse me," I said, "but do you know where the monument is along the road here—the one that marks the spot where T. E. Lawrence had his fatal motorcycle accident?"

The man stared at me for a moment with ever-widening eyes and then exclaimed, "Looovely spych! Looovely spych! So yer a Yank, then, eh?"

I admitted to being a Yank and translated his opening comment as, "Lovely speech!" Here we had yet another Englishman charmed by my American accent, as filtered through the upper Midwest. To English ears, I imagine it has the dulcet tone of a table saw hitting a nail in a 2×4. Yes, our spoken "r" is hard and pure as a diamond.

"Ye've joost missed the monument," he said in a rich Dorset accent right out of a Thomas Hardy novel. "It's there in the woods, back up the road a few hundred feet. Ye can take that path along the fence."

Barb and I thanked him and followed the footpath. To our right was a tall barbed-wire fence bordering what appeared to be the motocross track from hell. In actuality, it was a British Army tank-training facility called Bovington Camp, famous as the home of the British Tank Museum.

And probably even more famous as the last place T. E. Lawrence—better known to the world as *Lawrence of Arabia*—set foot on solid ground before his death on May 13, 1935. He was on his way home from Bovington, headed for Clouds Hill—his nearby cottage in the woods—when he crashed his Brough Superior SS100. He'd ridden the bike down to the camp to send a telegram to a

London friend, confirming he'd be home that weekend. After the accident, he was taken to the camp hospital, where he died six days later from his head injuries.

We discovered a stone monument in the woods, said to be the spot where Lawrence's unconscious body was found, and another one along the road, marking the place where his bike left the pavement. I'd read that the road had been widened and straightened since Lawrence's day, so it wasn't easy to imagine exactly what happened. The standard story is that he came over a rise and found two lads on bicycles weaving along the road, headed in the same northerly direction. He swerved and/or slammed on the brakes, lost control, and was thrown onto the roadside. His Brough slid down the road and hit the back of one of the bicycles, damaging the rear wheel. The boy on the bike was only slightly injured.

I looked up and down the road, trying to envision it all, frequently stepping back on the shoulder to dodge lethally fast-moving cars. English country roads aren't the quiet, pastoral places they were in 1935. Or even in 1973, when Barb and I drove around the island in a rented Mini. There seem to be cars everywhere now, all of the time. More trees too. Accident-scene photos from 1935 show a brushy, relatively open landscape with the road dipping and curving across the hills. The road looks like a lot more fun in the old pictures, more inviting to a person on a bike.

So what were Barb and I doing in this green little corner of southwestern England?

Well, we were taking an endlessly planned and long-delayed celebration-of-retirement vacation. We'd arrived early that very morning in the port of Southampton, having left New York seven days earlier on the *Queen Mary 2*, and were driving our rental car up to the Cotswold Hills for a six-day hiking tour.

In between those two featured events, however, we'd set aside a couple of days for a side trip down to Dorset to find both Lawrence's cottage and a place called Max Gate, the country home of novelist Thomas Hardy. Oddly enough, those two homes were only about 6 miles apart, near the city of Dorchester. Hardy and his wife used to ride their bicycles to visit Lawrence, and he in turn would ride his motorcycle or bicycle to visit them. England is rich in historical overlap like this, condensed and compacted for easy visitation.

After five years ...the first motion picture from the creators of "The Bridge On The River Kwai."
Columbia Pictures presents The SAM SPIEGEL · DAVID LEAN Production of

LAWRENCE OF ARABIA

ALEC GUINNESS · ANTHONY QUINN
JACK HAWKINS · JOSE FERRER
ANTHONY QUAYLE · CLAUDE RAINS · ARTHUR KENNEDY
OMAR SHARIF as Ali · PETER O'TOOLE as "LAWRENCE"
ROBERT BOLT · SAM SPIEGEL · DAVID LEAN
SUPER PANAVISION 70° · TECHNICOLOR®

Less than a mile from the crash site, Clouds Hill is a charming little two-story whitewashed stone forester's cottage (built in 1808) set back in the woods. Barb and I pulled into a small parking lot and walked down a wooded path to the house. A friendly man in a small British Trust ticket booth/book stall sold us a pair of tickets as I scanned the bookshelves behind him. There were Lawrence's own works, *Seven Pillars of Wisdom*, *Revolt in the Desert* (an abridgment of *Seven Pillars*), *The Mint*, and his translation of Homer's *Ulysses*. And there were biographies— lots of them—four or five of which I've somehow managed to accumulate over the years.

Why so many biographies of this particular man?

Well, Lawrence seems to fascinate a wide variety of people—World War I historians, Middle East specialists, archeologists, students of Crusader castle architecture, professors of literature, Peter O'Toole fans, cinema buffs, practicing masochists (Lawrence apparently had a few kinks in his private life), and—of course—motorcyclists. And who better than a genuine masochist to own seven British motorcycles?

Yes, the man was a personal friend of George Brough, who built the exquisite self-proclaimed "Rolls-Royce of motorcycles," and Lawrence owned, serially, seven of these beauties. And of course he was killed on the last one. Besides that, his personal letters and books contain some wonderful passages about the joys of riding fast on a fine motorcycle. All this, along with his brilliant and enigmatic personality, combine to make him one of the cult figures of the twentieth century.

It also probably didn't hurt that he was a nice-looking chap, whose manner gave the appearance of reserve and modesty. This is a big help if you want to be a cult figure. Look at Charles Lindbergh. Or Amelia Earhart. Or Robert E. Lee, for that matter. It also helps to be portrayed by Peter O'Toole, Jimmy Stewart, Hilary Swank, or Martin Sheen in a big-budget movie.

Anyway, the O'Toole film is where I came in, so to speak.

I went to see *Lawrence of Arabia* when I was fourteen, almost exactly at the moment when the motorcycle gene kicked in, flooding my young mind with adrenaline and hard-wiring its circuits in favor of two-wheeled adventure. I'd already built my own minibike, and suddenly we had an epic David Lean film (winner of seven Academy Awards) opening with a charismatic hero who kick-starts a throaty-sounding V-twin and hurtles down the narrow green lanes of England, obviously enjoying himself.

The hook was set. Never mind that Lawrence crashed and killed himself. I figured that when I got my own British twin I would simply swerve around those two bicycles and continue riding for the rest of my life. Which, surprisingly, I've done—with only a few emergency-room detours. As Bob Dylan once said in a song, "I can't help it if I'm lucky."

Anyway, I've been a Lawrence buff ever since, and apparently I'm not alone in this. I have a couple of riding friends whose bookshelves are virtual altars to the lore of T. E. Lawrence, lacking only votive candles, incense, and a brass gong to be completely over the top. I'm not quite that fixated, but I had to set aside a few days of our trip to see that famous spot on the fatal road. And Clouds Hill.

On entering Lawrence's cottage, I soon realized it's perfectly geared to appeal to the ascetic minimalism that lurks in the hearts of most motorcyclists. The building is smaller than I expected but quite welcoming and comfortable in a rustic way. Fireplace downstairs, with a big slab-sided reading chair designed by Lawrence himself and a tray across the arms to hold a book and hot drink. Or cold drink, if there is such a thing in England. There's a raised bunk with shelves built under it and a bathroom with a huge bathtub and boiler cleverly fed from a nearby spring. Lawrence's one temporal flaw was his weakness for a hot bath. There's no toilet. That was out in the woods, presumably with a crescent moon on the door.

No kitchen, no fixed meal times. Weekend guests (such as George Bernard Shaw and his wife, Charlotte) were expected to snack from cans of tinned food so meals wouldn't interrupt conversation—or listening to music. Upstairs is the music room, a very comfortable open space with a wood-beamed ceiling, leather-upholstered chairs, and a Victrola with a large horn. Beethoven, Mozart, and Elgar were favorites, though I suspect he would have enjoyed the *Lawrence* soundtrack by Maurice Jarre if he'd lived long enough. The room is lined with more bookshelves. There are paintings of General Allenby and Emir Feisal, which Lawrence referred to as his "dual masters." Outside in the yard is a neat shed Lawrence had built to hold his latest SS100—the last of which is now in the British War Museum.

Over the front door is a stone lintel—designed by Lawrence himself—with a Greek inscription loosely translated as, "Who cares?" I can barely read the Greek letters on a fraternity house, but I nevertheless bought a small souvenir copy of this stone and have it sitting on my desk right now. For inspiration.

So. Motorcycle, cottage, books, fireplace, music, and a vast network of some of the most charming winding roads on earth, just beyond the driveway. Not a bad retirement, really.

Unfortunately, he hadn't been retired long when he died. Hoping to escape his own fame and his disappointment at the arbitrary borders imposed on the Arabs after World War I (a problem that haunts us to this day), he sought refuge in anonymity. During the '20s and early '30s he served under assumed names as an enlisted man in both the RAF and the Tank Corps. He rented Clouds Hill as a refuge from barracks life while serving at Bovington in the early '20s and later bought the place and fixed it up. He'd only just finished his twelve-year enlistment in the RAF when he died.

Barb and I drove to the nearby village of Moreton (population 270), where Lawrence is buried in a simple grave just across the street from St. Nicholas Church. This country church has a second claim to fame because a random Luftwaffe bomb blew out its ancient stained-glass windows in 1940, and the noted artist Sir Lawrence Whistler designed a set of beautiful engraved-glass windows for the church. When we were there, a BBC crew had just finished doing a TV documentary on the church and its windows. It occurred to me that if it weren't for two terrible wars, there'd be very little tourism in Moreton. More strange historic convergence.

After a visit to the gravesite, Barb and I climbed back in our rental car and merged into the hectic flow of traffic, headed north for our week of hiking through the rural landscape and fourteenth century villages of the Cotswolds. We were temporarily back in the twenty-first century but headed for yet another attempt to defeat modernity in a quiet corner of England. And Clouds Hill may have been exactly this kind of refuge for Lawrence. The peacefulness and simplicity of the cottage left us with an odd feeling that he'd just been there, had just gone out for a ride, and that it might still be the spring of 1935.

I sometimes wonder if it was the Brough Superior that captivated me when I first saw *Lawrence of Arabia* fifty-two years ago or if it was simply the romantic vision of those empty English roads from a bygone era. Or the heroic legend that connected them both. Maybe it was all three. Motorcycling is never just about the bike.

CLASSIC REMATCH

A **FEW WEEKS AGO,** with summer truly here and the locust trees in full bloom, I flipped open my ancient cell phone and gave editor Mark Hoyer a call at the *CW* office in California.

"What I have sitting in my workshop at this moment," I said, pausing for dramatic effect, "are two rival superbikes from the mid-'70s—a 1974 Norton Commando and a 1976 BMW R90S—and they're both in pretty nice shape. One is quite British and the other is very German. I think it would be neat if you could fly out here to Wisconsin for a little classic comparison test/ tour and take some photos before I drop one of them in the driveway and ruin everything. Or the Norton wears out."

"Where were you thinking to go?"

"Oh, probably through the western Wisconsin hill country toward the Mississippi. Stay in some small towns where they have craft breweries—maybe try some English-style porters and German bocks. We could take the back roads down to Galena, Illinois, a restored old mining town and river port. It's also the home of U. S. Grant. If you stayed an extra day, we could play a little guitar."

Hoyer, a dark-beer enthusiast, Norton owner, guitar aficionado, and history buff who likes riding on our twisty rural lanes, showed up a short time later. If you can think of any buttons I failed to push, let me know.

In truth, the idea for this little outing was more than a sudden whim. The kernel of the idea went back almost exactly forty years. Let me explain:

One fine September morning in 1975, my wife, Barbara, dropped me off, helmet in hand, at a motorcycle shop called Madison Suzuki/BMW/Norton. I was there for the joyous business of taking delivery on my new black-and-gold Norton Commando. I'd chosen the Interstate version—with the oversize 7.3-gallon tank—because Barb and I harbored illusions of extended transcontinental travel. Those were optimistic times.

When I arrived, the bike was parked in front of the showroom, right next to a brand-new BMW R90S—then in its second year of production—with a lovely two-tone Silver Smoke paint scheme. This was another highly tempting bike on my personal radar at the time, but it was almost unimaginably expensive. Nearly twice as much as my new Commando, which was heavily discounted because the Norton factory was about to close its doors.

In a way, these two bikes were crossing at the upward and downward arcs of their factories' fortunes; Norton was going out of business after seventy-three years of building legendary motorcycles, and BMW was ascending new heights because the glamorous R90S was rescuing the company from its staid image and finding a legion of first-time buyers.

Nevertheless, those two bikes made a nice snapshot, sitting there in front of the showroom. The BMW was elegant, tidy, and very Teutonic in its purpose-fulness. The Hans Muth–designed bodywork had a beautiful unified flow to it, and the misted paint made the bike look like some kind of Black Forest wraith beaming itself through patches of light and dark. Quite Wagnerian.

The Norton was more a harmonious collection of exquisite artifacts than a single, unified design concept, but those pieces had somehow all landed in the right place. The polished transmission and engine cases wrapped tightly around the mechanical bits inside, and the whole bike looked spare, waspish, and hand-some. I sighed at the inexpressible rightness of life, pulled out my checkbook, and headed into the shop.

When I emerged with my Norton keys and temporary registration, I was accompanied by the new owner of the R90S. I recognized him right away as the famous artist-in-residence at the University of Wisconsin, Marko Spalatin, whom I'd met before at various motorcycle shops. Marko was a native of Croatia who'd escaped from Communist Eastern Europe to a life of great artistic success in the West.

We stood for a few minutes admiring our new bikes, and Marko said, "So this is your new Norton?"

"Yes."

He gazed at the bike wanly and nodded. "I had a Norton . . ." he said. Then he grinned and punched me lightly on the shoulder. "Someday," he said, "you'll buy a BMW."

We both had a good laugh, but mine was probably not as hearty as his. As a British-car mechanic at the time, I understood his meaning perfectly. Never-theless, I honestly wanted the Commando more than any BMW, regardless of price, reliability, or future parts availability. I was a British-bike guy, and I'd spent a couple of years staring at those seductive Norton ads just inside the front cover of *Cycle World*. I had to have one, and nothing else would do.

So Marko and I shook hands, put on our helmets, and rode off happily into the future.

Or at least he did.

My bike died at the first stoplight. And at all subsequent stoplights. Then on the way home it . . . Well, don't get me started. Let's just say the Commando was not a paragon of reliability. At 3,000 miles it seized a valve in Missoula, Mon-tana, while Barb and I were attempting to ride to Seattle, and we had to send it home in a Bekins moving van. After that, we continued our trip by train and Greyhound bus. The best thing I can say about this trip is that I wrote a story about it and got my first-ever article published here in *Cycle World*.

I've often wondered what life would be like if I'd come home with Marko's BMW that day instead of the Commando. Would *CW* have bought a story called "Young Couple Successfully Reaches West Coast on Reliable German Motorcycle"? Probably not. Maybe life unfolds exactly as it should, and this is the best of all possible worlds.

In any case, Marko's prediction eventually came true. I've owned several BMWs since 1975, and last fall I bought a Silver Smoke 1976 R90S—almost exactly like his. But I've never lost my affection for Nortons, either, and have owned and restored a series of Commandos. I seem to be addicted for life.

My current Commando is a black-and-gold 1974 Roadster that was given to me a couple of years ago by a friend who wanted to see it restored rather than parted out. It had been in a shed for twenty-five years and needed everything. It took me one full winter—and plenty of money and new parts—to restore the bike, but I've been riding it now for more than a year without any trouble. It's stock, except for electronic ignition, alloy Production Racer–style rims, and a sleeved-down brake master. Also, I left the rear hubcap off because I like the look of the inner casting.

The R90S is a clean and unmolested bike, originally from San Francisco, still with its original paint and only 44,000 miles on the odometer. I bought it late last fall from my friend Mike Mosiman in Fort Collins, Colorado. He put it up for sale when he suddenly realized, to his horror, that he had one too many airheads—and that the bike's low bars hurt his back. Also, he's a good guy and knew I'd been looking for a nice R90S for several years.

So of course I sold two of my other old bikes to buy this long-coveted item and trailered it home from Colorado exactly one day before our first big snow-storm. This is what passes for "life simplification" in my universe. After that the BMW became a static display item that warmed my heart every time I turned on the lights in my workshop. But now it's summer.

Editor Hoyer flew in and showed up with two photographers, Drew and Carter, whose handy rental car allowed me to take the hard bags off the BMW and my ancient Eclipse tank bag off the Norton, so as not to distract from their aesthetic purity. Mark had never ridden an R90S (gasp), so he started out on that bike, and I took the Norton.

I climbed aboard the Commando, and it started first kick, which it usually does even though I've left out the seldom-used choke slides for the sake of sim-plicity. So you simply "tickle" the twin Amal carbs (which sounds more mirthful and less messy than it is) and kick it over with a mighty leap. Riders weighing less than 150 pounds need not apply.

The 828cc parallel twin roars to life and soon settles down into a regular idle that has the engine bouncing ever so lightly up and down on its rubber Isolastic mounts. Those two big pistons rise together on the 360-degree crank and would like to fly to the moon, but the connecting rods hold them back. Usually. The front fender vibrates at an amplitude of about 2 inches, so even the hard of hearing will know when the Norton is running.

Snick the lovely gearbox into first (one up and three down on the right-side foot lever) with a well-oiled click and we're off. At about 2,000 rpm the Isolastics drop into sympathetic harmony with the engine, and the Norton accelerates with almost glassy smoothness through the gears. The exhaust has a regular, mellow, but hard-hitting punch that may be one of the nicest sounds in motorcycling. Throttle response is instantaneous, and the bike accelerates in an asphalt-spitting rush, feeling remarkably quick and muscular even by modern standards. This combination of smoothness and performance has prompted many British bike enthusiasts to name the Commando "most tourable" of British vertical twins.

Meanwhile, on the R90S, Mark turns on his fuel taps, pushes down the choke lever on the left side of the engine cases, and merely hits the starter button. No gasoline is slathered. The engine fires almost immediately with a rocking motion, and the pumper Dell'Orto carbs let it idle with a slightly hollow and metallic exhaust note. The left-shifting gearbox (one down and four up in the modern mode) accepts first with a reluctant grunch and is then slightly notchy on all shifts that follow. It's one of the enduring mysteries of the late twentieth Century that BMW, builder of long-lived, precision engines, didn't produce a truly slick gearbox in that era. It works okay but never endears itself to your left toe.

As we accelerate out onto the highway, the R90S has no trouble staying with the Norton but lacks its immediacy. The Commando accelerates like a Rottweiler tearing across the lawn to bite your leg, but the BMW is more like a greyhound that's been trained to build speed in linear fashion. Not as exciting, but possibly more rational.

A number of subsequent top-gear roll-on contests over the next three days will reveal that the more explosive Norton can always pull away by a couple of bike lengths, at any speed—until we approach 100 mph, and then the BMW starts to move inexorably ahead. We didn't proceed much over 100 mph because (a) gosh, that would be illegal; (b) we have a lot of nervous deer around here; and (c) the Norton has two pistons that would like to fly to the moon. Suffice it to say that these two bikes are so close in performance as to be an almost perfect match on a backcountry ride.

We stopped for lunch in the small Swiss village of New Glarus, home to the venerated New Glarus Brewery and Puempel's Olde Tavern, where Braunsch-

252 // THE TEENS

weiger and Limburger sandwiches terrorize the olfactory glands of the weak and timid. The green hills of Wisconsin support some sixty craft cheese factories, and a large number are found around New Glarus. And the same steep hills that tip over your tractor—and therefore encourage the grazing of dairy cows—also give you really good motorcycle roads. The landscape looks like the Swiss border in *The Great Escape*, only the local Germans are friendlier and there's no razor-wire fence to jump over.

We traded bikes and wicked it up a few times on the nearly empty farm roads, stopping for a handling comparison conference. "The BMW feels like a bike with a very deep keel," Hoyer concluded, "almost gyroscopic. It's very formal in its handling. You set up for a corner properly, turn in, and it just stays planted, all the way through. The Norton is nimbler and quicker steering, more adaptable to sudden changes in the road, but not as settled."

I agreed completely. "With the Norton," I said, "you flare your elbows out and attack the corner; with the R90S you tuck in and dispose of it. The BMW is more stately and less manic, better at the big sweepers."

Brakes? We both agreed that the BMW's brake pads were made of some hardwood but couldn't decide between mahogany and oak. The Norton lever has a more sensitive and progressive feel, probably because I installed a sleeved-down master cylinder to encourage this trait. Both bikes stop pretty well when they really have to.

We sped along on County Highways H and F, down into the old lead mining district of southwestern Wisconsin, where towns have names such as Lead Mine, Mineral Point, and New Diggings. The ready availability of lead in the early nineteenth century pulled in thousands of miners from Cornwall and other exotic places, such as Missouri, creating much friction with the local Indians. Tons of lead was mined out of these hills, some of which is still said to be embedded in the forests around Gettysburg and Shiloh.

Turning straight south on Highway O, we crossed the Illinois border and took back roads into the beautiful old river port of Galena—named for a variety of lead ore and now a mecca for antique hunters. Here we checked in at the historic DeSoto House Hotel, built in 1855. They had a nice covered parking garage, where we checked over the bikes.

The sharp-eyed Hoyer noticed that the pinch bolt had jittered out of the Norton's front axle. Not critical, as long as the axle nut was in place, but we'd have to find a hardware store in the morning. We had dinner at the hotel, then went down Main Street to look for the Galena Brewing Company so we could try a pint of Uly's Dark, an oatmeal stout with a picture of General Grant on the label. But a sign on the pub said it was closed on Monday nights.

In the morning we went to U. S. Grant's home, a nice old brick structure overlooking the town. It was closed on Mondays and Tuesdays. I considered naming this "the Closed Mondays and Tuesdays Tour." My advice to the reader is just to read Grant's autobiography and have a beer at home. This will save me a lot of descriptive typing.

Next stop, hardware store. We replaced the pinch bolt on the Norton, and I noticed quite a bit of oil drooling from the area around the left side cover. Seems my ingenious homemade catch bottle/breather canister, designed to keep the Commando's oil out of the air cleaner and off the rear tire, was slightly overfull. As I knelt on the ground, cleaning the oil up with contact cleaner and a filthy piece of paper towel, Hoyer said, "I have to admit, this is the kind of thing you seldom see a BMW owner doing on the roadside."

After that small repair, however, the Norton minded its manners, and we motored across the Mississippi bridge into Dubuque and cut north along the high riverbanks of Iowa. A long gravel road took us down a valley to the dock of the Cassville Ferry, and we crossed back to the Wisconsin side. A fuel stop revealed similar fuel mileage for the two bikes—both in the low 40s—but the BMW could safely go about twice as far on its 6.3-gallon capacity as the Norton with its svelte 3.0-gallon tank. Still, 100- to 120-mile fuel stops can sometimes be a welcome break from sitting.

Speaking of which, Hoyer and I both agreed the riding position on the R90S suited us perfectly. When you assume the position, you feel like a cast human figure who's been clicked into exactly the correct spot on a model motorcycle. The Norton is pretty good too—with the lower European bars installed—but those beautiful forged footpeg brackets are a bit far forward. You sit *on* the Norton and *in* the BMW, almost enveloped by it.

Nightfall found us at yet another historic old stone hotel/B & B, the Walker House, in Mineral Point, with a restaurant and pub called Brewery Creek just across the now-missing railroad tracks. Nice hotel, friendly owners, good food, several fine beers. We'd hit pay dirt. One of the hotel owners was a retired college professor, so my bedtime reading was an English translation of Andre Gide's *The Immoralist*. Quite different from the usual Gideon Bible, and when we left in the morning I was philosophically confused.

Nevertheless, Hoyer and I stopped on the way back to my place to discuss motorcycle philosophy over lunch—in New Glarus again, at a Swiss restaurant called the Glarner Stube. I posed this deep question: "If you didn't already own a Norton Commando and could take just one of these bikes back home for your own, which one would it be?"

He thought for a few moments and said, "The Norton. It's just more exciting and agile on these back roads. The BMW is too formal for me. You have to set up for corners and do what the bike wants, as though you're just along for the ride. The Norton just does what you want to do. What about you?"

"That depends," I hedged. "On a one- or two-hour ride, I'd take the Norton—which I usually do. If I were repeating this 350-mile route we've just

254 // THE TEENS

finished—or if Barb and I were trying to go to the West Coast again—I'd automatically take the BMW. Over a long distance, my soul is more at rest on the R90S. The BMW always has its eyes on the horizon, while the Norton is focusing on the next apex."

When we got back to my workshop late that afternoon, we put the bikes on their centerstands, sat back, opened a beer, and looked quietly at them for a while. I told Mark, "I've decided to conclude that the BMW is a sublime motorcycle and the Norton is a sublime experience. What do you think?"

He tilted his beer toward me in a small toast and said, "That's it."

Thinking about it now, I'm not sure these bikes were ever direct rivals for the same territory, either on the road or in your soul. One is really a sport-touring or GT machine, and the other more a pure sportbike—never mind that big "Interstate" gas tank on our old Commando, which was mostly a matter of wishful thinking. So maybe the Commando and R90S don't so much rival as complement one another. A friend with a Norton shop told me some years ago that if his customers owned a non-British bike, it was most likely to be a BMW.

Makes perfect sense to me and sounds like the best of all possible worlds.

DOWN TO THE CROSSROADS

A Tale of Pilgrims and Indians on the Loose in Barbecue, Blues, and Bayou Country

IF YOU'RE THE SORT OF MOTORCYCLIST who likes to "strafe corners," a trip down Highway 61 from Memphis to New Orleans will probably save you a lot of money on ammo. There are a few gentle curves along the Mississippi, but most of the corners in this land of bayous and cotton fields are crossroads, both literally and figuratively. So why go there?

Well, I suppose the answer for some of us would simply be: the music.

Memphis is the birthplace of rock 'n' roll, New Orleans is the home of jazz, and between them lies a stretch of rich bottomland called the Mississippi Delta, the land where the blues began. Also, there's a lot of good food and drink along these 400 miles of river road—smoked barbecue, fried catfish, seafood gumbo, beignets, French Roast coffee, and the famous hurricane drinks of New Orleans.

As a fledgling blues fan and apprentice omnivore, I first headed down there from Wisconsin in 1978 on my 400F Honda, and since then I've made three return trips—one in my coffee-colored 1963 Cadillac and one on a brand-new Triumph T100 Bonneville in 2003. I also went back on vacation with my wife, Barb, a couple of years ago. There's some magical combination of music, food, history, and ambiance that keeps drawing me back.

So when editor Mark Hoyer called a few weeks ago and asked if I'd like to make the trip again with him on a couple of 2016 Indians, I automatically said yes. I have to get my Highway 61 music and food fix every few years or I become erratic and morose. Even more than usual.

Apparently, Hoyer was suffering from this same syndrome, even though he'd never been in this part of the Deep South before. As a guitarist and blues fan, he felt the inevitable, distant pull of the Delta, and it didn't hurt that he also loves smoked barbecue, Cajun food, and the more opaque brands of bourbon and rye. It seems we share a genetic preference for all things smoky, whether music, food, or drink.

"We need to fly into Memphis," Mark said, "and pick up the Indians at a local dealership. Then we'll drop them off in New Orleans and fly home. You make the hotel reservations."

The first hotel choice was easy. As Mississippi author David Cohn famously wrote back in 1935, "The Delta begins in the lobby of the Peabody Hotel in Memphis and ends on Catfish Row in Vicksburg." So I was compelled by literary tradition to get us a couple of rooms at the elegant old Peabody. Andrew Jackson, William Faulkner, and The Rolling Stones had all stayed there, so we knew they'd have a decent bar.

I flew into Memphis on a Sunday afternoon and met Mark at baggage claim when his plane got in from California. "Welcome to Memphis," I said. "You are now an honorary Memphian."

"After sitting in an airplane all day," he said, "I feel more like a Memphibian."

We mulled that over for a minute and decided that a Memphibian is a creature that can walk on dry land but also drink like a fish on Beale Street.

At car rental we picked up a blue Toyota Sienna for the use of our photographers, Nik Wogen and Drew Ruiz, who were coming in later. As we cruised toward the Peabody in air-conditioned comfort, Mark plugged some John Lee Hooker into the sound system then suddenly said, "Can you imagine John Lee Hooker driving around in this minivan?"

I shook my head. "The Japanese don't do blues-mobiles very well," I said. "On the other hand, you probably wouldn't want John Lee Hooker to design your climate-control system."

We entered the beautifully ornate lobby of the Peabody with its big marble fountain and famously trained ducks, which come ceremoniously down the elevator from the roof every morning and return in the evening. It's a ritual that packs the lobby with tourists twice daily, and they had just left. You could sense the vacuum.

We tossed our lumpish gear bags into our rooms and walked down to Beale Street, with its neon-lit blues clubs and restaurants. In the past century, this was the glittering music row of the Delta, home of Southern blues and good times. But it went into decline, and by the time I got here in 1978 it was a bombed-out shell of its former self, and the empty street was littered with broken glass. The desk clerk at the Peabody warned me not to go there, even in daylight. I did anyway. Then got on my motorcycle and rode south. Another piece of Americana gone.

But urban renewal and a blues resurgence turned the lights back on, and now you'd never know anything happened. Fully restored, brightly lit, and absolutely jumping on a Sunday night, the blocked-off street was full of pedestrians and music.

Mark and I had a late dinner of smoked ribs at the Blues City Café, and I ordered a local beer called Snopes, as I was right in the middle of reading William Faulkner's Snopes trilogy. The beer was superb, which is more than you can say for the Snopes family in the novel. Toward the end of dinner, photographers Drew and Nik cabbed in from the airport and joined us.

In the morning, we drove across the Mississippi on the I-40 bridge to Barton Powersports in West Memphis and picked up our Indians, which we immediately named Blackie and Fringie.

Blackie was an all-black version of the new Springfield model with a cop windshield and hard bags, while Fringie was a silver-and-black Chief Vintage with a similar windshield but tan leather saddlebags and seat with fringe and more relaxed rake at the forks. Both had the 111-inch faux-flathead V-twin engine, floorboards, and low, comfortable seats. When you pick them up off the sidestand, both feel dense and hefty at around 800 to 850 pounds but travel down the road at low, relaxed revs with nice torque. It's also calm and restful behind those big windshields, perfect for a flowing, laid-back trip down the river.

We crossed back over the Mississippi for a good view of the downtown, with the landmark Memphis Pyramid on our left, a glittering homage to the city's Egyptian name. The pyramids on the Nile, however, probably don't contain a Bass Pro Shop.

Mark and I turned down Union Avenue toward one of the great shrines of Memphis, the small but historically potent Sun Studio. As virtually everyone on earth knows, this is where a young Elvis walked in off the street and asked to make a record for his mother in 1953. Nice-looking kid with a good voice. Others who showed up for a shot at fame were Howlin' Wolf, Johnny Cash, Roy Orbison, Ike Turner, Jerry Lee Lewis, Carl Perkins, Rufus Thomas, Charlie Rich, etc., etc. Visionary Sun Studio founder Sam Phillips probably did more to change American culture than anyone since Columbus. But don't make me prove that in a doctoral thesis.

We took a tour and stood in the original recording studio where all those people once sang and played, and everyone got very quiet, as if listening for ghosts in the room. Those guys are all gone now, except for Jerry Lee. The Killer rocks on.

We'd hoped to visit Stax Museum as well, but we ran out of daylight because I got snagged by the Gibson Guitar Factory and its retail store. Just before this trip, I'd had several of my guitars stolen, so I was on the hunt for replacements. I found a really nice Derek Trucks signature model SG but decided against entrusting it to the tender mercies of the airlines on my way home.

That night we hit Beale Street in the company of the redoubtable Leo Goff, a Memphis native and famous engine builder, tuner, drag racer, and motorcycle collector. He's also a professional bass player whose tracks may be heard on 173 albums and CDs, and he plays in three different Memphis blues bands.

As we walked down Beale, every single bartender, musician, street person, and club barker shouted, "Leo, my man!" We ended up at the Rum Boogie Café, eating barbecue and listening to Gracie Curran and the High Falutin' Band, an excellent blues combo who all nodded at Leo when he walked in. If he ran for mayor of Memphis, I think he'd win.

We took Elvis Presley Boulevard out of town the next morning and stopped at Graceland, lining up with visitors from all over the world to take a tour. It's a beautiful house and grounds and a great place to grasp the true cultural weight of Elvis's life and career, which is equal parts American success story and tragedy. In the museum room of gold records and movie posters, you can sense the relentless pressure on him to keep this huge money machine in motion. Which he is still doing. The tour tickets were $80 each, and the line is endless.

We toured the house, where poor Elvis had his tastes in furniture and carpeting permanently frozen in the '70s—something none of us would like to have done to us—and we filed quietly past the family graves on the side lawn.

John Lennon once said, "Before Elvis, there was nothing." I wouldn't quite go that far, but when my older sister bought a copy of "Hound Dog" in 1956, I played it on my little record player about a thousand times, watching that label spin around and trying to imagine what planet this wonderful, mesmerizing sound had come from. And now I was there.

We hooked up with Highway 61 South, crossed the Mississippi state line, and were on the open road at last, into the Delta.

The first few miles of the highway were lined with huge gambling casinos, but the true Delta of small towns, sprawling cotton plantations, and crop dusters reappeared around Robinsonville, where the great bluesman Robert Johnson once lived and worked on the Abbay and Leatherman Plantation.

We stopped for lunch at the nearby Hollywood Café, noted blues joint and sometime local hangout for author John Grisham. It's been said that Mississippi has produced more great writers per square foot than any state in the US, an honor roll that includes William Faulkner, Eudora Welty, Truman Capote, Tennessee Williams, Walker Percy, Shelby Foote . . . as with blues musicians, the list goes on and on. There's just something about this place. Maybe it's the soil.

The Delta was once called "the Great Panther Swamp," an impenetrable jungle of hardwoods that happened to sit on about 25 feet of the richest black soil on earth, deposited by centuries of river flooding. Much of it was cleared after the Civil War by a huge workforce of former slaves and Anglo planters who were willing to risk yellow fever and floods for profits in the cotton trade.

Meanwhile, the Scots-Irish and their music moved down the Appalachians into the hill country and bluffs above the Delta. Quite a mixture.

I've often thought that if the Delta had been settled by a European mono-culture—say the Swiss or Germans—instead of a crazy quilt of Brits, Celts, and African Americans, we'd be coming down here for Polka Fest, and the Delta would be about as funky a tourist attraction as the cornfields of central Illinois. You need a little of everything and everybody to make American music, and this is the crossroads.

We got off the four-lane Highway 61 and took Old 61 south toward Clarks-dale on our big comfortable Indians. I liked Blackie best, for its slightly smoother engine (better break-in?) and quicker, sportier-feeling steering, but Fringie had a certain magnificence, and its laid-back rake made it feel more stable when we hit stretches of gravel road along the levees. Both bikes have excellent brakes, nicely damped suspension with reasonable travel, and a bottomless well of smooth, low-rpm torque that makes downshifting optional at most road speeds. They're all-day comfortable touring bikes whose only drawback is weight, when you want to pull a quick U-turn or back out of a parking spot. Don't be ashamed to ask for help.

Dusk found us pulling up at a place called the Shack Up Inn, near Clarksdale. Situated on the old Hopson Plantation, it's a collection of weather-beaten sharecropper shacks that have been rehabilitated into clean but funky motel units, gathered around a big, old corrugated-iron cotton-gin building that houses an excellent bar, restaurant, and music stage. Lots of musicians stay there, and we arrived just as a harmonica workshop was in progress. Thank God it wasn't Banjo Days.

The restaurant was closed for a group dinner, so we rode into Clarksdale, epi-center of blues country, just as all the restaurants closed—except for one upscale bistro that could just as easily have been in Portland. The salmon special was excellent, however, and we shared the dining room with a large, cheerful HOG chapter from Padova, Italy.

Our sense of authenticity was rescued when we stopped at Crossroads Liquor, right on the famous junction of Highways 61 and 49, and I bought a bottle of Evan Williams bourbon, my favorite. This corner is where the great bluesman Robert Johnson was supposed to have sold his soul to the Devil in exchange for his unearthly musical talent. I don't believe this story, however, because Johnson and his evil pal would have been instantly run over by a truck. This is one of the busiest crossroads in Mississippi. Also, Johnson himself never claimed this happened. I believe it was a theory developed by jealous musicians who didn't practice enough.

Back at the Shack Up Inn we had a late-evening nightcap on the front porch of Nik's cabin, drinking bourbon and watching a lightning storm play out over the Delta. The cabin was short on drinking glasses, so Nik drank his bourbon from a cereal bowl. When his left eye wandered upward toward the moon—which was reemerging spookily from behind a storm cloud—and his other eye slammed shut, we decided it was time to go to bed.

In the morning we rode down the river road to Rosedale (mentioned in the Robert Johnson song "Cross Roads Blues") and had lunch at the White Front Café, where chef/owner Barbara Pope serves nothing but her famous tamales. Then we rode a few miles down to Beulah, where the crossroads in the movie of that name were supposed to have been filmed. We didn't find them, so we chose our own. As Mark said, "The crossroads are personal and spiritual."

We didn't have time to wait until midnight for the Devil, so we headed west toward Greenwood, where the unfortunate Mr. Johnson is possibly buried in one of three reputed graves. Legend has it he was killed by a jealous husband who sent a poisoned drink up to the stage one night at a juke joint in Three Forks. His death certificate says he was buried at the Zion Church, of which there are several in the area. Since no one knows for sure, I led our little band of pilgrims to the one with the best headstone, just off Highway 7 north of Morgan City.

A lovely, quiet little spot where I like to ponder the list of songs on his monument. Our garage band plays about five of them, as best we can, and a hundred great bands have played the rest. "Love in Vain" is a thing of beauty.

Noon found us in the beautiful hilltop town of Vicksburg, where Grant spent many months in 1863 trying to take this important river citadel away from the Confederacy. He eventually succeeded, but the surrounding hills are covered in tombstones.

At the River Town Grille in Vicksburg, I had the best meal of the trip—catfish smothered in a crawfish étouffée—and we kept the theme going after lunch by looking for the legendary Catfish Row where the Delta is supposed to end. This once-notorious row of riverfront dives is now a pleasant little playground with a big fountain for children to frolic in. We left before someone's mom called the police about the guys in motorcycle boots and black leather.

Next stop, New Orleans.

We had to make tracks that hot afternoon. The Big Easy was still several hundred miles away, so we got on I-10 and hammered our way east on the elevated highway over the vast swamps. The Superdome and skyline hove into view; we turned off on the Vieux Carré exit and soon found ourselves pulling into the parking garage of the Hotel Monteleone. This place is famous as "the writers' hotel," sometime residence of Hemingway, Faulkner, and Williams, and now Hoyer and Egan . . . in no particular order, mind you.

We peeled our sweat-soaked leather jackets off, cleaned up, and hit the streets of the French Quarter—my favorite neighborhood in one of the only two major cities in which I would consider living. Paris is the other one. It must be the French influence on food.

After a shrimp- oyster- and crawfish-based dinner at the unpretentious but excellent Remoulade, we all got ourselves some big old hurricanes at an outdoor stand and strolled down Bourbon and Royal Streets, people watching. To paraphrase a song, the street goes on forever, and the party never ends. Our own evening ended with a Sazerac cocktail or two at the Monteleone bar—a hyperlively scene for sharp-dressed twenty-somethings and thirty-somethings on dates. Or looking for dates. Or something. They had a knockout jazz band.

New Orleans in early morning is the very picture of the term "the morning after." It's subdued and muted, with only the sounds of the street cleaners washing the sticky pavement. The famous Café du Monde had a waiting line of slightly hungover patrons, so we got our French Roast coffee and beignet fix at the nearby Café Beignet on Royal Street and walked around St. Louis Cathedral on Jackson Square.

At noon, we finally had to mount up and return our Indians, riding out to Indian Motorcycle of New Orleans on the Airline Highway—which is good old Highway 61. Nice people there, and they gave us some black T-shirts with the Indian-head logo and "New Orleans" printed beneath. Hard to beat as a final souvenir of this trip.

We blues-mobiled our Sienna back to the French Quarter, had a last fine dinner of aquatic swamp creatures in smoky, dark beurre roux, and then took a last walk down Bourbon Street. On a street corner sat a thin, young, white guy in a large black hat, playing an old Epiphone guitar through a small amp. Behind him was a beat-up 100th Anniversary Harley Sportster, painted flat black, with a huge box on the back to carry all his belongings.

He was playing some of the most beautiful slide guitar I've ever heard, in a haunting and complex melodic style. We listened for a long time and put some money in his guitar case. I asked his name and he quietly said, "Stoker," without looking up. "Stoker Homeboy."

On the way back to the hotel I said to Mark, "That guy's a genius, and he's sitting in front of his old motorcycle, playing on a street corner. We came looking for the real blues, and I think we finally found 'em."

ROAD TEST: TRIUMPH T120 BONNEVILLE

Another Great Leap Forward for Hinckley—and the Meriden School of Fine Art and Design

WELL HERE'S SOMETHING you don't see every day—a late adopter like yours truly actually coughing up $12K (plus tax, licensing, etc.) of his own money for a motorcycle we've not yet tested here in the magazine.

Yes, last month I went out on a limb and bought a new 2016 Triumph Bonneville T120—right out of the crate—and took it in just yesterday for its 500-mile break-in service. Which was actually a 640-mile break-in service because I couldn't stay off it for a full weekend.

Truth be told, this was not completely a blind-impulse purchase. I'd previously visited our local Triumph dealership, Team Triumph in Janesville, Wisconsin, to take a look at the first of these new liquid-cooled 1,200cc Bonnevilles when it came in. It was Cranberry Red and Aluminum Silver.

I sat on the bike and was relieved to find a little more legroom than I had on my old 2008 Bonneville, as the seat was about an inch and a half higher relative to the pegs. Nice bars too. A little flatter and lower.

Also, the overall level of finish had taken a pleasing jump in quality (as it well should have, for the approximate $3,000 price hike), and it came stock with a centerstand, passenger grab rail, heated grips, ABS, and stock mufflers that actually sounded rich and euphonious, rather than stolen off a Lawn-Boy. Also, the engineers had taken the dreaded kink out of the exhaust system. It seemed complete, in need of no costly options.

So first impressions were good, but of course I would have to politely ask for a test ride before making any expensive decisions.

At that moment a sales associate named Kristi Hall came out of the office and hung a "Sold" tag on the handlebars.

"A man who looked at this bike yesterday just called and said he'd take it," she explained.

So much for my theoretical test ride.

"Are you getting another one in this color?" I asked. The other options were solid red or black tank with contrasting shiny bits, or the "none more black" version for that matte Gothic look, but I was sold on the traditional red-scallop-on-silver paint scheme, reminiscent of the 1969 and '70 Bonnevilles.

"I don't think so," she said. "Maybe in the fall, when the 2017s come out."

Bummer. My shoulders slumped, and I tried to radiate an aura of abject defeat and depression.

It apparently worked because two days later Todd and Darcy Ligman, the owners of the shop, called to say they might be able to get a red-and-silver bike out of a dealership in northern Illinois, if they made a rather complex three-way trade involving a red-and-black bike and maybe some Manchurian Railroad bonds. Was I still interested?

Oh, boy, the pressure was on.

"Yes," I said, after giving it five or six seconds of deep thought.

Luckily, by the time the Bonneville arrived a few days later, they'd also gotten in a black T120 demo bike, so I was able to give that a pretty long test ride on

some of my favorite roads along the Rock River before finalizing the deal. I returned suitably impressed and said, "Where do I sign?" Or words to that effect.

And 640 miles later?

Without sounding too effusive, I would say the only new bikes I've enjoyed this much in the first month of ownership were my 1975 Honda 400F and my 1991 Ducati 900 Supersport. To paraphrase Pontius Pilate, I can find no fault with this motorcycle. So far.

It's as if someone at Triumph had asked owners for a list of all the things that could be improved on the last-generation Bonneville (of which I've owned two) and then acted on it. First, the engine.

It's gone from 865 to 1,200cc, and a 1,200 is a big, beefy engine for a bike this size—old-time Harley FLH big—but now with liquid cooling, fuel injection, overhead cams, and four valves per cylinder. The magazine's test T120 put out 72 bhp at 6,330 rpm and 72 pound-feet of torque at a mere 3,280 rpm, a torque increase of 54 percent from the last generation. What these numbers don't really get across is the smooth, effortless, do-everything hustle of this engine. In town, it's docile and sweet running as a low-compression Triumph Twin of the '50s, but when you roll on the throttle it moves out with a muscular, locomotive force and a deep, throaty purr from the exhaust. Kind of like a cat the size of your house. It's not a two-stage engine that suddenly comes up on cam but a refined, willing powerhouse that simply does whatever you ask it to do, without any fuss.

Traditionalists have complained that it no longer has a 360-degree crank, like its many predecessors, and that the 270-degree crank lacks that snotty, ripping sound of yore and makes it sound too much like a V-twin. It does have a more laid-back shuffle than previous Bonnies, but—mated to the new six-speed transmission with taller gearing—the sound is a lot less busy and tiring on the road. Personally, I like it.

On my last Bonneville, I was always looking for a sixth gear that wasn't there; with this one I often find myself cruising serenely in fourth or fifth on the highway only to realize (properly embarrassed) that I've got a gear or two left. At 70 mph, it's turning an effortless 3,100 rpm, with almost 4,000 left on the tach before redline. The engine doesn't mind revving, but after about 5,500 rpm there's not much need. It's a smooth torque monster on the highway, and around town it shrugs off lugging and lazy shifting.

Speaking of which, the new six-speed may be the slickest and most precise-shifting gearbox I've experienced on a bike. This and a nicely weighted, progressive clutch and powerful but linear dual front brakes make this bike pleasantly easy to ride on a winding back road, as if you're using just your fingertips to control the bike. This sense is enhanced by the neutral/friendly handling characteristics.

I went on a ride last week with my friend Mike Collins, who now owns my 2008 red-and-silver Bonneville, and we both agreed after back-to-back rides that the old bike has a slight gyroscopic resistance to turn-in, while the T120 simply heels over and goes exactly where you think it should. Mike, incidentally, said he will probably buy a new Bonneville this fall. The old bike is still fun, charming and good looking, and (I think) has more of a traditional, direct mechanical feel, so making that trade is not necessarily a slam-dunk option, but both of us were won over by the power and solid, unified feel of the roomier—but slightly heavier—new version.

Also improved is the suspension, which I would rate as being in the firm-but-compliant school. The T120 doesn't get the fully adjustable Showa fork of the café-racer Thruxton R, or that bike's Öhlins rear shocks, but it's still a step up from the last generation in damping and road feel through the fork.

So the basic functional architecture is there for a bike that handles, stops, and goes. My main complaint with the last Bonneville was that cramped seating position for my long legs, and I thought a modern 865cc bike should have more power—or at least be as quick as, say, a Ducati 620 Monster. Also, I didn't like that bent exhaust system. If Triumph had fixed just those three things, I would have been happy to buy another one. Well, the Hinckley company did, but it has also gone far beyond those improvements. Let us count the ways.

There are stock heated grips, for instance, with a neat two-position switch on the left handgrip. These are a big deal when you live only a few hours from Lambeau Field, home of the frozen tundra. Not to mention cheerleaders. Also on the left bar is an Information button that cycles effortlessly through overall mileage, present fuel mileage, overall fuel mileage, two trip odometers, and a digital clock. It's so simple even I can use it, intuitively. The almost invisible ABS takes the stress out of sudden stops at sandy or gravel-strewn intersections.

Then there's liquid cooling. I winced a bit when I first heard this, but the engineers did a nice job of blending in the flat-black radiator—which is only a little bigger than the old oil cooler—and there's much to be gained, such as mileage. Triumph claims mpg is up 36 percent in this generation, and my T120 cruising Wisconsin back roads has delivered about 55 mpg versus the typical 45 on my old (admittedly carbureted) T100. The nutters testing at *CW* HQ turned in a 47-mpg best, which suggests they should relax and enjoy the scenery a bit more. Nonetheless, with its 3.8-gallon tank, the T120's range comfortably approaches 175 miles before fear and foreboding set in.

I suppose liquid cooling will make the bike more complicated to restore thirty years from now, but my doctor has promised me I won't live that long. In the meantime, I like that radiator.

For those hooked on big, rangy adventure-tourers or pure, high-horsepower sportbikes, this is obviously not one of those. It's basically a standard motorcycle that brings a lot of fun back into riding by being both versatile and easy to live with—and easy to park and move around the garage, sort of like a sophisticated Honda CB350 on steroids. But it's also a standard that has upped the game in performance, finish, and refinement, taking the concept to the next level of modernity, where all the components cooperate with the will of the rider. It's a complete motorcycle, with no lingering list of should-have-dones.

Oddly, the more modern the Bonneville becomes, the more it generally resembles those '60s versions I admire. It has fuel-injection throttle bodies that look like old Amal Monoblocs (sans cables), the best-looking exhaust system in years—with a catalytic converter hidden under the engine—and a nicely finned head and cylinders with a camouflaged radiator in front of them. Yet it looks clean and simple and works better than any British twin I've owned.

As an heir to the original 1959 Bonneville, has it become too refined and painless to use, without enough hair-shirt edginess?

Not for me. I love the new Bonneville T120. But then I generally have an old British bike in the garage to restore and work on when I need to bask in the elegant simplicity (and occasional heartbreak) of the past.

In the meantime, I like to ride as much as possible while the sun is still shining. Preferably on a bike I enjoy looking at when it's parked.

COMMANDO AT FIFTY

I**T'S FUNNY** how your tastes can change with time.

For instance, when I first tried a sip of homemade corn liquor as a youth I thought it tasted like paint remover. But I tried some again recently and decided just the opposite is true.

Also, when the first Norton Commando was introduced in September of 1967 at the Earl's Court show in London, I examined the photos of the new Fastback and immediately decided it was not for me. Too swoopy and radical, not traditionally British enough. "Repelled" is probably too strong a word, but the look of that bike drove me firmly back into the Triumph camp, where I normally resided, at least in my dreams. I owned a secondhand Honda CB160 at the time, which was all I could afford as a college sophomore, what with squandering perfectly good bike money on textbooks.

Now, half a century later, when I see a Commando Fastback at a vintage bike show, it stops me in my tracks, and I find it to be quite a lovely thing, and if I were collecting Nortons I'd probably have to have one. But, at the time, that too-daring styling put me off, as it did many others. The Commando was initially a slow seller, despite its impressive superbike performance and the magical rubber engine mounts that gave it an almost unearthly smoothness (for a British vertical twin) on the highway.

In any case, it took the more conventionally restyled Commando 750 and then 850 Roadsters of the early '70s to win my heart. I spent hours gazing at those full-color Commando ads inside the front cover of every major bike magazine, charmed by the pure elemental beauty of the bike and of course the beauty of the "Norton Girl" who stood alluringly nearby, pouting at me because I didn't yet own a Norton. The Roadsters had a spare and rangy look about them, without flab or artifice. As with early Harley Sportsters, they were like the Chesterfield or Lucky Strike of motorcycles: pure nicotine, no filter.

Gears meshed in my febrile brain, and I knew beyond any doubt that I would eventually own a Commando. And in 1975 I finally bought one, brand new, by selling a dead-reliable Honda CB350 and using all the money I had in the world. It was, by far, the most expensive thing I'd ever purchased.

The dream wilted somewhat on my ride home from the dealership when the bike quit running at every single stop sign and stoplight. And during my first few months of riding, about six major things went wrong with the Commando, but none of them (I was told) could be covered under warranty. The dealer pronounced every failure a clear case of "abuse." By default, I learned to fix everything myself and became a self-taught British-bike mechanic.

So you might say I owe the Commando for a free technical education—free except for the parts, of course, and the cost of the Whitworth wrenches I still own.

Later that year, the Commando seized and bent an exhaust valve in Montana while Barb and I were attempting a ride from Wisconsin to Seattle, and we had to ship the bike home from Missoula in a Bekins moving van, continuing the trip by bus and train. I wrote a story about the trip and got my first article published right here in *Cycle World*.

So it seems I owe my journalism career to that Norton as well. If I'd bought a Honda, God knows what I'd be doing now. Possibly something useful to humanity. That or sleeping under a bridge.

Incidentally, that valve seizure in Montana was attributed to "abuse" and naturally not covered under warranty, so I learned how to install valves, guides, and pistons. Self-taught, again. The Norton was making me brilliant.

I sold the bike soon after that, chafing under the travel restrictions dictated by the bike's apparent lack of long-distance stamina. I loved looking at the Norton in the garage, but I also wanted to go places far away, and the Commando had an invisible bungee cord of doubt that kept me near home.

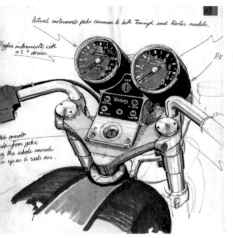

Actual instruments pods common to both Triumph and Norton models.

Veglia instruments with 45° dial.

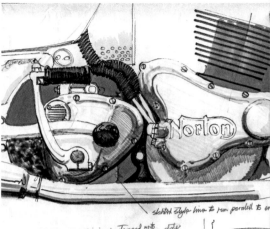

But that was a long time ago, and time either heals all wounds or causes Alzheimer's because I've owned four more Commandos since then and just did a full restoration on another black-and-gold 850 Roadster about two years ago. It appears I'm addicted to them.

Friends have accused me of having a "love/hate relationship" with Nortons, but it might be more accurately described as a "love/hope relationship." I know all their foibles but keep thinking that just the right upgrades to modern materials, electronics, and sealants will render them virtually as useful and reliable as any modern motorcycle. And I know people who have made that theory work for them. My friend Bill Getty, who owns a British parts business called JRC Engineering, has now put 130,000 miles on his 1974 850.

And of course Editor-in-Chief Mark Hoyer has an 850 Commando that he rides everywhere with impunity—after a certain amount of (ahem) "sorting out." He now swears by this bike far more often than he swears at it. And then there's my old friend Brian Slark, who was West Coast service manager for Norton from 1969 to 1975, and he affirms that there is now "a fix for everything."

The big question, of course, on the fiftieth anniversary of the Commando, is why has so much latter-day development time, expense, and sheer effort been lavished on a British twin that's now half a century old? Along with the 1959–1970 Triumph Bonneville, the Commando has clearly emerged as one of the two most popular and venerated bikes of its era. It has a worldwide following and support network, not to mention a cultish aura of cool that seems to work on riders of all ages. Why so?

I put this question to Brian Slark this morning, and he said, "For one thing, it's really the only classic British bike you can ride at current speeds and not have it shake apart. Also, it's eminently tunable, with many upgrades available, and great parts availability as well."

He also pointed out that the parallel twin is a compact, sensible, and generally charismatic engine design for motorcycles and that nearly every major manufacturer is now building one for those very reasons. "Interesting," he said, "that after all these years we've come full circle, back to the parallel twin."

I asked him about Norton's sketchy reputation for reliability, and he said, "Well, when you own a bike you're more aware of its problems. We tend to forget that a lot of Japanese bikes at the time also had serious problems: transmissions that packed up, crank failures, piston seizures, and so on."

Fair enough. I had friends in that era who found the repair of worn Japanese bikes economically unfeasible and simply abandoned them. Conversely, I'd never heard of anyone throwing a Norton away.

But of course much of the Commando's appeal lies outside the bounds of mere reason. There's romance to consider.

The Commando is really almost an accident of history, an unlikely amalgam of old and new ideas put together as a stopgap solution to the problem of rapidly advancing technical progress in the motorcycle market. Norton didn't have enough money or engineering staff to design an entirely new engine, and many British-bike enthusiasts (me included) didn't want them to. We wanted something that looked more or less like a Norton Atlas but that didn't shake as much or leak oil.

So Norton tilted the Atlas engine forward and adapted it to a new frame that isolated the entire drivetrain from the rider, using shimmed rubber motor mounts that allowed the engine to jump up and down but not sideways. Thus good handling was retained and the dreaded Atlas engine vibration no longer caused the screws in your sunglasses to fall out.

Use of the old Atlas 750 engine (mildly updated) allowed Norton to retain the charisma, torque, and sound of this venerable long-stroke twin while building a superbike that could go head to head in performance with the latest Japanese multis and Italian V-twins. Also, they took a bike already festooned with beautiful pieces and castings and added more, with a polished-aluminum primary cover, stainless-steel fenders, and lovely steel footpeg brackets. The result was a bike of bone-deep beauty that I once remarked looked like a collection of exquisite paperweights, all harmoniously blended into one motorcycle.

And when the Commando was updated to an 850 in 1973, it got even more torque, much-improved "Superblend" crank bearings, and a mild styling update of the seat and instruments, resulting in what is probably my favorite version, the 1974 Roadster. In black and gold, of course.

In 1975, Norton added an electric starter that was incapable of turning the engine over, so they called it a "starter assist" and changed the air cleaner and mufflers to a less traditional—but US-compliant—design. But touches like this didn't help much. It seemed the inability to make an electric starter that could spin the crank of an internal combustion engine was no longer amusing to

customers, and years of indifferent execution of an essentially good design finally came home to roost. By the end of that year it was all over for a once-great company with a long tradition of racing excellence and classic beauty.

But the bikes are still with us, now as popular as they were when new—or more so. And they still have that heady combination of smooth locomotive power and untamed wild-animal spirit that's not quite like anything else I've ridden. And the Commando is still my wife, Barbara's, favorite motorcycle. It's never been bested, in her opinion, for its combination of acceleration, sound, and sheer presence.

A heartfelt endorsement, coming from a woman who helped me push a broken Commando through the streets of Missoula, forty-one years ago.

As a postscript here, I should mention that I no longer own that last black-and-gold 850 Roadster I restored. It turned out beautiful, but I suffered a stroke while trying to kick-start it for a first ride in the spring last year. Thanks to a clot-busting drug administered at the VA hospital, I made a complete recovery, but I soon sold that bike to my friend Bill Hall. Even though it was guilty of nothing but clogged idle jets, the bloom was off the relationship, and my doctor recommended I buy a bike with a starter button on the handlebars.

When I wrote about this last year, a couple of physicians weighed in and suggested that the Norton probably did not cause the stroke. More likely, I was already having one that morning, and the Commando's failure to start saved my life because I had the stroke at home, 6 miles from a hospital, rather than out on a distant country road while riding alone.

It's quite possible they're right. In which case I can now thank the Norton Commando for my mechanical training, journalism career, and current good health.

And the ownership of all those Whitworth wrenches. Which I used just yesterday on a 1965 Triumph engine with low oil pressure and a rod knock.

Some of us never learn. And don't really want to.

A SHORT HISTORY
OF HITTING MY HEAD

JUST BEFORE WE TOOK OFF for Florida last week on a spring-break vacation, Barb's sister Pam and her husband, Richard, called from Fort Myers. "A good friend of ours named Scott Fischer is the local Harley dealer," said Pam, "and when he heard you were coming to visit us, he said he could lend you a Harley while you're here."

"Great!" I said, eyeing the small carry-on suitcase I'd just begun to pack. "I'll just bring a larger suitcase so we can take a couple of helmets along."

"Oh, you don't need a helmet in Florida," she said. "It's just like Wisconsin—we don't have a helmet law down here."

I held the phone and stared into space for a moment, scanning my memory for images of traffic in coastal Florida at the height of the winter tourist season. Lots of cars, many of them quite large and driven by elderly folks whose heads were not quite visible above their seatbacks, so that you were never really sure if the car ahead of you had a driver at the wheel or not. Often, it made no difference.

My parents lived in Florida for many years, and I used to joke (rather cruelly) that if you blew up a paper bag and popped it loudly, half the state population would die of a heart attack. Now that I'm a little closer to that age myself, it doesn't seem quite as funny, but I still stand by the scientific principle.

Anyway, Florida didn't seem like the best state in the Union in which to go helmetless, even if there was a certain warm-weather appeal to letting your freak flag fly and being free to do your own thing and ride your machine and not be hassled by the man, etc. I knew from previous trips that, while there were plenty of great places to ride in Florida, there would also be many pale-yellow Lincoln Town Cars with white vinyl tops on their way to the Early-Bird Senior Special at the Crab Shack, so you had to keep your wits about you. Also lots of half-lost visitors like me careening around.

"Well, I think I'll bring helmets anyway," I told Pam. "I just had my life saved by a helmet about six months ago, so I'm in kind of a helmet mood."

I may have been overstating the case, as I have no proof that the helmet in question—a dual-sport Arai XD—actually saved my life, but I'd guess it did. If nothing else, it certainly saved me from a good spell in rehab, trying to guess (wrongly) how many fingers the therapist is holding up now.

It was a dirt-bike crash in Wyoming last year that broke my foot and a bunch of ribs. During the accident, my helmet also took a pretty good bounce off a rock, and the impact was hard enough to leave my ears ringing for a few minutes. The helmet just had a small scuff mark and paint chip, and I didn't even have a headache after the accident. Or maybe I did, but I was too busy grousing about my ribs and foot to notice. Anyway, I'm still here, after having my bell well and truly rung.

Actually, looking back at a lifetime of high adventure mixed with natural clumsiness, I would say helmets have spared me to ride another day at least three other times. One was a crash in the Barstow-to-Vegas Dual Sport ride, during which I flew over the handlebars of my XL500 and failed to attain lift, alighting amid some rocks on that portion of the helmet where my bare forehead would normally have been found. The other two were roadracing crashes—at Grattan and Riverside—where I lost the front end and low-sided, smacking my face into the pavement like somebody bobbing for blacktop, then slid for so long that I became bored and tried to stand up, falling again. In those last two cases, it was the chin bar on the helmet that took most of the impact.

You'd think those last two hits would have taught me a lesson, but—illogically—I still own a couple of open-face helmets and wear them quite a bit for street riding on those bright, sunny days when my superstition and foreboding levels are especially low. I read an interview a few years ago with one of my heroes, four-time 500cc World Champion John Surtees, and he said he still prefers to wear an open-face helmet when doing track sessions and exhibition races, mainly because he's always liked the openness of vision and hearing, the added peripheral awareness of his surroundings, that an open helmet provides.

I feel the same way. If I wear a full-face helmet, I adapt to it instantly and don't give it a second thought. But when I switch to an open helmet, I feel strangely liberated and more attuned to what's going on around me, like a guy who's just put the convertible top down on his car.

Wearing no helmet at all adds yet another dimension of freedom, of course, unless it's cold, windy, dusty, buggy, or rainy, at which time that lack of helmet becomes just another of life's many aggravations, like losing your gloves during a dogsled race. As so often happens here in the north.

Anyway, when it was time to pack for Florida last week, the helmet I chose was an open-face Shoei J-Wing with a dark-tinted flip-up shield. Never mind my long and violent history of chin-smacking; it just seemed like the right thing for Florida.

And it was. I picked up a nearly new Road Glide from my new friends at Harley-Davidson of Fort Myers and was soon cruising down the wide boulevard that is Highway 41, headed toward Naples, with a short swing out toward Sanibel Island.

Palm trees along the highway reflected in the chromed gas cap on the Harley, and a light sea breeze wafted up the sleeves of my open Levi's jacket. Bright red bougainvillea bloomed in front of homes with iridescently green lawns. The Big Twin was percolating nicely, with a relaxed and muted burble.

Ah, Florida. And warm air and sunlight and bridges and blue water passing by. It was my first ride in three months, and I'd almost forgotten what those motorcycles in my garage were for. They were for exactly this.

"Good to be here," I said to myself. Then I thought about it for a moment and added that famous Keith Richards afterthought, "Good to be anywhere."

ZEN AND THE ART
OF THE OIL CHANGE

THESE DAYS, a lot of younger, less experienced riders come up to me and say, "Mr. Egan, you have an almost legendary reputation for being able to change the oil and filter on your motorcycles without spilling more than about 30 percent of the oil onto the garage floor or your own clothing. How the heck do you do it?"

I tell them, "Well, kids, part of it is experience. I worked for almost a decade as a foreign-car mechanic, and I've also owned and maintained a lot of motorcycles in my life. But basically, it's a Zen thing; you have to work thoughtfully and carefully, planning every move and wasting no motion. You have to be at one with your motorcycle and the molecular flow of lubricants in the universe."

I've been asked this question so often, I thought it might be beneficial to our readers if I walked them through the stages of one of my typical oil changes. Let's take the case of my Buell Ulysses, whose oil I changed just last weekend.

Naturally, I didn't have an oil filter on hand, so I rode 60 miles to Mischler's Harley-Davidson/BMW in Beaver Dam to get one.

There are Harley dealers closer than this, of course, but they don't have BMWs to look at as well as Harleys. And it's important to remember that at least 60 percent of the reason we ride is to go look at other motorcycles. I'm told some people do it just for the scenery and fresh air, which I suppose is possible, but it seems rather shallow.

So I arrived at Mischler's and—after confirming that they didn't have a good, used black BMW R1100S for sale—went straight to the parts counters and asked my friendly parts-man Aaron if he had an oil filter for a 2009 Buell Ulysses. Harley is long since out of the Buell business, as we know, but I was told when I bought my bike that parts and service would be available for the next nine years. This sounded fine to me.

When you're in your mid-sixties, nine years sounds like eternity, which it very well may be, depending upon the results of your last EKG. And if, for some reason, you happen to live longer than that, there are always parts on eBay. No worries here.

Anyway, Aaron looked up the filter and said, "Do you want just one?"

He asked it in a tone that implied that most wise shoppers buy at least two filters at a time or maybe a six-pack. "Better give me two," I said grandly,

privately mourning the lost opportunity to take another long, pointless ride to a motorcycle dealership.

So I took my filters and headed home. I could have bought some genuine Harley-Davidson oil, too, but I use 20W50 Valvoline racing oil (with mystical ZDDP) in a racing car and have a couple cases of the stuff stacked in my workshop. Should be okay for the Buell, I figured.

Back home, I followed the oil-change instructions in the owner's manual and began my sublime work. Here's where the specific instruction kicks in. Pay careful attention.

Step 1: Place a "suitable container" under the sump or oil reservoir—which, in the Buell's case, is in the hollow swingarm above the end of the muffler—and remove the plug. A stream of scalding hot oil will run down over the rear of the muffler and cascade into the pan, like Niagara Falls in a nightmare. Some will run down to the far end of the muffler and onto the floor. Or trickle warmly down your forearm and into your sleeve.

Step 2: While oil is dripping from the drain hole and muffler, remove the small chin fairing and place another pan under the oil filter. Remove the filter with a web-type tool, and stand back as oil from the engine and filter run over the front of the muffler and into the pan. Much of the oil will follow the bottom of the muffler and run onto the floor. Expect some to drip off the filter wrench onto your blue jeans. Accidentally drop the slippery, hot filter into the pan for a nice splash effect.

Step 3: Carefully fill the new filter with oil, spilling hardly any at all, then screw it into the engine and put the drain plug back in. Here's where you give the drain pan an accidental kick so that a small tidal wave of oil flops onto the floor. Then refill the reservoir using a funnel with too small an opening so that it overflows immediately and burps oil onto the swingarm. Before putting the chin spoiler back on, use massive amounts of contact cleaner/degreaser to clean up the muffler and floor, along with ecologically friendly piles of oil-soaked paper towels.

Step 4: Carry the main oil drain pan across the workshop and dump it down a large funnel into a disgustingly filthy, oil-streaked, red plastic 5-gallon gas can with the words "DRAIN OIL" scrawled across it so people don't accidentally drink from it.

Step 5: Check to make sure this can isn't already almost full. Otherwise, about 2 quarts of dirty drain oil will well up around the sides of the funnel and run onto the floor, as mine did. Expect some oil to run down the back side of the pouring spout on the drain pan and drip onto your running shoes.

Step 6: Mop up the oil spill with more paper towels and wring them out over your drain pan. Clean the whole area with half a spray can of contact cleaner, but don't breathe any of the fumes. When everything is cleaned up, start the bike and check it for oil leaks. Mine was fine; not a sign of a drip.

Step 7: Wipe your tools carefully, put them away, and then go into the house. Throw all your clothes—including the running shoes—into the washer and then take a shower. Put on clean clothes and return to the workshop to have a beer and ponder the evening's work. Now, you're done.

The sharp reader will note that some oil was actually spilled during this process, but that the majority of it ended up in either the bike or some kind of container.

Is there a truly perfect, Zen-like way to change your oil, working calmly and logically, without spilling a drop?

I suppose somebody somewhere can do it, but not me. There's a remote possibility that I'm too impatient and impulsive or just too unskilled.

In any case, I've found the best substitute for skill is to work alone. That way, no one knows you're not at one with the serene, clock-like machinery of the universe. Or how much you swear.

THE PARENTAL CONSENT FORM

SOMETIMES I WONDER if I'd have any social life at all without old motorcycle parts. Yesterday morning, for instance, I was staring forlornly into the kitchen cupboard, trying to decide whether to have Cheerios or Grape Nuts, when the phone rang. It was my friend Lee Potratz.

"I found a really good Victor 441 chain guard in a box of old BSA parts in my workshop," he said. "I could drop it off at your place or we could meet for lunch at the bakery in Brooklyn."

Lee was speaking here not of Brooklyn, New York, but of the small nearby village of Brooklyn, Wisconsin. You can tell the difference because the Wisconsin version has no bridge. Also, the police force used to consist of just one officer, who was known by the name of "Radar Bob." I believe he's retired now, but I still ride very slowly when I enter that village, like a cowboy expecting an ambush in a narrow canyon. In his prime, Radar Bob cost me plenty.

Nevertheless, I fearlessly headed toward Brooklyn through the rain in my elderly green Jeep Wrangler. When someone says he's found a good used Victor chain guard, you don't hesitate. BSA Singles tend to gnaw both their chain guards and front fenders in half from engine vibration, so a good original one is a rare thing, indeed. It's like finding an undamaged U-boat after World War II. They almost don't exist.

So Lee met me at the bakery for lunch, and we sat at a table in the front window drinking coffee and talking.

Somehow we got onto the subject of our first motorcycles, and Lee mentioned that his parents had absolutely no interest in them and forbade him from owning one while in high school. He didn't buy his first bike—a Honda XL350—until he came home from flying helicopters in Vietnam in 1973.

I told Lee my parents took an extremely dim view of bikes, as well. My dad had been on exactly one motorcycle in his life, and it hadn't left a good impression. He was temporarily stationed at the Brooklyn Navy Yard during World War II and billeted in an old ship. When he returned to base one rainy night, another sailor gave him a ride on the back of a Harley. My dad said the guy swooped back and forth between piles of cargo and loading cranes at high speed, and the whole thing was terrifying.

So when I told my dad I'd like to get a motorcycle, he looked at me as if I'd expressed a sudden interest in the occult.

"Dad, how come we never celebrate a black mass around here or sacrifice a goat?" That sort of look. My mom seconded that emotion.

But I was not to be dissuaded, and both my parents finally caved in—under intense lobbying—and allowed me to buy a new Bridgestone 50 because I convinced them it was just a harmless little scooter and not a motorcycle at all. And that, as they say, was the camel's nose under the tent.

After that, I escalated to progressively larger bikes, and they hardly noticed the difference. But, as I recall, none of my motorcycle buddies in high school had parents who had ever ridden a motorcycle, either, or even wanted to.

I think there were three things going on here, culturally speaking. First, our parents had all lived through the Depression and the war, and they didn't believe in spending money on frivolous things (to include electric guitars, I soon learned). Second, the 1950s and early 1960s were a time when most Americans aspired to a cleaner, brighter, and more sophisticated future, and motorcycles of that period—mostly loud and shuddering oilleakers—looked like some kind of throwback to a darker time. It really took the "You Meet the Nicest People on a Honda" advertising campaign to turn that perception around with the older generation.

And third, our parents thought motorcycles were dangerous. The basic job of parents from time immemorial has been to keep children alive until they're old enough to develop a glimmer of common sense, and a lot of parents saw bikes as a threat to that plan.

And, of course, motorcycles are somewhat dangerous, as are most things worth doing—flying, mountain climbing, horseback riding, defending your country, skydiving, arresting felons, football, auto racing, boxing, firefighting, scuba diving, etc. You don't do these things to be safe; you do them after deciding what kind of life you want to lead, careful or exciting. An exciting one can easily take you out of the gene pool early, and that's a difficult choice for parents to make on someone else's behalf.

Even now, friends will say to me, "Our son wants a motorcycle. Do you think he should have one?"

I just smile and fall back on the Sergeant Schultz from *Hogan's Heroes* defense: "I know nothing!" I almost always tell them it's between them and the kid. I already fought that fight and won, but I'm not going to tell anyone else what to do. If the kid wants a motorcycle badly enough, he or she will get one. Eventually. If not, the kid can take up golf or some other perfectly nice pastime. It's not my decision.

After lunch, I took my excellent new/used BSA chain guard home. While driving, I began to wonder if I knew anyone (other than my wife, Barbara) whose parents actually encouraged him or her to buy a bike. When I got home I called a couple of the usual suspects, riding buddies Mike and Lew, to see what their story was.

"Are you kidding?" Mike said. "My dad was a doctor, and he called them 'murdercycles.' I joined the air force specifically so I could leave home and buy a motorcycle. I bought a Kawasaki Trail Boss 100 when I was stationed in Okinawa. Two weeks after I got there."

Interesting. Bikes are unsafe at home, so Lee becomes a helicopter pilot in Vietnam and Mike ends up installing bombs on F-4 Phantom jets in Okinawa. I think this is called the Law of Unintended Consequences.

When I called Lew, he said, "My parents absolutely didn't want me to get a bike. My dad was a skilled auto mechanic who owned his own shop, but he had no use for motorcycles—or the people who rode them. I finally talked my folks into letting me buy a Cushman scooter."

"What was your first real motorcycle?"

"A BSA 650 Lightning."

"Wow! How did you manage that?"

"I traded my beautiful black 1951 Cadillac hearse straight across with a friend who had the BSA. My dad was actually very glad to see the hearse go."

Brilliant strategy, I thought to myself. Just plain brilliant.

JUST WHEN I WAS COMFORTABLY RETIRED for almost four months, had everything I needed for a simple saint-like existence, and thought my checkbook was at long last safe from the predations of desire, the email arrived.

It was from a man named Gary Ackatz, who lives near the small town of Kewaskum, Wisconsin. Gary, it seemed, had a black-and-gold 1974 Norton Commando seriously in need of restoration. It had been sitting in his shed, unridden, for twenty-three years. There was a time when he thought he might restore the thing, but he was older now, and that time had passed.

Still, he wanted it to go to a good home and possibly get restored back to its original beauty and be made to run again. If someone were willing to take up this challenge, he would give the bike away—yes, free, with no strings attached—to that person. The bike even had a title. Was I interested?

Apparently Gary had been reading my column over the years and had noticed that I (a) had a soft spot for Norton Commandos and (b) was inclined to take on projects that most people wouldn't touch with a 10-foot pole fired from a giant steam-powered catapult some distance away.

Oh, Lord. Did he have any pictures?

Yes, and he emailed them to me. Seen poking out into the sunlight from his shed like a timid groundhog, the Norton was pretty much as it had been when Gary bought it from his uncle in Colorado twenty-five years ago—extended fork, high-rise handlebars, forward footrests of twisted, chromed iron bar, and aftermarket shorty mufflers. All the shiny parts were fairly rusty. It had a single Mikuni carburetor, and the front fender was missing.

Still, when you substituted stock fork legs, bars, and mufflers, what you had here was a fairly unmolested black-and-gold Norton 850 Commando from 1974—a good year for these bikes. The 1973 and later 850 Commandos had the much-improved "Superblend" crankshaft bearings with tapered rollers, unlike the earlier 750s, which were famous for whipping their straight-cut rollers into expensive chunks of metal.

So, as you can understand, my Norton x-ray vision allowed me to see beauty and possibility where others might only see six months of long nights in the workshop. Truth be told, I was looking for a fun-yet-elaborate winter project, and the idea of those long nights (and days, now that I'm retired) in the shop

held no terrors for me. And it was a Norton, after all. These bikes have their flaws (God knows), but their polished engine cases, gearbox covers, footrests, valve covers, and other shiny bits collectively form the world's finest collection of Victorian jewelry outside the Tower of London, all embedded in a motorcycle that has no bad shapes anywhere. Commandos look great, have thunderous torque, and sound better than . . . well, just about anything.

So, of course, I told Gary I'd come and get the bike. How can you turn down a free Norton? I hooked up my aluminum bike trailer to my new VW Jetta TDI wagon and sped off in the direction of Kewaskum, two and a half hours away. My fellow motorcycle-restoration sage, Lee Potratz, went with me on a cold Saturday morning with snow flurries gusting out of the north.

Pushed out of the shed and into daylight, the Norton actually looked better than I'd expected. A clean, bone-dry fuel tank with no dents. The engine turned over, and the gearbox clicked through the gears. Before we left, Gary served us a lunch of his custom-recipe Tex-Mex chili that could probably take first place at the Terlingua cook-offs and gave me all of his Norton shop manuals. Very nice guy with a good heart. He could easily have parted this Commando out and made some money, but he just wanted to see it restored and running again. I invited him to drive over and check on its progress whenever he could.

Back home, Lee and I rolled the bike onto my Handy lift and elevated it to idol/inspection height. I needed to ponder the Norton for a few days before I started taking it apart, so I invited our motorcycle gang over for an evening of "Free Norton Worship." I turned down the shop lights, lit candles around the base of the lift platform, and put my skull candleholder on a shop towel that read "The Unapproachable Norton." Food was served, obscure bitters and black porters were drunk, Gregorian chants and the music of Screamin' Jay Hawkins were played. Quite occult. Many who were there have never been the same. Others were not the same even before they got there.

That was two weeks ago. Now there's nothing left on my lift but a bare frame. Today I got the engine out of the bike, piecemeal—head, barrels, and bottom end—and removed the gearbox and cradle. Tomorrow the steering-head bearings come out. Then I can have the frame painted. I've already bought 50 pounds of new glass bead and blasted the battery box, taillight mount, head-steady, etc. Powdercoat or paint on these bits? I must think.

Yesterday a huge box of new parts arrived from my old California friend Bill Getty, who runs a British-bike parts business called JRC Engineering. Mufflers, fork tubes, Isolastic motor mounts, etc., all at friendly prices. Bill, too, has a good heart and wants to see Nortons run. He has 130,000 miles on his own Commando.

So I am, as my dad would have said, going to town. I've had several Commandos in the past but always played catch-up with repairs and never taken one down to do the whole thing right. With this one, I'm painting the frame, putting it on new Excel shouldered alloy rims with polished hubs, new bearings, stainless spokes, and Dunlop K81s, and moving on from there. One piece, done as well as I can do it, at a time.

Friends have pointed out it's probably not economically sensible to restore an old Norton that needs virtually everything. They tell me I could find a nice one that's already running for a lot less money, with no long hours spent at the bead blaster and the parts cleaner. And they're right, of course.

But I just shrug and say, "What fun would that be?" I'm retired, and this is my winter art project. Also, I have a weakness for Nortons and making things whole again. This is how I straighten out my little corner of the universe. Call back in the spring.

THE FIVE-STROKE NORTON

Sometimes You Kick the Bike.
Sometimes the Bike Kicks You.

YES, I KNOW MOST PEOPLE believe the Norton Commando is a four-stroke motorcycle, but this is not always the case. Let me explain.

Several months ago, I awoke on a warm and sunny morning—perhaps the first really nice day of spring—and decided to take a motorcycle ride. Pondering the many options in my vast four-bike collection, I decided it was time to get my 1974 Commando out of its winter mothballs and fire it up.

I unhooked the battery tender, topped up the oil, adjusted and oiled the chain, checked the tires, and put on my leather jacket. I turned on the fuel taps, tickled the Amals until they wept, flicked on the key, and kicked.

Nothing. So I kicked it again. And again. Finally it started, but it immediately died. About five times in a row. Oh, boy. I was getting hot and tired, so I took off my helmet and jacket. After a few more kicks and stumbles, I took off my sweatshirt.

My friend Ed Zender always says that if a Norton doesn't start in about two kicks, there's something wrong, and you should stop kicking and fix it. I figured the idle circuits were probably gummed up from sitting all winter, but cleaning your carbs is not a fun job on a nice spring morning.

"One more kick," I said to the Norton imperiously, "and then I'm taking another bike." The Commando probably sensed from the tone in my voice that I meant business. Big mistake. I was soon to learn that you should never threaten a Norton.

I leapt into the air and gave it one more mighty kick, and the whole right side of my body went instantly numb, as if someone had thrown an electrical switch. My right arm and leg seemed to have carbonated ginger ale running through them, and my right jaw and eyelid felt as though they'd gotten a massive novocaine injection at the dentist's office. Even the right side of my nose was numb, and the left side felt normal. Right down the middle.

"Well, this is not good," I said aloud, surprised to find my speech quite normal—assuming that a small-town Wisconsin accent is normal. My balance was okay, too, and I could walk. Sensing an imminent hospital visit, I walked up to the house, took off my clumpy motorcycle boots, put on some comfortable loafers, and made a few phone calls. Barb was gone for the morning, volunteering at a no-kill cat shelter, and our neighbors were at church, so I drove myself to the local hospital, only 6 miles away on a country road, which was faster than calling an ambulance.

Long story vastly shortened, they checked me out and sent me on to the Madison, Wisconsin, VA hospital, where the neurology department did a brain scan and determined I'd had an ischemic stroke (blood clot) in the reptilian core of my brain and then gave me a big injection of TPA, the miraculous clot- busting drug. Within twelve hours all the stroke symptoms had gone away, except for some residual numbness in my right hand and forearm. After I'd spent three days in the ICU, they let me go home. They said that except for the small matter of having a stroke, I was one of the healthiest sixty-eight-year-old Vietnam vets they'd ever seen, but they gave me some parting health tips anyway:

- Cut down your salt intake.
- Walk every chance you get.
- Don't kick-start big motorcycles—"They have bikes now that start with these magic little buttons on the handlebars," the doctor explained. "You should try one."

When I got home, I sat in my workshop all evening, looking at the Norton and brooding. Could I really let it go? I'd spent an entire winter restoring the thing, and it looked beautiful. But as my old friend George Allez likes to say, "It'll look just as beautiful in someone else's garage."

In the morning, I called ace British-bike restorer Dale Mattison, who'd rebuilt the engine for me, and asked if he could get the bike tuned and starting well so I could sell it. He said, "Just clean the carbs, and it should start right up after a few kicks."

"The trouble with that advice," I said, "is the 'few kicks' part. I don't think the VA will take me back for a second miracle cure."

So I trailered it down to Dale's Cycle, and he cleaned the carbs and did a full tune-up. When I picked it up, of course, I immediately broke my own vow by starting it (first kick!) and taking a ride. It ran beautifully and sounded great. As usual. Maybe I'd been too hasty in thinking of selling it. The stroke was probably just a strange anomaly . . .

The next day, I decided to risk all and take another ride. The Norton started immediately, and I was soon coursing down the green, winding roads of the Wisconsin countryside, listening to the lovely beat of that big twin. Then I missed a turn I'd intended to take and stalled the engine while making a U-turn in the road. The pavement was off-camber, so I pushed the bike slightly uphill to a flatter spot, where I could set it firmly on the centerstand and give it a kick. It was a hot, muggy day. The Norton started briefly, then spit back and stopped, so I foolishly tickled the carbs and flooded it slightly. It took six more kicks to clear it. When it finally fired up, I was wringing wet and out of breath. I put my head down on the tank, heart pounding and right arm tingling like a Lucas voltage regulator.

As I rested there, a favorite last line from a James Joyce short story called "Araby" popped into my head: "Gazing into the darkness, I saw myself as a creature driven and derided by vanity, and my eyes burned with anguish and anger." Also salty sweat, in this case.

When I got home from the ride, I called my friend Bill Hall, who'd gotten back into bikes recently and was looking for a nice Commando. He drove his pickup truck over a few days later and bought the Norton. It started first kick for him.

The next morning, I headed down to a shop called Team Triumph in Janesville, Wisconsin, and ordered a brand-new Triumph T120 Bonneville. It's a beautiful silver and red and has one of those magic buttons on the handlebars.

Sometimes a moment comes when you need to count your blessings and move on. Also, there are worse things in life than having a doctor's prescription to purchase a new motorcycle you were looking for an excuse to buy anyway.